THIS UNIQUE BOOK

has been designed to reward the casual
reader and the language student alike.
When you open it, your eye will light
upon two different languages. On the
left-hand page you will find the authentic
text of a renowned work of German literature;
on the right, a graceful rendering into
English which is both modern and faithful
to the original.

This Dual-Language Book will enable even
those readers with only a limited knowledge
of the language to enjoy a German literary
masterpiece in its original form. Notes
on background material are included as a special
aid to the student and reader.

Learn the literature through the language,
the language through the literature.

JOHANN WOLFGANG VON GOETHE

THE SUFFERINGS OF YOUNG | DIE LEIDEN DES JUNGEN

WERTHER | WERTHER

A BANTAM DUAL-LANGUAGE BOOK

Edited by Harry Steinhauer
Western Reserve University

with a translation, critical introduction,
notes and vocabulary by the editor

BANTAM BOOKS / NEW YORK

THE SUFFERINGS OF YOUNG WERTHER

A Bantam Dual-Language Book
Published November 1962

*Bantam Books are published by Bantam Books, Inc. Its trade-mark,
consisting of the words "Bantam Books" and the portrayal of a bantam, is registered in the United States Patent Office and in other
countries. Marca Registrada. Printed in the United States of Amer-
ica, Bantam Books, Inc., 271 Madison Ave., New York 16, N. Y.*

CONTENTS

INTRODUCTION

In May 1772 Goethe arrived in Wetzlar, an old Imperial town on the river Lahn, the seat of the Supreme Court of the Holy Roman Empire. Young lawyers went there to acquire their final polish, and the more important members of the Reich maintained embassies. Following the wishes of his overbearing father, the young graduate from law school inscribed himself as a probationer at the Imperial court.

But Goethe had no more genuine interest in the law then than he had displayed during his student days. It was literature that drew him, and the society of people who would be raw material for the man of letters. He attached himself to a group of young lawyers and diplomats who met at a local inn for talk and jest. Goethe was the youngest among them, but he stood out at once as a brilliant eccentric who, moreover, commanded respect as the author of some published verse and of a still unpublished drama about the medieval knight, Götz von Berlichingen.

Several weeks later, on June 9th, Goethe met Charlotte Buff at a dance in the nearby village of Volpertshausen, virtually under the same circumstances as those in which Werther meets Charlotte (letter of June 16, 1771). He was deeply in love almost at once—before he knew that the girl was already betrothed to Johann Christian Kestner, secretary in one of the embassies at Wetzlar. For the young man of twenty-two it was his fourth love, if that word may be used to cover the various degrees of emotional commitment which he had experienced up to this time. His passion developed approximately like Werther's in the first book of the novel. Some of the scenes described there actually occurred. The tension between Werther and Albert

1

is a piece of life, though Kestner was a far more admirable person than the Albert whom Goethe put into the novel. Early in September Goethe realized that Charlotte was wholly devoted to Kestner and would never give him anything but friendship. After a final meeting with the two lovers (a meeting that is fairly literally transcribed in the last letter of part one, September 10, 1771) Goethe packed his bags and left Wetzlar without saying good-by, leaving behind a note for Kestner and one for Charlotte, in which he described his desperate state of mind.

He went up the Rhine to Ehrenbreitstein, where he was introduced into the La Roche family. He found consolation in the company of Sophie La Roche, the novelist, and even more in that of her sixteen-year-old daughter Maximiliane, with the wonderful black eyes that made him forget Charlotte temporarily. Back in Frankfurt he was visited by Kestner, and the old wound began to bleed again. He bombarded the couple with letters which frankly avowed his love for Charlotte. Two months later his passion drove him to Wetzlar for a few days. The visit accomplished nothing; he left in an emotional state that was in no way relieved or improved.

Late in November he heard from Kestner about the suicide of Carl Wilhelm Jerusalem, which had occurred on October 30th. Goethe had known Jerusalem casually when they were both students at Leipzig; he had seen Jerusalem at Wetzlar occasionally; he felt deeply enough about the gifted young man's tragic end to ask Kestner for a full account of it. Many details from Kestner's report went into Goethe's description of Werther's death. Jerusalem, who was the secretary of the Braunschweig legation at Wetzlar, had been a melancholiac by temperament. He had been badly treated by a superior officer in the service; and he was involved in a hopeless passion for the wife of a colleague. These factors together had made life intolerable for him.

In April of 1773 Kestner married Charlotte in Wetzlar. Goethe knew of the event in advance, was in constant touch with the couple, insisted on ordering the wedding rings for them, and revealed in his letters a state of pro-

found agitation, which was only increased by the marriage. But in January 1774 Maximiliane Brentano, née La Roche, of the black eyes, came to live in Frankfurt as the wife of a wholesale grocer, a man more than twice her age and who shared none of her intellectual or aesthetic interests. The young wife of eighteen became the stepmother of five children and lived in an apartment above her husband's business. Goethe began to frequent the house; ardent scenes ensued between Tristan and Isolde, which King Mark did not relish. A month later the young lawyer and writer was forbidden to enter the Brentano house.

The materials for the novel *Die Leiden des jungen Werther* were there; they assembled themselves rapidly in Goethe's mind and took shape as one of the great novels of world literature. Without making a plan, rereading the letters he had written to his friend Merck and Kestner's report to him about the suicide of Jerusalem, Goethe began writing. In a few weeks the book was finished; Goethe sent it to a publisher at Leipzig, and it appeared at Michaelmas of 1774.

What drew Goethe to Charlotte is described in *Werther:* the fact that her sedate, steady character was the antipode of his turbulent one; she seemed to offer him that peace of mind he so sorely needed. This turbulence Goethe himself acknowledged many years later in his autobiography, *Dichtung und Wahrheit.* What he says there is corroborated by his friends and acquaintances of the "Werther" years. Goethe's emotional turmoil during this period is attested to in his letters and in the tone and mood and even the content of his early writings. His mental condition during this time, as we gather from his own repeated statements—both direct and oblique—in his writings, was characterized by terrible loneliness, by the inability to focus his mind on what he was doing, and by a rapid alternation between the extremes of joy and grief, pleasure and pain, idealism and despair. His ambivalence admits into the same breast superiority, conceit, arrogance—to the point of contempt for the opinion of others—and submissiveness and diffidence close to despair. He is self-centered and domineering and therefore unpopular; but he is also pliable and sensitive

3

to the climate that surrounds him and careful not to ruffle sensibilities. Consequently, even those who shake their heads about him are consumed with reverence and adoration and predict greatness for him in extravagant terms. "Emotion running riot," "a chaos of feeling"—these are the terms which students of Goethe apply to his pre-Weimar personality. He is unstable in temperament, in the life he leads, in the work he produces. Professor Fairley finds him intellectually immature in comparison with other poets like Keats, Shelley, or Hölderlin. And Emil Staiger, commenting on the fragmentary nature of his early writings, on the fact that he began so much and finished almost nothing, asks: "Has any other writer made such a spendthrift, planless beginning?" Goethe compares himself to Cain, Tantalus, Philoctetes, Orestes, St. Sebastian. He repeatedly reverts to the images of the chameleon, the weathercock, the peep show (*Raritätenkasten*), a ship in a storm, to describe himself and the literary characters who are the projections of his own image in the writings of these years. And the thought of suicide is often in his mind as the only release from the unhappiness that consumes him.

This state lasted about ten years (1765–1775) and was accompanied by a serious physical breakdown, the nature of which has never been precisely determined. The best description of Goethe's mental state is that given by Barker Fairley in *A Study of Goethe* (pp. 4–59); this able critic and admirer of Goethe does not shrink from employing the term "pathological" to characterize Goethe's state of mind. The harsh word is justified; but it should not be forgotten that this same disturbed, pathological young man had accumulated a solid education, had taken a law degree, was actually practicing law (in however desultory a fashion), was creating literature of high excellence—including lyric poetry that has remained within the canon of the world's best. And the evidence is there in abundance that, even before he became the famous author of *Werther,* Goethe impressed his contemporaries, to the point of extravagant enthusiasm, by his striking personality and abilities.

4

Goethe was not alone in this turbulence of mind. These "Werther" years (c. 1765–1785) are known in the history of German literature as the period of "Storm and Stress" (*Sturm und Drang*). It was an era of violent emotional reaction against the intellectualism of the Enlightenment (*Aufklärung*). The course of this rebellion parallels similar movements in England and France; indeed it received a strong impetus from those parallel developments. A wave of emotionalism had already inundated the *Aufklärung* itself; in Germany it began about 1740 and rose steadily through the following decades, as *Aufklärung* merged into *Sturm und Drang*. The English weeklies like the *Spectator, Tatler,* and *Rambler;* the novels of Richardson, Sterne, and Goldsmith; the lugubrious poetry of the "graveyard school"; the "tearful comedy" of Destouches and Nivelle de La Chaussée, and the bourgeois tragedy of Diderot; above all, the writings of Rousseau—were all influences which combined with native German tradition and the legacy of Pietism to promote the rebellion against cold Augustan reason, classical control, and good taste, in the name of freedom, individualism, and emotion.

Sturm und Drang is the first stage in the evolution of German romanticism, and it already shows all the later basic attitudes that we associate with romantic sensibility: enthusiasm for the natural, the rustic, and the primitive; the rebellion against rules and bonds, tradition and authority (political, social, religious); the cult of extreme individualism—indeed of extremism in general, symbolized by the yearning to break through the bounds of the finite and settle for nothing less than the infinite. It even bore within itself the paradox that characterized later romanticism: along with rebellion against tradition went a reverence for the national past.

The artistic credo of the *Sturm und Drang* was also basically that of later romanticism. The young titans rebelled against the neoclassical canon of good taste, based on rules. Against these rules they championed originality, native genius, organic growth, rather than mechanical regularity; they wanted free scope for the imagination and feelings; they showed enthusiasm for the "interesting," the

"picturesque," the rustic, the irregular, the rugged, the sublime as opposed to the "beautiful" (to which the eighteenth century assigned the attributes of regularity, symmetry, balance, correct size, and polish). The *Sturm und Drang* ideal of literary diction approximated that which Wordsworth later championed: the language of every day, the homely realism of the common man, the loose syntax of natural speech. Much of the power of Goethe's *Werther* derives from its diction, which conforms to the spirit of *Sturm und Drang* aesthetics.

This elaborate excursion into the historical background of Werther, into Goethe's personal involvement in the events and sentiments which form the raw material of his novel, requires some justification. The "biographical heresy" has been out of favor for some time in literary criticism. The new critics would have us pay no attention to the external circumstances in a writer's life, nor to the *Zeitgeist* as possible guides to an interpretation of the created work of art. "The play's the thing"; nothing else matters. Goethe himself, in the *Westöstlicher Divan,* berated the "anecdote hunters" who wish to see a *roman à clef* in every work of imaginative literature. But Goethe also made the oft-quoted statement that all his writings were fragments of a great confession. He meant that he was a subjective writer who used the raw materials which his own life had provided for him as the thematic content of his art, who created out of his personal experience rather than from a sheer empathic imagination. In his own activity as a literary critic Goethe was an early, perhaps the first, champion of the genetic method, which assumes that an awareness of the constellation that came together in the production of a work of art does help to enhance our aesthetic appreciation of the work. The preliminary sketches of a great painter, the notebooks of Beethoven which show the evolution of a phrase into a motif, the *brouillons* of Flaubert's *Madame Bovary,* are all pertinent to intelligent appreciation of the finished work. When we have studied the various elements that Goethe pulled together to make his *Werther,* our aesthetic appreciation is

bound to be the more intense. Consider, for instance, the last two sentences in the novel. Goethe took them from Kestner's report on the suicide of Jerusalem. The fact that Goethe realized their climactic value and put them at the very end of the tragic history affords us an insight into his genius that would otherwise be lacking; we can appreciate Goethe's skill as an artist when we see what he did with Kestner's report. The profound value in retracing the history of *Werther* comes from following Goethe's mind as his creative imagination weaves a pattern out of these disparate elements involving external events in the lives of three separate groups of people (Goethe and the Kestner's; Jerusalem and his colleague; Goethe and the Brentanos), but even more in observing with what wonderful skill and artistry he wove into this plot the intellectual and emotional factors that move these characters in this great tragic drama.

For *Werther* is a drama. Goethe first thought of writing it in dramatic form; and though what we now have is a subjective, "lyrical" presentation of a chain of events, seen almost entirely from the point of view of the hero-victim, there is intense drama everywhere in these pages, a constant state of conflict between protagonists, one of whom is always Werther, while the other is sometimes Albert, sometimes Wilhelm (the recipient of the letters, whose function it is to urge Werther to exercise control and common sense), again Werther's employer the Count, or the aristocratic group whom he offends, or the society with which he is constantly at odds. Even Lotte may be regarded as his antagonist, for she, like everyone else, places limits on his emotional expansion.

We have drama, too, inasmuch as the action of the novel may be divided into two acts, each with its cycle of initial calm, rising to a climax of excitement, and ending in a resolution of the conflict. Because Goethe ultimately did not choose to tell his story in the form of dialogue, he was able to exploit the relationship between Werther and the nature that surrounds him to a degree that the dramatic form would have made impossible.

But what is the theme of this drama? With some notable

7

exceptions among the more discriminating, generations saw in it the sentimental tale of a young man who cannot take defeat in love, who commits suicide because he can't "get the girl." They could, like Napoleon, wallow in the romance of it and possibly emulate Werther's behavior or, like Thackeray, ridicule the silly lover:

> Werther had a love for Charlotte,
>   Such as words could never utter,
> Would you know how first he met her?
>   She was cutting bread and butter.
>
> Charlotte was a married lady,
>   And a moral man was Werther,
> And for all the wealth of Indies
>   Would do nothing that might hurt her.
>
> So he sighed and pined and ogled,
>   And his passion boiled and bubbled;
> Till he blew his silly brains out,
>   And no more was by them troubled.
>
> Charlotte, having seen his body
>   Borne before her on a shutter,
> Like a well-conducted person
>   Went on cutting bread and butter.

Today we know better. *Werther* is not primarily a novel about a tragic love, but a profound character study of a psychological type who has become more and more central in our Western culture: the disillusioned or frustrated man, who cannot find a place for himself in society; for whom all life turns sour, the world becomes a prison; in whom these sentiments or attitudes assume pathological intensity. Goethe himself supplied the key to his intentions in a terse note written almost immediately after he had finished the original version of the novel. On June 1, 1774, he described it as "a novel in which I depict a young person who, endowed with profound and pure sensibility and true penetration, loses himself in romantic dreams, undermines himself through speculation, until finally, deranged by added unhappy passions—specifically an infinite love—

8

puts a bullet through his head." It is clear that Goethe saw in the love motif in *Werther* no more than an illustration of Werther's general character.

The skill with which Goethe makes Werther reveal himself in the early letters is one of the strong features of the novel. In a most natural way Werther exposes the principal traits of his character to us before he ever sees Lotte. If we go back to these early letters, we can see with what inevitability his later fate develops.

The fundamental trait in Werther's character is his emotionalism. He is a man of feeeling, with a noble scorn for the rationalism of his age as it is embodied in Albert. ". . . my heart," Werther writes in the letter of May 9, 1772, "which is really my sole source of pride, and which alone is the source of everything, of all my strength, all my bliss, and all my misery. Ah, what I know, everyone can know—my heart is mine alone." And in the argument with Albert on the subject of suicide (August 12, 1771), he throws down the gauntlet to the smug, sensible rationalists. "Oh you sensible people!" he exclaims with a smile. "Passion! Drunkenness! Madness! You stand there so calm, so unsympathetic, you moral men. You condemn the drunkard, abhor the insane man, pass by like the priest and thank God like the Pharisee that He did not make you as one of these." When Albert condemns suicide on the conventional grounds that it is a cowardly way of evading the responsibilities of life, Werther counters heatedly that it is, on the contrary, an act of exemplary courage like that of a rebel against an unbearable tyranny. And he makes a generalization that is of singular importance for understanding his psyche: "If energy is strength, why should excessive strain be its opposite?" In other words, he despises moderation as a sign of weakness; for passion is to him not a vice, but a higher degree of emotion and therefore a good thing. In his thinking he anticipates Nietzsche and modern psychology which recognizes that much bourgeois moderation has its source in timidity and cowardice (*Thus Spake Zarathustra:* Of the Pale Criminal). Friedrich Gundolf, in fact, described Werther as a "titan

9

of feeling," a companion to other Goethean figures of this period, to Prometheus the titan of creativity, to Caesar the titan of activity, to Faust the titan of effort.

What values does Werther's heart dictate to him? Foremost, perhaps, a powerful feeling for nature in all her moods. The second letter in the book contains the magnificent apotheosis to verdant nature, one of many such glorious tributes in the book. But Werther savors nature in her stormy and gloomy moods as well. Nature gives him that same feeling of expansion, of harmony with the cosmic order that Wordsworth recorded so memorably. She also offers him relief from the tension which is his normal state. The progress of his malady is reflected in the novel in the changed face of nature. In Book Two Werther sees her no longer in her happy moods but in her gloomy and threatening aspects. If this side of nature gives him comfort too, it is a masochistic comfort, the wry pleasure that the hypochondriac derives from the fact that all is unwell.

Werther is a man of nature in another sense too—in the Rousseauistic sense of championing the natural against the artificial conventions of society. He loves children and the common people, the downtrodden, the "innocent" criminal; he loves simplicity, naïveté, the primitive, the original, persecuted genius.

The insult to his dignity which Werther suffers at the hands of the aristocratic circle in which he moves—one of the central motifs of the novel—brings out this Rousseauistic quality in his character. That these empty-headed aristocrats should reject him as an unfit associate merely because he was not born with a handle to his name is an affront to nature. That his pedantic superior in office should censure his vivid, dynamic style in favor of mechanically correct syntax and vocabulary is equally unendurable to him. For in art, too, Werther is a man of feeling. Art should express emotion, not be shaped by reason. Accordingly in his very first letter he praises the late Count's garden because it bears the marks of having been laid out by a feeling heart rather than a cold, scientific mind. He brushes off with lofty contempt the neoclassical respect for rules in art.

10

A man who follows the rules will produce a "correct" work of art, just as a good bourgeois who obeys the rules of society will live a correct life. But how barren this is in comparison with the dynamic, though unbridled, life of the genius, or the vigorous, expressive, natural (though irregular) work of art of the Promethean creator.

But all this does not necessarily lead to a prognosis of suicide. After all, the history of human endeavor is filled with rebels against mass values who lived out their lives and repaid humanity for its neglect and hostility by leaving to posterity great works of art or thought or statesmanship. What makes the difference in Werther's case is two further features of his character: his urge to infinity and his inner disharmony.

Werther's statement, quoted above, about energy and excess of energy is an expression of his extremism. For the common-sense answer to his logic is that experience shows us repeatedly that an excess of even a good thing may be bad. But Werther is what is now called a perfectionist; nothing but the extreme, the absolute, will satisfy him. And since the search for the absolute is bound to end in frustration, he is perpetually frustrated in life. Even his adored nature becomes a disappointment to him; she cannot offer him lasting satisfaction. For in her, too, he sees a revelation of that infinity which is his ideal; but later on he finds that the glorious nature he so adored is nothing but a lacquered picture, without life; and he can no longer live in her, but stands aside and observes her apathetically.

For Werther the outside world is but a reflection of his inner mental state. Things exist only in the meaning which he assigns to them. He is one of the first of those modern men whose attitude is summed up in the words of Schopenhauer: the world is my representation. Since this inner representation is on a high level, reality fails him at every point. "Our imagination, compelled by its nature to elevate itself, nourished by the fantastic images of literature, creates a series of beings of whom we are the lowest, and everything outside ourselves seems more splendid to us, everyone else more perfect than we are. The process is quite natural" (October 20, 1771). His lot is perpetual disillu-

11

sionment: in nature, in his association with his fellow men, in love. This subjectivity in his approach to life is expressed in one of his favorite images: life is a dream; in his predilection for the half-light, his will to illusion. A consequence of this subjectivism is that he never seriously blames himself for his failures and unhappiness; it is always the fault of society or of the world order, of that *Schicksal* which plays an altogether disproportionate role in German thinking.

This subjectivism leads to a slighting of reality. For one thing, Werther can only see the restrictions which are put in the way of his will to achieve. Besides, the rhythm of life as it is lived by ordinary people becomes trivial to him; time and energy are wasted in carrying out the pointless chores of daily existence. We are on the way to the absurd universe of the existentialists.

As the universe becomes trivial, so Werther himself grows more and more exalted. Commentators on the novel have noted the Biblical language which Werther applies to himself in his later letters. He draws parallels, in situation and language, between his fate and that of Jesus as recorded in the Gospel of John. An examination of the relevant passages makes it clear that Werther regards himself as suffering a martyrdom similar to that of Jesus; he too is an innocent victim of human malevolence; he too is abandoned by God and goes to join God the Father in Heaven. This analogy is all the more striking as Werther is not an orthodox Christian, not a churchgoer, even rejecting altogether the mediation of Christ. To a Christian reader this identification of himself with Christ must look like blasphemy, unless it be interpreted as the excrescence of a disordered mind. If we remember that Werther was conceived as a warning rather than an example, it is clear that this latter interpretation is the one which Goethe intended to be taken from this Biblical analogy. He wished to show the logical end to which Wertherism leads. What more striking way could he have chosen to do so?

When we speak of a titan, we think of an indomitable, intrepid fighter like Prometheus or Oedipus. A titan seeks to break through the limitations which nature, his environ-

ment, his fellow-men—indeed the gods themselves—have placed in his path. Does Werther qualify for this distinction? Hardly. His passivity has often been noted. He himself more than once speaks of his emotional waywardness as a failing. Near the very beginning of the novel (May 13, 1771) he writes to Wilhelm: "You have never seen anything so uneven, so unsteady as this heart." And he continues in the same vein, referring to his swings between the poles of euphoria and melancholy, concluding that he pampers his heart as one pampers an ailing child, granting its every wish.

Goethe took great pains to underscore the weaknesses in Werther's character; he emerges as anything but a titanic being. His lofty superiority to all the Philistines he encounters and his sense of self-righteousness in every situation are but the surface camouflage for a deep feeling of insecurity which he recognizes as existing at the core of his being. "When we lack ourselves, we lack everything" (August 22, 1771). "Good Lord, Who hast given me all this, why didst Thou not withhold half of it and give me self-confidence and contentment? . . . We feel so often that we lack many things, and the very things we lack someone else often seems to us to possess, and we also attribute to him all that we have ourselves, and a certain ideal contentment into the bargain" (October 20, 1771).

It is difficult, in writing about Goethe's *Werther,* to avoid using the psychological jargon of our day; for some basic syndromes which modern psychiatry has made familiar to us are strikingly anticipated in the book. Two thorough studies—one by Ernst Feise in 1926, the other by Stuart Atkins in 1948, both elaborately documented—have explored the manifestations of depth psychology in Goethe's novel. From them Werther emerges as a neurotic character, suffering from a strong sense of inferiority which he attempts to overcome by making a masculine protest through nonconformity, rebellion, and contempt for his fellow men—to whom he applies such unflattering epithets as "dogmatic puppets," "fools," "rogues," "dogs," "weird eccentrics," "funny faces." The whole letter of May 22, 1771,

is a studied insult to average humanity. And this is the Werther who boasts of his love for the common folk. He is a highly self-centered narcissist, who refers all events and all values back to his own interest. He parades as a political and social revolutionary, and as such he is regarded by his contemporaries; but how much genuine principle is there behind his profession? For instance, he is not against class distinction as such, but only against those distinctions which work against him. His naturalistic or "biological" view of human relations meets his subjective needs. For him all nature shows a perpetual interacting between opposing forces, both material and spiritual, some creative, others destructive. This necessary interaction of forces is what we call destiny; both our physical and mental life are the products of natural laws over which the human will has little control. It is therefore meaningless, in his view, to apply ethical judgments to human behavior; one can at best trace it back to its causes and seek to "understand" it. This is a philosophy of life that is tailored to the needs of a weak-willed man, which Werther is. Atkins draws up a catalogue of Werther's accomplishments during the eighteen months covered by the action of the novel; it is not impressive. Feise goes further still and suggests that Werther has the will to fail. He cunningly sets himself goals that are impossible for him to attain, so that he need not exert himself to attain them. He can always console himself with the thought that he had the best intentions, and blame society or the environment for frustrating them. He can then indulge himself in the negative satisfaction of the hypochrondriac who enjoys his bad health and his failures.

This is also the pattern of his behavior in his affair with Lotte. If Werther is really so superior to Albert as he thinks he is, and if Lotte is the discriminating person he thinks she is, why does he not make a positive gesture to take her away from Albert before the marriage? We know from Kestner's diary that the real Charlotte had made it quite clear to the young Goethe that her lot was definitely tied to that of Kestner and that her interest in Goethe did not go beyond that of friendship. The Lotte of the novel is by no means so single-minded, neither before nor after her mar-

riage, and even less so in the first version of the book. Why then doesn't Werther exploit his conviction that Lotte is not indifferent to him? His correspondent Wilhelm puts this question to him and he replies to it in the letter of August 8, 1771. He tells Wilhelm that he will not be speared on the horns of an either-or dilemma. Can one expect, he asks, that a person suffering from a lingering disease shall suddenly thrust a dagger into his bosom and put an end to his torment? Does not his very disease rob him of the power to do something to liberate himself from its ravages? And then he answers another objection raised by Wilhelm: is it not preferable to lose one diseased limb and save the rest of the organism? He evades this. But it is significant that he has, in this discussion with Wilhelm, examined only the one of the two alternatives offered him: he has considered the "or" but not the "either." The idea that he might win Lotte away from Albert is not touched upon. Feise's suggestion that he no more wants to succeed in this venture than in any other is indeed plausible. During their last stormy interview Lotte says to him: "I fear it is only the impossibility of possessing me that makes this wish so attractive to you." H. A. Korff has an apt comment to make on this situation: Werther gives the impression of savoring the pain which his unhappy love affords him, so that he may not feel the terrible inner emptiness which increasingly takes possession of him as he goes through life.

Werther's constant need of excitement, change, and novelty makes the normal man's rhythm of tension and relaxation unacceptable to him. Like Faust he has two souls within his breast, each pulling in opposite directions. Basically we have in Werther that ambivalence of attitude which Thomas Mann later made familiar to us through his gallery of artist-intellectuals who feel both superior and inferior to the run-of-the-mill bourgeois. Yet, with all his need for change and excitement, Werther's fundamental character trait is perhaps sloth, which keeps him in an almost constant state of irritation. The letter of July 1, 1771, deals specifically and powerfully with this theme of sloth or ill-humor. Werther works himself into a passion against those who embitter life for their fellow men

through their ill-humor. For these others he recommends an act of will power and a dose of self-control. He calls them spoil-sports, who are fundamentally dissatisfied with themselves and envious of others who live in inner peace. "We see happy people," he continues, "whom we have not made happy and find this unendurable." He runs on for a while, using this revealing "we." Why is he so vehement on this subject, even bursting into tears? Is it because this impersonal "we" is really a very personal "I"? Is the final example which he gives of this type of sadism an instance in which he was more than a mere spectator, was in fact the actual cause of the unhappiness he describes? At any rate, one does not go far wrong in regarding this tirade as one that is directed at the speaker himself.

For in the following month he will write about himself: "It's a catastrophe, Wilhelm, my active powers have atrophied into a restless idleness; I can't be idle and yet can do nothing" (August 22, 1771). In his last letter to Wilhelm (December 20, 1772) he is more direct still: "It was simply my destiny to sadden those to whom I owed joy." Here we have the psychological mechanism at work: sloth leading to guilt and self-condemnation irritates him against the outside world, whereupon he proceeds to take vengeance by tormenting others. But "sadden" is an understatement. Like every masochist he is a sadist too, however unconsciously. What a cunning revenge he takes on the couple who have thwarted his love, through the way he takes his life. He blows out his brains with one of Albert's pistols, tells Lotte how happy he feels to have received it from her hands, and underscores the suggestion that his Christ-like passion is for her—he is shedding his blood in order that she may be happy with Albert! The effect of his cruel behavior is registered tersely in the third from the last sentence of the novel: "Lotte's life was feared to be in danger."

If, in the course of this discussion, little has been said of the love motif, it is because this theme is no more than one concrete illustration of Werther's method of handling a problem—any problem. But it would be critical blind-

16

ness to deny that the element of love plays a special role in the novel. Balzac, for instance, regarded it as a manual of love that provides a key to almost every situation of the human heart in love. That the work has so persistently been regarded as a romantic love tragedy, like *Romeo and Juliet,* is due to the fact that the love action does occupy most of the space in the book and is the principal event in it; but even more it is a tribute to Goethe's artistic powers. Himself endowed with a strong attraction to the Eternal Feminine, he knew superbly how to develop a love-entanglement and bring it to an inevitable conclusion.

There is, however, one aspect of Goethe's treatment of the love motif that may be described as novel: it is the fusion between love and religion, or the blurring of the distinction between heavenly and earthly love. Werther's love for Lotte is idealized passion in the courtly-love tradition, at least on the surface. He puts into it the spiritual energies which a Christian ought to reserve for his God and his religion. Werther tells us specifically that he is not a believing Christian; he conceives God as a creative force active in nature, to be apprehended through nature, which is, in the words of Faust, "God's living garment." The spiritual energy, which a man of Werther's sensibility must have in rich quantity, attaches itself to the object of his love, since he is too narcissistic to bestow it on anyone or anything else in life. His relation to his mother is one of unconcealed hostility; Wilhelm seems to exist for the sole purpose of receiving Werther's letters and executing various commissions for him. There is no one in Wahlheim with whom he is on a truly intimate footing except Lotte. So it is she who receives all the idealization that he is capable of giving, an idealization which serves the further purpose of covering over the fundamentally sensual nature of his desire. This sensuality comes out in various places; but generally Werther tries to conceal it from himself by emphasizing the sacred, spiritual nature of his feeling.

Since a good deal has been written about Werther's "religion," it is relevant to add one more comment on the subject. In 1939 Herbert Schoeffler published an essay arguing that in *Werther* Goethe had written a secular pas-

17

sion in imitation of the Passion of Christ, a serious parody of Christ's redemption of man through His sacrificial death on the Cross. Werther, too, dies a sacrificial death (if not for all mankind, at least for Albert and Lotte), so that the lovers may have a life of greater happiness. By following the Biblical account, Schoeffler argues, Goethe indicated that he regarded Werther's passion as being of equal importance with that of Christ: to sacrifice oneself for a profound love is, for modern man, as significant as Christ's otherworldly sacrifice for humanity. Werther is, in this interpretation, a good man animated by a noble passion which brings about his destruction because of the essential imperfection of the world order.

At the other end of the spectrum is Emil Staiger, who interprets Werther's turning to religion as a symptom of his malady: it is an attempt to submit once more to a way of thinking from which he has long become estranged and to murmur words of a reverent faith, which may be genuine enough, at a crucial time when emptiness stares him in the face. In other words, Staiger sees Werther's "religion" as one of those deathbed returns to faith which are attributed to certain eminent atheists and agnostics. Between these two extremes stands the thesis of Professor E. L. Stahl, who also sees *Werther* as a religious novel. The central theme, in Stahl's view, is Werther's relation to God, rather than his conflict with society. Werther rejects society because he feels close to God, in immediate contact with Him, as Jesus did. So he needs no mediator between himself and God, as other men do. Hence, when both society and nature fail him, he clings to God and goes to join Him. His suicide is therefore not weakness, but strength. Schoeffler's view seems to be obviously wrong, inasmuch as it assumes that Goethe intended Werther to appear as an admirable character. The documentary evidence, both within and outside of the text, refutes this assumption beyond dispute. If Schoeffler had argued that Werther regards himself as a Christ-like figure and his passion as in some form a parallel to that of Christ, he would have been on more solid ground; indeed such a view is more acceptable than that of Staiger. In Werther's confused and overexcited mind a fusion de-

velops between the most disparate elements: he mixes the sacred and the profane, the intellectual and the emotional. As Albert points out: making distinctions is not his strong point. Werther being what he is, it is very likely that, in his growing sickness, which includes wounded vanity, egoism, self-righteousness, and persecution mania, he would hit upon the analogy between his suffering and Christ's. Goethe was able to diagnose this clinically without presenting it sympathetically.

It is not unfair to interpret Goethe's intention in this sense; because Werther invests all his energy and all his idealism in this hopeless passion for Lotte, instead of diverting it, as Goethe did, into some other form of activity, whether social, personal, or aesthetic, when this passion fails, he has nothing left but suicide. Viewed from this perspective, the theme of love has a special symbolical value in the novel, and our former formulation must be revised, though it is still clear that the love motif is no more than an illustration of Werther's psychological problem. May not Goethe have been writing *pro domo?* By the time he composed *Werther,* he was already bothered by a pattern of behavior in love that had established itself in him: after an intense and wholehearted involvement, he would extricate himself ·and leave, even as Werther leaves at the end of the first book, though in a different spirit. May not Goethe unconsciously have depicted Werther's fate as an apology for his own behavior: if I had not extricated myself from these involvements, my character would have brought me to this?

We may now formulate the theme of *Werther* as the destruction of an extreme idealist by his contact with inexorable reality. This confrontation produces disillusionment or a series of frustrations, which lead him to question the value of life itself and ultimately to condemn it. For Werther's highly developed inner life cannot find any external activity, any objective correlative, to balance it or use it up. We see, or Werther would have us see, a natural genius stifled by narrow convention, an artistic soul forced to live in a society of Philistines, a pure and intense lover whose spiritual passion is frustrated by the circumstance that the

object of his love betrays him. All these setbacks desiccate his mind, so that he feels completely dead inside, unable to respond to anything in life, and thus becomes a forerunner of that totally alienated man whom the modern existentialists have rediscovered. Since he has nothing to live for, he decides to drain the bitter cup which fate has handed him and thereby achieve a signal blood-sacrifice for those he leaves behind him.

There remains the question: what does suicide mean for Werther? Here again it is worth going back to Goethe's own experience. There is ample documentation to indicate that Goethe, in his Werther period, seriously contemplated suicide as an escape from his mental turmoil. He even kept a dagger at his bedside and made repeated attempts to plunge it into his breast. But as he could never get it in very far, he decided to live. He made no effort to romanticize this ultimate act of negation by ascribing to it other motives than the selfish one of escape from the intolerable burden of life. But he did introduce into both *Werther* and *Faust* a metaphysical justification for suicide. Both Werther and Faust see in this act the realization and the fulfillment of those aspirations which they have been unable to realize here on earth. They regard suicide as the only possible liberation from the finiteness of this world; it makes possible a swifter union with God in the beyond. Both Werther and Faust see death, not as the end of life, but as the beginning of a new life. If one should object that such a belief is inconsistent with Werther's and Faust's undogmatic, vague, quasi-agnostic pantheism, the answer is that they both do believe in a spiritual realm beyond earthly reality. The texts are not intelligible on any other assumption. At any rate it is clear that Werther appeals to God the Father to receive him when he leaves this world and is confident that God will indeed receive him. Nor is there for him any ethical problem in this act of suicide; for he views suicide, like everything else, from the "biological" point of view. He is a mentally sick man, for whom the only remedy is suicide. He has as much moral right to make use of this cure as the physically sick man has to take the medicine that science offers him.

In his famous essay *On Naïve and Sentimental Literature* Schiller condensed into one marvelous paragraph a critique of Goethe's *Werther*. It is quoted here as a summarizing statement of the points made in the foregoing essay in interpretation:

"A character who embraces an ideal with glowing emotion and flees from reality to wrestle with an insubstantial infinite; who is incessantly seeking outside himself what he is incessantly destroying within himself; for whom dreams alone are reality, while his experiences are mere barriers; who finally sees nothing but a barrier in his own existence and, as is natural, tears down this barrier too in order to penetrate to the true reality—this dangerous extremism of the sentimental character became the raw material for a creative writer in whom nature is at work more faithfully and more purely than in any other and who, among modern writers, has perhaps moved the least distance away from the sensuous truth of things. It is interesting to see with what happy instinct everything that provides nourishment for the sentimental character has been compressed into Werther: romantic, unhappy love, sensibility to nature, religious feelings, the spirit of philosophical contemplation; finally, if we are to forget nothing, the gloomy, formless, melancholy world of Ossian. If one adds to this in what an uninviting, indeed hostile light reality is placed, and how everything in the outside world combines to drive the tormented man back into his ideal world, one can see no possible way in which such a character could escape from such a circle."

The form in which Goethe chose to cast the novel has taken nothing from the dramatic quality of its material. It enjoys the same classical simplicity of plot as Flaubert's *Madame Bovary,* together with the advantages accruing from the more open novel form. It is idle to repeat all the *post factum* justifications that have been given for the epistolary form in which the book has been cast. The novel in letters was a novelty that had established itself as a fashion. There was no "higher necessity" at play in the choice, except that it is especially appropriate that a sub-

jective hero like Werther should be allowed to tell his own story. Goethe's genius lies in having him tell a story that is so different from the one he thinks he is telling. While Werther believes he is justifying himself, the alert reader sees him for what he really is.

The plot is as simple as the dramatic conflict which it carries. After weathering some sort of emotional crisis, Werther arrives in a new town, begins to feel happy in nature and in the human contacts he makes. He meets Lotte and falls deeply in love with her. Her fiancé arrives and the classic triangle is formed. Werther leaves the town suddenly (Book I). He takes a diplomatic post, but is unhappy in his relations with his superior. Moreover, he suffers an unearned insult from the petty aristocrats with whom he associates. He therefore resigns his post and returns to the town in which Lotte, now married, lives with Albert. His love for her grows; since he sees no possibility of its fulfillment, he takes his own life (Book II).

To this simple plot Goethe has added a number of episodes designed to act as parallels to the main action, or to reveal character, or just to create atmosphere: such are the episodes of the nut trees; the peasant who experiences for his widowed employer a love similar to Werther's; the insane flower picker; the rustic scenes; the allusion to a former love; the relationship with Fräulein B.

Each of the two books is constructed dramatically: it begins with a tense calm and rises to a climax, followed by an explosion. While it is true that the book belongs to Werther, Goethe has nevertheless maintained a nice balance in distributing the lights and shadows on Albert and Lotte. He does not present a clear conflict between Werther at the one end of the seesaw and Albert and Lotte at the other, but rather with Werther and Albert at either end and Lotte at the center, bending alternately in either direction (though quite unconsciously), so that our suspense is maintained throughout the action. For, with all her resolution and straightforwardness and sound, bourgeois morality, Lotte is a woman; she appreciates fun and male attention. Here, much more than in Lessing's *Emilia*

22

Galotti, one could speculate on the "guilt" of the heroine in helping to produce the catastrophe.

It would require too much space to analyze in detail the artistic devices that Goethe uses to enhance the reader's aesthetic delight as he follows the unfolding of the action. These devices include the masterful handling of the natural landscape to create the proper atmosphere in each of Werther's varying moods; the hundreds of small allusions to men, events, and attitudes of the day—things that were familiar to the educated reader of Goethe's time, but must unfortunately be explained in footnotes today; the motivation and preparation of the principal events in the story; the gradual deterioration of Werther's own mind; the careful introduction and development of the suicide motif.

When we ask what it is in this novel that has held the attention and won the admiration of generations of sophisticated readers to this day, we are compelled to single out the rich variation in tone, imagery, and mood which the work presents. The idyllic and the rapturous, the humorous and the satirical, the casual sketching-in of genre scenes, matter-of-fact reporting, the deeply emotional descriptions of mental crisis, the worlds of Homer and Ossian and the everyday tone of modern realism—all are there in the right places and proportions.

Detailed studies have been made of the imagery and leitmotifs in which the novel abounds. There is a cluster of imagery that belongs to the preromantic world of Ossian and the folk ballad: the picturesque, the patriarchal, the idyllic, solitude, highly charged passion, the sentimental. There is the imagery taken from political struggle: freedom, prisons, chains, restriction, walls, the curtain lifted. There is the rich imagery of the Bible: God and Devil, heaven and hell, angels, prophets, saints, the blessed and the damned, pilgrims and Pharisees. But above all there is the imagery of disease and health: fever, intoxication, dizziness, madness, oppression, torment, anguish, pain, healing, comfort, balsam, and refreshment. These manifold images work like musical leitmotifs to keep the spirit of the book before the reader's mind. The title itself is a masterful example of artistic ambiguity. *Leiden* means suf-

fering, whether physical or mental. Goethe wants to imply both; for mental suffering is for Werther a physical disease, in line with his holistic view of life. There is another type of leitmotif which pervades the work: what is called in German the *"Dingsymbol."* There is a recurrent reference to fountains, to Lotte's melody, to trees.

On every page there is evidence of a striving for realism: in the use of homely language, in the broken sentences to suggest high emotion, in the repetitions and stammerings, in the fiction of an editor, in the footnotes and asterisks to conceal names. *Werther* is one of the first works in European literature to be composed in spoken, as opposed to literary, language. The vocabulary and rhythm are those of the spoken language, not those of rhetoric or high literature. This feature lends the work an exemplary freshness.

But the greatest artistic triumph which Goethe achieved is to make us feel, as Thomas Mann observed, the mortal weakness of his hero as exuberant strength. Even his exit from life seems to be that of a victorious conqueror. It is only when we read the text closely that we see the pathetic creature that Goethe has put before us. To have created a character on these two levels is a triumph. But it may well be that Goethe, realizing how much of Werther there was in himself, set out to make a "hero" of Werther, to vindicate him by blaming society for his fate. But his artistic eye saw clearly that the fault lay in Werther, not in his stars. As a man he felt sympathy for Werther's plight; as an artist he felt compelled to condemn him.

Werther became famous at once, not only in Germany but abroad too. Its fame reached even China, where scenes from the novel were used to decorate chinaware. Sentimental young men sported Werther's costume: blue coat and yellow trousers and vest; some lovelorn creatures followed his example and committed suicide with copies of the novel in their pockets. There has been much sneering at *Werther* as a typical product of German sentimentality. It is well to remember that the *Werther* craze was European in scope, that it lasted a long time—though in attenuated form—and that there was strong opposition to

"Wertherism" in Germany too. There were many imitations of the novel in European literature, adaptations, parodies, attacks both from the camp of the rationalists and from narrow orthodox Christians, who saw in the work an apology of *Weltschmerz* rather than a warning against it. Kestner protested at the uncalled-for publicity which it brought him and Charlotte (those were different times!) and Goethe had some explaining to do. At first he was proud of the work; later he developed a strong aversion to it. In 1780 he reread it for the first time since its appearance and expressed astonishment at the book. Two years later he began to revise it; the revision was not completed till 1786; it is the version which has become standard and is reprinted here. He did not read the novel again until 1824, when the publisher of the original work, Weygand of Leipzig, suggested issuing a de luxe reprint to commemorate the fiftieth anniversary of its publication and asked Goethe to write a preface to the book. Goethe read the proofs of this reprint and was strengthened in the aversion which he had expressed in conversation to different people over the years. Instead of a preface he composed the poignant poem *An Werther,* in which he envies his hero for having escaped from this world so early, leaving his creator to relive Werther's sufferings over and over again:

Noch einmal wagst du, vielbeweinter Schatten,
Hervor dich an das Tageslicht,
Begegnest mir auf neu beblümten Matten,
Und meinen Anblick scheust du nicht.
Est ist, als ob du lebtest in der Frühe,
Wo uns der Tau auf Einem Feld erquickt
Und nach des Tages unwillkommner Mühe
Der Scheidesonne letzter Strahl entzückt;
Zum Bleiben ich, zum Scheiden du erkoren,
Gingst du voran — und hast nich viel verloren.

Du lächelst, Freund, gefühlvoll, wie sich ziemt:
Ein gräßlich Scheiden machte dich berühmt;
Wir feierten dein kläglich Mißgeschick,
Du ließest uns zu Wohl und Weh zurück.
Dann zog uns wieder ungewisse Bahn

Der Leidenschaften labyrinthisch an;
Und wir, verschlungen wiederholter Not,
Dem Scheiden endlich — Scheiden ist der Tod!
Wie klingt es rührend, wenn der Dichter singt,
Den Tod zu meiden, den das Scheiden bringt!
Verstrickt in solche Qualen, halbverschuldet,
Gab ihm ein Gott zu sagen, was er duldet.*

For Goethe was once more involved in a hopeless love—this time for the young Ulrike von Levetzow.

In seeking to account for the unending popularity that *Werther* has enjoyed we must realize that Goethe made a good choice of material. The Werther malady was particuuarly rife throughout the romantic period of European literature. This is shown not only by the high regard in which Goethe's work was held, but by the many imitations that appeared during the following half-century. It is therefore rather futile for German historians of literature to seek an explanation for its hold on people in the conditions of German life and thought that existed in the Werther years; this could at best account for the book's popularity in its own day. Goethe himself saw more deeply when he told Eckermann in 1824 that *Werther* captures a definite situation in the life of young people everywhere and at all times. Wertherism, in other words, is a world phenomenon, not a provincial, eighteenth-century German affair.

But the most fundamental question is: why is it Goethe's *Werther* that has survived and not the romantic heroes of Benjamin Constant or Ugo Foscolo? The answer is that Goethe's *Werther* is incomparably superior to all its progeny. Despite its passages of intolerable sentimentality, it

* Once more you venture, much bewept shadow, forth into the light of day, confront me on new flowering meadows, and do not retreat before my view. It is as if you were living in the early morning, when the dew refreshes us on one field, and after the unwelcome effort of the day the last ray of the parting sun delights us; I—chosen to stay, you to depart; you went ahead—and did not lose much.

You smile, friend, with deep feeling, as is proper: a gruesome parting made you famous; we celebrated your wretched misfortune, you left us behind for weal and woe. Then the uncertain, labyrinthine path of the passions drew us once more; and we, entwined in repeated distress, finally for parting—parting is death! How touching it sounds when the poet sings, to avoid the death which parting brings! Enmeshed in such torments, half involved in guilt, a god gave him the power to say what he endures.

is richly endowed, in its structure, psychological penetration, its fresh, vigorous imagery and diction, with the attributes of greatness.

EDITOR'S NOTE

The proposal for a dual-language edition of Goethe's *Werther* came from the publisher. It struck the editor as a happy thought: to make this world's classic available to a large public at modest cost, in a form that will permit a careful reading of the work in German at an early stage in the study of the language. The foreign-language lists of most publishers are heavily weighted in favor of ultra-modern, ephemeral meteors of yesterday and today. This unhappy trend is being reversed by Bantam Books in its bilingual series, which is building up a collection of the best literature of Europe. The decision to include Goethe's *Werther* in this series will surely be welcomed by every serious teacher of German.

Bearing in mind the needs of this special public, the editor has had to make a number of choices in preparing the edition. On the one hand, he set himself the goal of producing a scholarly text, with corresponding notes, and a critical introduction, so that it might be used with profit even by advanced students of German. The text offered here has been arrived at after consulting the *Jubiläumsausgabe* of Goethe's works, the *Hamburgerausgabe,* edited by Professor Erich Trunz, and the *Artemis* Goethe, edited by the late Ernst Beutler. All these have modernized the spelling and punctuation of the original editions. To make the book accessible to learners of German, the present editor has gone a little further than these authorities in handling spelling, punctuation, and elisions. This seems all the more justified inasmuch as the editors of the above-mentioned Goethe editions differ among themselves on these matters.

Among the works consulted in the preparation of this book, two deserve special mention: the edition of *Werther*

by Ernst Feise (Oxford University Press), and that by Erich Trunz in the *Hamburgerausgabe*.

My thanks are also due to Mr. Theodore Lustig for his careful reading of my translation and his many excellent suggestions for improving it.

THE SUFFERINGS
OF YOUNG WERTHER

Was ich von der Geschichte des armen Werther nur habe auffinden können, habe ich mit Fleiß gesammelt, und lege es euch hier vor und weiß, daß ihr mir's danken werdet. Ihr könnt seinem Geiste und seinem Charakter eure Bewunderung und Liebe, seinem Schicksale eure Tränen nicht versagen.

Und du gute Seele, die du eben den Drang fühlst wie er, schöpfe Trost aus seinem Leiden, und laß das Büchlein deinen Freund sein, wenn du aus Geschick oder eigener Schuld keinen nähern finden kannst.

ERSTES BUCH

Am 4. Mai 1771

Wie froh bin ich, daß ich weg bin! Bester Freund, was ist das Herz des Menschen! Dich zu verlassen, den ich so liebe, von dem ich unzertrennlich war, und froh zu sein! Ich weiß, Du verzeihst mir's. Waren nicht meine übrigen Verbindungen recht ausgesucht vom Schicksal, um ein Herz wie das meine zu ängstigen? Die arme Leonore[1]! Und doch war ich unschuldig. Konnt' ich dafür[2], daß, während die eigensinnigen Reize ihrer Schwester mir eine angenehme Unterhaltung verschafften, daß eine Leidenschaft in dem armen Herzen sich bildete! Und doch — bin ich ganz unschuldig? Hab' ich nicht ihre Empfindungen genährt? Hab' ich mich nicht an den ganz wahren Ausdrücken der Natur, die uns so oft zu lachen machten, so wenig lächerlich sie waren, selbst ergötzt, hab' ich nicht — Oh, was ist der Mensch, daß er über sich klagen darf! Ich will, lieber Freund, ich verspreche Dir's, ich will mich bessern, will nicht mehr ein bißchen Übel, das uns das Schicksal vorlegt, wiederkäuen, wie ich's immer getan habe; ich will das Gegenwärtige genießen, und das Vergangene

Whatever I have been able to discover about the story of poor Werther, I have collected with diligence and am putting before you, and I know that you will thank me for it. You will not be able to refuse his spirit and his character your admiration and your love, nor his fate your tears.

And you, good soul, who feel the same anguish as he, derive comfort from his sufferings, and let this little book be your friend if your destiny or your own fault prevent you from finding a closer one.

BOOK ONE

May 4, 1771

How glad I am to be gone! Dearest friend, what is the heart of man! To leave you, whom I love so much, from whom I was inseparable, and yet to be glad! I know you will forgive me. Were not my other attachments deliberately designed by fate to torment a heart like mine? Poor Leonore! And yet I was innocent. Could I help it that, while her sister's striking charms provided me with pleasant entertainment, a passion for me grew in her unfortunate heart? And yet, am I wholly innocent? Did I not encourage her emotions? Did I not find delight in the wholly sincere expressions of nature which so often made us laugh, though they were hardly ridiculous? Did I not—oh, what is man, that he dare accuse himself? I will, dear friend, I promise you, I will improve; I will no longer, as I have always done, ruminate upon the bit of misfortune that destiny puts in our path; I will enjoy the present, and the past shall be past for me. Of course you are right, my dear friend, there would be less suffering among men if they did not—God knows why they are so made—expend so much zeal and

31

soll mir vergangen sein. Gewiß, Du hast recht, Bester, der Schmerzen[3] wären minder unter den Menschen, wenn sie nicht — Gott weiß, warum sie so gemacht sind — mit so viel Emsigkeit der Einbildungskraft sich beschäftigten, die Erinnerungen des vergangenen Übels zurückzurufen eher als eine gleichgültige Gegenwart zu ertragen.

Du bist so gut, meiner Mutter zu sagen, daß ich ihr Geschäft bestens betreibe und ihr eh'stens Nachricht davon geben werde. Ich habe meine Tante gesprochen und bei weitem das böse Weib nicht gefunden, das man bei uns aus ihr macht. Sie ist eine muntere, heftige Frau von dem besten Herzen. Ich erklärte ihr meiner Mutter Beschwerden über den zurückgehaltenen Erbschaftsanteil; sie sagte mir ihre Gründe, Ursachen und die Bedingungen, unter welchen sie bereit wäre, alles herauszugeben, und mehr als wir verlangten. — Kurz, ich mag jetzt nichts davon schreiben; sage meiner Mutter, es werde alles gut gehen. Und ich habe, mein Lieber, wieder bei diesem kleinen Geschäft gefunden, daß Mißverständnisse und Trägheit vielleicht mehr Irrungen in der Welt machen als List und Bosheit. Wenigstens sind die beiden letzteren gewiß seltener.

Übrigens befinde ich mich hier gar wohl. Die Einsamkeit ist meinem Herzen köstlicher Balsam in dieser paradiesischen Gegend, und diese Jahreszeit der Jugend wärmt mit aller Fülle mein oft schauderndes Herz. Jeder Baum, jede Hecke ist ein Strauß von Blüten, und man möchte zum Maienkäfer werden, um in dem Meer von Wohlgerüchen herumschweben und alle seine Nahrung darin finden zu können.

Die Stadt selbst ist unangenehm, dagegen ringsumher eine unaussprechliche Schönheit der Natur. Das bewog den verstorbenen Grafen von M . . ., seinen Garten auf einem der Hügel anzulegen, die mit der schönsten Mannigfaltigkeit sich kreuzen und die lieblichsten Täler bilden. Der Garten ist einfach, und man fühlt gleich bei dem Eintritte, daß nicht ein wissenschaftlicher Gärtner, sondern ein fühlendes Herz[4] den Plan gezeichnet, das seiner selbst hier genießen wollte. Schon manche Träne hab' ich dem Abgeschiedenen in dem verfallenen Kabinettchen geweint, das

imagination in recalling the memory of past misfortunes, instead of enduring an indifferent present.

Will you be good enough to tell my mother that I will look after her business as best I can and report to her about it as soon as possible. I have spoken to my aunt and found her anything but the disagreeable woman we make of her at home. She is a lively, impetuous woman with the best of hearts. I explained to her my mother's complaints about the portion of the inheritance that has been withheld from her; she told me her grounds, reasons, and the conditions under which she would be prepared to give up everything, even more than we ask for.—In short, I don't want to write about the matter now; tell my mother that everything will come out all right. And, my dear friend, I have found once again in this little affair that misunderstandings and indolence cause more error in the world than cunning and malice. At least the latter two are much rarer.

For the rest, I feel very comfortable here. The solitude in this heavenly region is a precious balm for my heart, and this youthful season warms my often shivering heart with its abundance. Every tree, every hedge is a bouquet of blossoms; and one would like to turn into a cockchafer, to be able to float upon this sea of perfume and to find all his nourishment in it.

The town itself is disagreeable, but the surrounding country has an inexpressible natural beauty. That is why the late Count von M— was induced to lay out a garden on one of the hills which cross each other in the most beautiful variety and form the loveliest valleys. The garden is simple, and the moment you enter it you feel that it was planned, not by a scientific gardener but by a feeling heart which wanted to enjoy itself here. I have already shed many a tear for the deceased in the ruined summerhouse which was his favorite spot and is mine too. I shall soon be master

33

sein Lieblingsplätzchen war und auch meines ist. Bald werde ich Herr vom Garten sein; der Gärtner ist mir zugetan nur seit den paar Tagen, und er wird sich nicht übel dabei befinden.

Am 10. Mai

Eine wunderbare Heiterkeit hat meine ganze Seele eingenommen, gleich den süßen Frühlingsmorgen, die ich mit ganzem Herzen genieße. Ich bin allein und freue mich meines Lebens in dieser Gegend, die für solche Seelen geschaffen ist wie die meine. Ich bin so glücklich, mein Bester, so ganz in dem Gefühle von ruhigem Dasein versunken, daß meine Kunst darunter leidet. Ich könnte jetzt nicht zeichnen, nicht einen Strich, und bin nie ein größerer Maler gewesen als in diesen Augenblicken[5]. Wenn das liebe Tal um mich dampft und die hohe Sonne an der Oberfläche der undurchdringlichen Finsternis meines Waldes ruht und nur einzelne Strahlen sich in das innere Heiligtum stehlen, ich dann im hohen Grase am fallenden Bache liege und näher an der Erde tausend mannigfaltige Gräschen mir merkwürdig werden; wenn ich das Wimmeln der kleinen Welt zwischen Halmen, die unzähligen, unergründlichen Gestalten der Würmchen, der Mückchen näher an meinem Herzen fühle und fühle die Gegenwart des Allmächtigen, der uns nach seinem Bilde schuf, das Wehen des Allliebenden, der uns in ewiger Wonne schwebend trägt und erhält; mein Freund, wenn's dann um meine Augen dämmert[6], und die Welt um mich her und der Himmel ganz in meiner Seele ruhn wie die Gestalt einer Geliebten, dann sehne ich mich oft und denke: Ach, könntest du das wieder ausdrücken, könntest du dem Papiere das einhauchen, was so voll, so warm in dir lebt, daß es würde der Spiegel deiner Seele, wie deine Seele ist der Spiegel des unendlichen[7] Gottes! — Mein Freund! — Aber ich gehe darüber zugrunde, ich erliege unter der Gewalt der Herrlichkeit dieser Erscheinungen.

Am 12. Mai

Ich weiß nicht, ob täuschende Geister um diese Gegend

34

of the garden; the gardener has become attached to me in these few days I've been here, and he will not regret it.

A wonderful serenity has taken possession of my whole soul, like the sweet spring mornings which I enjoy with all my heart. I am alone and am enjoying my life in this region, which was made just for souls such as mine. I am so happy, my dear friend, so completely absorbed by the feeling of peaceful existence, that my art is suffering. I couldn't draw now, not a stroke, and yet I have never been a greater painter than at these moments. When the lovely valley around me is shrouded in mist and the high sun rests on the surface of the impenetrable darkness of my forest, and only single rays steal into the inner sanctuary; when I lie in the tall grass beside the cascading brook, and close to the ground a thousand varieties of tiny grasses fill me with wonder; when I feel this teeming little world among the stalks closer to my heart—the countless, unfathomable forms of tiny worms and gnats—and feel the presence of the Almighty, Who created us in His image, the breath of the All-loving One who, floating in eternal bliss, bears and sustains us; my friend! when my eyes then grow misty and the world about me and the sky lie wholly within me like the form of a beloved woman—then I often think with yearning: oh, if you could express this once more, if you could breathe onto the paper what dwells so fully, so warmly within you, so that it became the mirror of your soul, as your soul is the mirror of infinite God!—My friend —but this will destroy me, I succumb to the power of these glorious manifestations.

May 12

I don't know whether delusive spirits hover about this

schweben, oder ob die warme himmlische Phantasie in meinem Herzen ist, die mir alles rings umher so paradiesisch macht. Da ist gleich vor dem Orte ein Brunnen[8], ein Brunnen, an den ich gebannt bin wie Melusine[9] mit ihren Schwestern. — Du gehst einen kleinen Hügel hinunter und findest Dich vor einem Gewölbe, da wohl zwanzig Stufen hinabgehen, wo unten das klarste Wasser aus Marmorfelsen quillt. Die kleine Mauer, die oben umher die Einfassung macht, die hohen Bäume, die den Platz rings umher bedecken, die Kühle des Orts, das hat alles so was Anzügliches[10], was Schauerliches. Es vergeht kein Tag, daß ich nicht eine Stunde da sitze. Da kommen dann die Mädchen aus der Stadt und holen Wasser, das harmloseste Geschäft und das nötigste, das ehemals die Töchter der Könige selbst verrichteten. Wenn ich da sitze, so lebt die patriarchalische Idee so lebhaft um mich, wie sie alle, die Altväter, am Brunnen Bekanntschaft machen und freien[11], und wie um die Brunnen und Quellen wohltätige Geister schweben. Oh, der muß nie nach einer schweren Sommertagswanderung sich an des Brunnens Kühle gelabt haben, der das nicht mitempfinden kann.

Am 13. Mai

Du fragst, ob Du mir meine Bücher schicken sollst? — Lieber, ich bitte Dich um Gottes willen, laß mir sie vom Halse! Ich will nicht mehr geleitet, ermuntert, angefeuert sein, braust dieses Herz doch genug aus sich selbst; ich brauche Wiegengesang, und den habe ich in seiner Fülle gefunden in meinem Homer[12]. Wie oft lull' ich mein empörtes Blut zur Ruhe; denn so ungleich, so unstet hast Du nichts gesehn als dieses Herz. Lieber, brauch' ich Dir das zu sagen, der Du so oft die Last getragen hast, mich vom Kummer zur Ausschweifung und von süßer Melancholie zur verderblichen Leidenschaft übergehen zu sehn? Auch halte ich mein Herzchen wie ein krankes Kind; jeder Wille wird ihm gestattet. Sage das nicht weiter; es gibt Leute, die mir es verübeln würden.

region or whether it is the warm, heavenly fantasies in my heart which turn everything about me into such a paradise. Just outside the town there is a well, a well which holds me in its spell like Melusine and her sisters. You go down a little hill and find yourself in front of an arch; about twenty steps lead down to a place where the clearest water flows from marble rocks. The little wall that surrounds the place above, the tall trees which shade it all around, the coolness of the spot—all this has something so attractive, so thrilling about it. Not a day passes that I do not spend an hour sitting there. The girls come from the town to fetch water, that most innocent and most necessary occupation, which at one time the daughters of kings performed themselves. When I sit there the patriarchal idea lives so vividly about me, I see how they, all those patriarchs, form their acquaintanceship and do their courting at the well, and how beneficent spirits hover about wells and springs. Oh, the man who cannot feel this with me can never have taken comfort from the coolness of a well after a hard day of summer walking.

May 13

You ask whether you should send me my books.—Dear friend, I beg you in God's name, don't saddle me with them! I don't want to be guided, encouraged, inspired any more, for this heart is bubbling enough by itself. I need lullabies, and these I have found in abundance in my Homer. How often I lull my seething blood to rest, for you have never seen anything so uneven, so unsteady as this heart. Dear friend! Need I tell this to you, who have so often borne the burden of seeing me pass from grief to wild exuberance and from sweet melancholy to destructive passion? Moreover I coddle my little heart like a sick child; I grant its every wish. Don't tell this to anyone; there are people who would resent it.

Die geringen Leute des Ortes kennen mich schon und lieben mich, besonders die Kinder[13]. Wie ich im Anfange mich zu ihnen gesellte, sie freundschaftlich fragte über dies und das, glaubten einige, ich wollte ihrer spotten, und fertigten mich wohl gar grob ab. Ich ließ mich das nicht verdrießen; nur fühlte ich, was ich schon oft bemerkt habe, auf das lebhafteste: Leute von einigem Stande werden sich immer in kalter Entfernung vom gemeinen Volke halten, als glaubten sie durch Annäherung zu verlieren; und dann gibt's Flüchtlinge[14] und üble Spaßvögel, die sich herabzulassen scheinen, um ihren Übermut dem armen Volke desto empfindlicher zu machen.

Ich weiß wohl, daß wir nicht gleich sind noch sein können; aber ich halte dafür, daß der, der nötig zu haben glaubt, vom sogenannten Pöbel sich zu entfernen, um den Respekt zu erhalten, ebenso tadelhaft ist als ein Feiger, der sich vor seinem Feinde verbirgt, weil er zu unterliegen fürchtet.

Letzthin kam ich zum Brunnen und fand ein junges Dienstmädchen, das ihr Gefäß auf die unterste Treppe gesetzt hatte, und sich umsah, ob keine Kameradin kommen wollte, ihr es auf den Kopf zu helfen. Ich stieg hinunter und sah sie an. — „Soll ich Ihr[15] helfen, Jungfer?" sagte ich. — Sie ward[16] rot über und über. — „O nein, Herr!" sagte sie. — „Ohne Umstände." — Sie legte ihren Kringen[17] zurecht, und ich half ihr. Sie dankte und stieg hinauf.

Den 17. Mai

Ich habe allerlei Bekanntschaft gemacht, Gesellschaft habe ich noch keine gefunden. Ich weiß nicht, was ich Anzügliches für die Menschen haben muß; es mögen mich ihrer so viele und hängen sich an mich, und da tut mir's weh, wenn unser Weg nur eine kleine Strecke miteinander geht. Wenn Du fragst, wie die Leute hier sind, muß ich Dir sagen: wie überall! Es ist ein einförmiges Ding um das Menschengeschlecht. Die meisten verarbeiten den größten

The common people of the place know me already and love me, especially the children. When I first sought their company and asked them about this and that in a friendly way, some of them thought that I wanted to make fun of them and even brushed me off rudely. I was not angry with them; I only felt most keenly what I have often noticed before: that people of some social position will always coldly keep at a distance from the common folk as if they thought they would lose something by closer contact; and then there are shallow minds and evil-minded pranksters who pretend to condescend only to make the poor people feel their arrogance the more keenly.

I know quite well that we are not all equal and cannot be so; but I hold that the man who thinks it necessary to keep himself aloof from the so-called mob in order to remain respectable is as much to blame as a coward who hides from his enemy because he is afraid of being defeated.

Recently I came to the well and found a young servant girl who had set her pitcher on the lowest step and was looking around to see if some other girl might be coming to help her place it on her head. I went down and looked at her. "Shall I help you, Miss?" I said.—She blushed deeply.—"Oh no sir," she said.—"It's nothing at all."—She adjusted her headgear and I helped her. She thanked me and walked up the stairs.

I have made all sorts of acquaintances, but have found no true companions yet. I don't know what attraction I must possess for people; so many of them like me and attach themselves to me, and then it hurts me when we can travel the same road only a short stretch. If you ask me what the people here are like, I must tell you, like people everywhere. The human race is a uniform commodity. Most people work the greatest part of the time to earn a

Teil der Zeit, um zu leben, und das bißchen, das ihnen von Freiheit übrig bleibt, ängstigt sie so, daß sie alle Mittel aufsuchen, um es los zu werden.[18] O Bestimmung des Menschen!

Aber eine recht gute Art Volks! Wenn ich mich manchmal vergesse, manchmal mit ihnen die Freuden genieße, die den Menschen noch gewährt sind, an einem artig besetzten Tisch mit aller Offen- und Treuherzigkeit sich herumzuspaßen, eine Spazierfahrt, einen Tanz zur rechten Zeit anzuordnen und dergleichen, das tut eine ganz gute Wirkung auf mich; nur muß mir nicht einfallen, daß noch so viele andere Kräfte in mir ruhen, die alle ungenutzt vermodern und die ich sorgfältig verbergen muß. Ach, das engt das ganze Herz so ein. — Under doch, mißverstanden zu werden, ist das Schicksal von unsereinem.

Ach, daß die Freundin[19] meiner Jugend dahin ist! Ach, daß ich sie je gekannt habe! — Ich würde sagen[20]: du bist ein Tor, du suchst, was hienieden nicht zu finden ist; aber ich habe sie gehabt, ich habe das Herz gefühlt, die große Seele, in deren Gegenwart ich mir schien mehr zu sein, als ich war, weil ich alles war, was ich sein konnte. Guter Gott! blieb da eine einzige Kraft meiner Seele[21] ungenutzt? Konnt' ich nicht vor ihr das ganze wunderbare Gefühl entwickeln, mit dem mein Herz die Natur umfaßt? War unser Umgang nicht ein ewiges Weben von der feinsten Empfindung, dem schärfsten Witze, dessen Modifikationen bis zur Unart alle mit dem Stempel des Genies[22] bezeichnet waren? Und nun! — Ach ihre Jahre, die sie voraus hatte, führten sie früher ans Grab als mich. Nie werde ich sie vergessen, nie ihren festen Sinn und ihre göttliche Duldung.

Vor wenig Tagen traf ich einen jungen V . . . an, einen offnen Jungen, mit einer gar glücklichen Gesichtsbildung. Er kommt erst von Akademien, dünkt sich eben nicht weise, aber glaubt doch, er wisse mehr als andere. Auch war er fleißig, wie ich an allerlei spüre, kurz, er hat hübsche Kenntnisse. Da er hörte, daß ich viel zeichnete und Griechisch könnte (zwei Meteore hierzulande), wandte er sich an mich und kramte viel Wissens[23] aus, von Batteux bis zu Wood, von de Piles zu Winckelmann, und versicherte mich, er habe Sulzers Theorie, den ersten Teil, ganz durch-

living, and the little bit of freedom that they have left causes them such anxiety that they ferret out every means of getting rid of it. Oh, destiny of man!

But they are a really decent sort. When I occasionally forget myself, and share with them the pleasures that are still granted to human beings, such as enjoying myself, in all frankness and sincerity, at a well-stocked table, arranging an excursion or dance at the right time, and so on, he effect on me is quite salutary; but I must not be reminded that so many other forces lie dormant within me, atrophying for lack of use, and which I must carefully conceal. Oh, how that constricts my heart!—And yet, to be misunderstood is the fate of a man like me.

Alas, that the friend of my youth is gone, alas that I ever knew her!—I would say: you are a fool; you are looking for what cannot be found here below; but I did possess her friendship, I did feel her heart, her noble soul, in the presence of which I seemed to be more in my own eyes than I really was, because I was everything I could be. Good Heavens! Was there any faculty of my mind that was idle? Could I not unfold before her the whole marvelous feeling with which my heart embraces nature? Was our association not an endless stirring of the most delicate emotions, the sharpest wit, the variations of which were all stamped with the mark of genius to the point of wantonness? And now!—Alas, the years that she had in advance of me led her to the grave before me. Never shall I forget her, never her firm mind and her divine patience.

A few days ago I met a young man, V—, a frank boy with most pleasing features. He has just left the university, does not exactly think himself wise, but still believes that he knows more than other people. He was diligent, too, for which I have all sorts of evidence; in short, he is quite well informed. When he heard that I do a lot of sketching and know Greek (two unusual accomplishments in this part of the country), he turned toward me and unloaded much learning, from Batteux to Wood, from De Piles to Winckelmann, and assured me that he had read through the entire

gelesen und besitze ein Manuskript[24] von Heynen über das Studium der Antike. Ich ließ das gut sein.

Noch gar einen[25] braven Mann habe ich kennenlernen, den fürstlichen Amtmann, einen offenen, treuherzigen Menschen. Man sagt, es soll eine Seelenfreude sein, ihn unter seinen Kindern zu sehen, deren er neun hat; besonders macht man viel Wesens[26] von seiner ältesten Tochter. Er hat mich zu sich gebeten, und ich will ihn eh'ster Tage besuchen. Er wohnt auf einem fürstlichen Jagdhofe, anderthalb Stunden von hier, wohin er, nach dem Tode seiner Frau, zu ziehen die Erlaubnis erhielt, da ihm der Aufenthalt hier in der Stadt und im Amthause zu weh tat.

Sonst sind mir einige verzerrte Originale in den Weg gelaufen, an denen alles unausstehlich ist, am unerträglichsten ihre Freundschaftsbezeigungen.

Leb wohl! Der Brief wird Dir recht sein, er ist ganz historisch[27].

Am 22. Mai

Daß das Leben des Menschen nur ein Traum sei, ist manchen schon so vorgekommen, und auch mit mir zieht dieses Gefühl immer herum. Wenn ich die Einschränkung ansehe, in welcher die tätigen und forschenden Kräfte des Menschen eingesperrt sind; wenn ich sehe, wie alle Wirksamkeit dahinaus läuft, sich die Befriedigung von Bedürfnissen zu verschaffen, die wieder keinen Zweck haben, als unsere arme Existenz zu verlängern, und dann, daß alle Beruhigung über gewisse Punkte des Nachforschens nur eine träumende Resignation ist, da man sich die Wände, zwischen denen man gefangen sitzt, mit bunten Gestalten und lichten Aussichten bemalt. — Das alles, Wilhelm, macht mich stumm. Ich kehre in mich selbst zurück und finde eine Welt! Wieder mehr in Ahnung[28] und dunkler Begier als in Darstellung und lebendiger Kraft. Und da schwimmt alles vor meinen Sinnen, und ich lächle dann so träumend weiter in die Welt.

Daß die Kinder nicht wissen, warum sie wollen, darin

first part of Sulzer's *Theory,* and possessed a manuscript by Heyne on the study of classical antiquity. I took his word for it.

I've made the acquaintance of another very nice person, the Prince's bailiff, a candid, sincere person. They say it is a joy to see him among his children—he has nine of them; they mention especially his oldest daughter. He invited me to his home and I will visit him very soon. He lives in one of the Prince's hunting lodges, an hour and a half away, where he was permitted to move after the death of his wife, since it was too painful for him to live on here in town at his official residence.

Apart from that, I have crossed paths with some eccentric characters whom I find completely intolerable, most of all in their demonstrations of friendship.

Good-by! You will like this letter; it's quite factual.

May 22

Many a man before me has felt that life is but a dream, and this feeling attends me constantly, too. When I observe the restrictions which are placed on man's active and contemplative faculties; when I see how all our activity merely serves to satisfy needs which in turn have no purpose other than to prolong our wretched existence; and then realize that our equanimity concerning certain points of inquiry is merely a dreamy resignation in which we decorate the walls between which we are imprisoned with gay figures and bright views—all this, Wilhelm, robs me of my speech. I turn back upon myself and find a world! But again more in imagination and obscure desire than in actuality and living power. And so everything swims before my senses, and I smile my way dreamily through the world.

All the highly learned schoolmasters and tutors are

sind alle hochgelahrten[29] Schul- und Hofmeister einig; daß aber auch Erwachsene gleich Kindern auf diesem Erdboden herumtaumeln, und wie jene nicht wissen, woher sie kommen und wohin sie gehen, ebensowenig nach wahren Zwecken handeln, ebenso durch Biskuit und Kuchen und Birkenreiser regiert werden: das will niemand gern glauben, und mich dünkt, man kann es mit Händen greifen.

Ich gestehe Dir gern, denn ich weiß, was Du mir hierauf[30] sagen möchtest, daß diejenigen die Glücklichsten sind, die gleich den Kindern in den Tag hinein leben, ihre Puppen herumschleppen, aus- und anziehen und mit großem Respekt um die Schublade umherschleichen, wo Mama das Zuckerbrot hineingeschlossen hat, und wenn sie das Gewünschte endlich erhaschen, es mit vollen Backen verzehren und rufen: Mehr! — Das sind glückliche Geschöpfe. Auch denen ist's wohl, die ihren Lumpenbeschäftigungen oder wohl gar ihren Leidenschaften prächtige Titel geben und sie dem Menschengeschlechte als Riesenoperationen zu dessen Heil und Wohlfahrt anschreiben. — Wohl dem, der so sein kann! Wer aber in seiner Demut erkennt, wo das alles hinausläuft, wer da sieht, wie artig jeder Bürger, dem es wohl ist, sein Gärtchen zum Paradiese zuzustutzen weiß, und wie unverdrossen dann doch auch der Unglückliche unter der Bürde seinen Weg fortkeucht, und alle gleich interessiert sind, das Licht dieser Sonne noch eine Minute länger zu sehn — ja, der ist still und bildet auch seine Welt aus sich selbst und ist auch glücklich, weil er ein Mensch ist. Und dann so eingeschränkt er ist, hält er doch immer im Herzen das süße Gefühl der Freiheit, und daß er diesen Kerker verlassen kann, wann er will.

Am 26. Mai

Du kennst von alters her meine Art, mich anzubauen, mir irgend an einem vertraulichen Ort ein Hüttchen[31] aufzuschlagen und da mit aller Einschränkung zu herbergen. Auch hier hab' ich wieder ein Plätzchen angetroffen, das mich angezogen hat.

Ungefähr eine Stunde von der Stadt liegt ein Ort, den

agreed that a child does not know why he wants something; but that adults, too, like children, stagger about on this earth of ours and do not know where they come from or where they are going; that they act just as little in accordance with true purpose and are governed just as much by biscuits and cake and birch rods—no one wants to believe that, and yet it seems to me that this is palpably so.

I'll gladly admit—for I know what you would like to say to me—that those people are happiest who live but for the day, the way children do, who drag their dolls about, dress and undress them, with deep awe haunt the drawer into which Mother has locked the cookies, and when they finally get what they want, stuff it into their mouths and cry, "More!"—They are happy creatures. They are happy, too, who give pompous titles to their shabby occupations, or even to their passions, and represent them as gigantic operations for the salvation and welfare of the human race. —Happy the man who can be like that! But he who recognizes in his humility what it all amounts to, he who sees how nicely every comfortable citizen is able to trim his little garden into a paradise, and how patiently even the unhappy man struggles on his way beneath his burden and how they are all equally interested in beholding the light of this sun for one more minute—yes, such a person is serene and shapes his world out of himself, and is even happy to be a human being. And however restricted he is, he always preserves in his heart the sweet feeling of freedom and the knowledge that he can leave this prison whenever he wants to.

May 26

You have long known my habit of settling down, putting up a little hut in some cozy place and keeping house there in a limited way. Here too I have found a little spot which has attracted me.

About an hour from town there is a place called Wahl-

sie Wahlheim* nennen. Die Lage an einem Hügel ist sehr interessant, und wenn man oben auf dem Fußpfade zum Dorf herausgeht, übersieht man auf einmal das ganze Tal. Eine gute Wirtin, die gefällig und munter in ihrem Alter ist, schenkt Wein, Bier, Kaffee; und was über alles geht, sind zwei Linden, die mit ihren ausgebreiteten Ästen den kleinen Platz vor der Kirche bedecken, der ringsum mit Bauerhäusern, Scheuern und Höfen eingeschlossen ist. So vertraulich, so heimlich[32] hab' ich nicht leicht ein Plätzchen gefunden, und dahin lass' ich mein Tischchen aus dem Wirtshause bringen und meinen Stuhl, trinke meinen Kaffee da und lese meinen Homer. Das erstemal, als ich durch einen Zufall an einem schönen Nachmittage unter die Linden kam, fand ich das Plätzchen so einsam. Es war alles im Felde; nur ein Knabe von ungefähr vier Jahren saß an der Erde und hielt ein anderes, etwa halbjähriges vor ihm zwischen seinen Füßen sitzendes Kind mit beiden Armen wider seine Brust, so daß er ihm zu einer Art von Sessel diente, und, ungeachtet der Munterkeit, womit er aus seinen schwarzen Augen herumschaute, ganz ruhig saß. Mich vergnügte der Anblick: ich setzte mich auf einen Pflug, der gegenüberstand, und zeichnete die brüderliche Stellung mit vielem Ergötzen. Ich fügte den nächsten Zaun, ein Scheunentor und einige gebrochene Wagenräder bei, alles, wie es hintereinander stand, und fand nach Verlauf einer Stunde, daß ich eine wohlgeordnete, sehr interessante[33] Zeichnung verfertigt hatte, ohne das mindeste von dem Meinen hinzuzutun. Das bestärkte mich in meinem Vorsatze, mich künftig allein an die Natur[34] zu halten. Sie allein ist unendlich reich, und sie allein bildet den großen Künstler. Man kann zum Vorteile der Regeln viel sagen, ungefähr was man zum Lobe der bürgerlichen Gesellschaft sagen kann. Ein Mensch, der sich nach ihnen bildet, wird nie etwas Abgeschmacktes und Schlechtes hervorbringen, wie einer, der sich durch Gesetze und Wohlstand modeln läßt, nie ein unerträglicher Nachbar, nie ein merkwürdiger Bösewicht werden kann; dagegen wird aber auch alle

* Der Leser wird sich keine Mühe geben, die hier genannten Orte zu suchen, man hat sich genötigt gesehen, die im Originale befindlichen wahren Namen zu verändern.

heim.* It has an interesting location on a hill, and when you leave the upper end of the village on the footpath, you suddenly look out over the whole valley. The hostess at the inn, a good woman who is pleasant and cheerful in her old age, dispenses wine, beer, and coffee; but the supreme attractions are the two linden trees which spread their branches over the little square in front of the church; the square is enclosed by farmhouses, barns, and farmyards. I have rarely found a spot that is so cozy and homely, and there I have my little table and chair taken out from the inn, drink my coffee, and read my Homer. The first time I came to the linden trees, by chance on a beautiful afternoon, I found the little square so solitary. Everyone was out in the fields; only a boy about four years old was sitting on the ground, holding between his legs another child of about six months, whom he pressed against his chest with both arms so that he formed a sort of chair for the infant; in spite of the liveliness which sparkled in his black eyes, he sat quite still. The sight pleased me; I sat down on a plow which stood across from them and made a sketch of the fraternal scene with great delight. I added the nearby fence, a barn door and some broken wagon wheels, exactly as they were ranged behind each other, and after an hour had passed I found that I had made a very interesting and well-arranged drawing, without adding anything of my own to it. This confirmed my resolve to stick to nature alone in the future. She alone is infinitely rich and she alone forms the great artist. You can say much for rules, about as much as one can say in praise of bourgeois society. A person who conforms to them will never produce anything bad or in poor taste, just as a man who allows himself to be molded by convention and decorum can never become an unbearable neighbor or a notorious villain; on the other hand, you may say what you will, all rules destroy a real feeling for nature and its true expression. You will say this is too harsh, the rule merely limits, prunes the rank growth of the vine, etc.—Dear friend, shall I give you an analogy?

* The reader need not trouble to seek the places named here; we found it necessary to change the names in the original letters.

Regel, man rede, was man wolle, das wahre Gefühl von Natur und den wahren Ausdruck derselben zerstören! Sag Du, das ist zu hart! Sie schränkt nur ein, beschneidet die geilen Reben usw. — Guter Freund, soll ich Dir ein Gleichnis geben? Es ist damit wie mit der Liebe. Ein junges Herz hängt ganz an einem Mädchen, bringt alle Stunden seines Tages bei ihr zu, verschwendet alle seine Kräfte, all sein Vermögen, um ihr jeden Augenblick auszudrücken, daß er sich ganz ihr hingibt. Und da käme ein Philister[35], ein Mann, der in einem öffentlichen Amte steht, und sagte zu ihm: „Feiner junger Herr! Lieben ist menschlich, nur müßt ihr menschlich lieben! Teilet eure Stunden ein, die einen zur Arbeit, und die Erholungsstunden widmet eurem Mädchen. Berechnet euer Vermögen, und was euch von eurer Notdurft übrig bleibt, davon verwehr' ich euch nicht, ihr ein Geschenk, nur nicht zu oft, zu machen, etwa zu ihrem Geburts- und Namenstage" usw. — Folgt der Mensch, so gibt's einen brauchbaren jungen Menschen, und ich will selbst jedem Fürsten raten, ihn in ein Kollegium zu setzen; nur mit seiner Liebe ist's am Ende, und wenn er ein Künstler ist, mit seiner Kunst. O meine Freunde! Warum der Strom des Genies so selten ausbricht, so selten in hohen Fluten hereinbraust und eure staunende Seele erschüttert? — Liebe Freunde, da wohnen die gelassenen Herren auf beiden Seiten des Ufers, denen ihre Gartenhäuschen, Tulpenbeete und Krautfelder zugrunde gehen würden, die daher in Zeiten mit Dämmen und Ableiten der künftig drohenden Gefahr abzuwehren wissen.

Am 27. Mai

Ich bin, wie ich sehe, in Verzückung, Gleichnisse und Deklamation verfallen und habe darüber vergessen, Dir auszuerzählen, was mit den Kindern weiter geworden ist. Ich saß, ganz in malerische Empfindung vertieft, die Dir mein gestriges Blatt sehr zerstückt darlegt, auf meinem Pfluge wohl zwei Stunden. Da kommt gegen Abend eine junge Frau auf die Kinder los[36], die sich indes nicht gerührt hatten, mit einem Körbchen am Arm und ruft von weitem: „Philipps, du bist recht brav." — Sie grüßte mich, ich

48

It's like love. A young fellow clings tightly to a girl, spends every hour of the day with her, squanders all his energy, his whole fortune, in order to express to her at every moment that he is completely and forever devoted to her. And then a Philistine comes along, a man who holds a public office, and says to him: "My dear young man, to love is human, but you must love within human bounds. Divide up your hours, use some for work and set aside your leisure hours for your girl. Assess your fortunes; I don't forbid you to give her a present from what is left to you after necessities, but not too often, say for her birthday or saint's day, etc." If he follows this advice then you have a useful young man and I myself would advise every prince to make him a member of his cabinet; but his love will be at an end, and if he is an artist, his art, too. O my friends! Why does the stream of genius burst forth so rarely, so seldom roar in high waves and shake you to the depths of your astonished soul?—Dear friends, comfortable gentlemen live on both sides of the river; their little summerhouses, tulip beds, and vegetable gardens would be ruined; they are therefore able to avert the future danger by building dams and ditches.

May 27

I see I have fallen into raptures, parables, and declamation and have forgotten in the process to complete my story about the children. I had been sitting on my plow for about two hours, completely absorbed in artistic contemplation which my letter of yesterday shows you in a very fragmentary form. Then, toward evening, a young woman with a little basket on her arm came up to the children, who had not stirred all this time, and called from a distance: "Philip, you're really a good boy."—She greeted me, I

49

dankte ihr, stand auf, trat näher hin und fragte sie, ob sie Mutter von den Kindern wäre? Sie bejahte es, und indem sie dem ältesten einen halben Weck gab, nahm sie das Kleine auf und küßte es mit aller mütterlichen Liebe. — „Ich habe", sagte sie, „meinem Philipps das Kleine zu halten gegeben und bin mit meinem Ältesten in die Stadt gegangen, um Weißbrot zu holen und Zucker und ein irden[37] Breipfännchen." — Ich sah das alles in dem Korbe, dessen Deckel abgefallen war. — „Ich will meinem Hans" (das war der Name des Jüngsten) „ein Süppchen kochen zum Abende; der lose Vogel, der Große, hat mir gestern das Pfännchen zerbrochen, als er sich mit Philippsen um die Scharre des Breis zankte." — Ich fragte nach dem Ältesten, und sie hatte mir kaum gesagt, daß er auf der Wiese sich mit ein paar Gänsen herumjage, als er gesprungen kam und dem Zweiten eine Haselgerte mitbrachte. Ich unterhielt mich weiter mit dem Weibe und erfuhr, daß sie des Schulmeisters Tochter sei, und daß ihr Mann eine Reise in die Schweiz gemacht habe, um die Erbschaft eines Vetters zu holen. — „Sie haben ihn drum betrügen wollen", sagte sie, „und ihm auf seine Briefe nicht geantwortet; da ist er selbst hineingegangen. Wenn ihm nur kein Unglück widerfahren ist, ich höre nichts von ihm." — Es ward mir schwer, mich von dem Weibe loszumachen, gab jedem der Kinder einen Kreuzer[38], und auch fürs jüngste gab ich ihr einen, ihm einen Weck zur Suppe mitzubringen, wenn sie in die Stadt ginge, und so schieden wir voneinander.

Ich sage Dir, mein Schatz, wenn meine Sinne gar nicht mehr halten wollen, so lindert all den Tumult der Anblick eines solchen Geschöpfs, das in glücklicher Gelassenheit den engen Kreis seines Daseins hingeht, von einem Tage zum andern sich durchhilft, die Blätter abfallen sieht und nichts dabei denkt, als daß der Winter kommt.

Seit der Zeit bin ich oft draußen. Die Kinder sind ganz an mich gewöhnt, sie kriegen Zucker, wenn ich Kaffee trinke, und teilen das Butterbrot und die saure Milch mit mir des Abends. Sonntags fehlt ihnen der Kreuzer nie, und wenn ich nicht nach der Betstunde da bin, so hat die Wirtin Ordre, ihn auszuzahlen.

thanked her, stood up, went over to her and asked her if she was the mother of the children. She said yes and, giving the older child half a roll, she lifted up the baby and kissed it with deep motherly love.—"I gave Philip the little one to hold," she said, "and went into town with my oldest boy to get white bread, sugar, and an earthen dish for his cereal." I saw all these items in the basket, from which the lid had come off. "I want to cook some soup for my Hans (that was the name of the youngest) for his supper; that rascal, the big one, broke the dish yesterday when he was fighting with Philip about the scrapings of the porridge." I asked her about her oldest; she had scarcely finished telling me that he was chasing a few geese in the meadow when he came running up, bringing the second boy a hazel switch. I went on talking with the woman and learned that she was the daughter of the schoolmaster and that her husband had gone to Switzerland to collect the inheritance left to him by a cousin. "They wanted to cheat him of it," she said, "and didn't answer his letters; so he went there himself. I only hope he hasn't met with an accident; I've heard nothing from him." It was hard for me to leave the woman; I gave each of the children a penny and I gave her one for the youngest, too, so that she could bring him a roll for his soup when she went to town; and so we parted.

I tell you, my dear friend, when my senses are on the point of failing me, all my inner turmoil is relieved by the sight of such a creature, moving in happy tranquility within the narrow circle of her existence, living from one day to the next; when she sees the leaves fall, she has no other thought than that winter is coming.

Since that time I have been out there often. The children are quite used to me; they get sugar when I'm drinking coffee, and in the evening they share my bread and butter and my sour milk. On Sundays they never fail to get their pennies, and if I am not there after the church service the landlady has orders to pay them.

51

Sie sind vertraut, erzählen mir allerhand, und besonders ergötze ich mich an ihren Leidenschaften und simplen Ausbrüchen des Begehrens, wenn mehr Kinder aus dem Dorfe sich versammeln.

Viel Mühe hat mich's gekostet, der Mutter ihre Besorgnis zu nehmen: sie möchten den Herrn inkommodieren[39].

Am 30. Mai

Was ich Dir neulich von der Malerei sagte, gilt gewiß auch von der Dichtkunst; es ist nur, daß man das Vortreffliche erkenne und es auszusprechen wage, und das ist freilich mit wenigem viel gesagt. Ich habe heut eine Szene gehabt, die, rein abgeschrieben, die schönste Idylle von der Welt gäbe; doch was soll Dichtung, Szene und Idylle? Muß es denn immer gebosselt sein, wenn wir teil[40] an einer Naturerscheinung nehmen sollen?

Wenn Du auf diesen Eingang viel Hohes und Vornehmes erwartest, so bist Du wieder übel betrogen; es ist nichts als ein Bauerbursch, der mich zu dieser lebhaften Teilnehmung hingerissen hat — ich werde, wie gewöhnlich, schlecht erzählen, und Du wirst mich wie gewöhnlich, denk' ich, übertrieben finden; es ist wieder Wahlheim und immer Wahlheim, das diese Seltenheiten hervorbringt.

Es war eine Gesellschaft draußen unter den Linden, Kaffee zu trinken. Weil sie mir nicht ganz anstand, so blieb ich unter einem Vorwande zurück.

Ein Bauerbursch kam aus einem benachbarten Hause und beschäftigte sich, an dem Pfluge, den ich neulich gezeichnet[41] hatte, etwas zurechtzumachen. Da mir sein Wesen gefiel, redete ich ihn an, fragte nach seinen Umständen; wir waren bald bekannt und, wie mir's gewöhnlich mit dieser Art Leuten geht, bald vertraut. Er erzählte mir, daß er bei einer Witwe in Diensten sei und von ihr gar wohl gehalten werde. Er sprach so vieles von ihr und lobte sie dergestalt, daß ich bald merken konnte, er sei ihr mit Leib und Seele zugetan. Sie sei nicht mehr jung, sagte er, sie sei von ihrem ersten Mann übel gehalten worden, wolle nicht mehr heiraten, und aus seiner Erzählung leuchtete so merklich hervor, wie schön, wie reizend sie für ihn sei, wie

They are intimate with me, tell me all sorts of things, and I find special delight in their passions and naïve outbursts of desire when other village children gather.

It was a great effort for me to relieve the mother of the anxiety that they might inconvenience the gentleman.

May 30

What I told you recently about painting is certainly true of literature, too. The point is that one should recognize what is excellent and dare to express it, and that is, of course, saying much in a few words. I experienced a scene today which, in a fair copy, would yield the most beautiful idyll in the world; but why talk of poetry, scene, idyll? Must we be eternally tinkering if we are to participate in a phenomenon of nature?

If you are expecting a lot of elevated and noble thoughts after this introduction, you will be badly deceived again; it is only a peasant lad who has moved me to feel this lively sympathy.—I shall tell my story badly, as usual, and as usual you will find that I exaggerate; it is Wahlheim again, always Wahlheim, that produces these extraordinary states in me.

There was a group outside under the linden trees drinking coffee. Because the company did not quite suit me, I stayed inside under some pretext.

A farm boy came out of a nearby house and got busy repairing the plow which I had recently sketched. Since I liked his manner, I spoke to him, asked about his circumstances; we were soon acquainted and, as usually happens to me with people of that sort, soon on familiar terms. He told me that he was in the service of a widow who was treating him well. He talked about her so much and praised her so warmly that I could soon see that he was devoted to her, body and soul. She was no longer young, he said. She had been badly treated by her first husband and refused to marry again; his words showed so clearly how beautiful, how charming he found her, how very much he wished that she might choose him to wipe out the memory of her first

sehr er wünsche, daß sie ihn wählen möchte, um das Andenken der Fehler ihres ersten Mannes auszulöschen, daß ich Wort für Wort wiederholen müßte, um Dir die reine Neigung, die Liebe und Treue dieses Menschen anschaulich zu machen. Ja, ich müßte die Gabe des größten Dichters besitzen, um Dir zugleich den Ausdruck seiner Gebärden, die Harmonie seiner Stimme, das heimliche Feuer seiner Blicke lebendig darstellen zu können. Nein, es sprechen keine Worte die Zartheit aus, die in seinem ganzen Wesen und Ausdruck war; es ist alles nur plump, was ich wieder vorbringen könnte. Besonders rührte mich, wie er fürchtete, ich möchte über sein Verhältnis zu ihr ungleich denken und an ihrer guten Aufführung zweifeln. Wie reizend es war, wenn er von ihrer Gestalt, von ihrem Körper sprach, der ihn ohne jugendliche Reize gewaltsam an sich zog und fesselte, kann ich mir nur in meiner innersten Seele wiederholen. Ich hab' in meinem Leben die dringende Begierde und das heiße, sehnliche Verlangen nicht in dieser Reinheit gesehen, ja wohl kann ich sagen, in dieser Reinheit nicht gedacht und geträumt. Schelte[42] mich nicht, wenn ich Dir sage, daß bei der Erinnerung dieser Unschuld und Wahrheit mir die innerste Seele glüht, und daß mich das Bild dieser Treue und Zärtlichkeit überall verfolgt, und daß ich, wie selbst davon entzündet, lechze und schmachte.

Ich will nun suchen, auch sie eh'stens zu sehn, oder vielmehr, wenn ich's recht bedenke, ich will's vermeiden. Es ist besser, ich sehe sie durch die Augen ihres Liebhabers; vielleicht erscheint sie mir vor meinen eigenen Augen nicht so, wie sie jetzt vor mir steht, und warum soll ich mir das schöne Bild verderben?

Am 16. Junius[43]

Warum ich Dir nicht schreibe? — Fragst Du das und bist doch auch der Gelehrten einer? Du solltest raten, daß ich mich wohl befinde, und zwar — Kurz und gut, ich habe eine Bekanntschaft gemacht, die mein Herz näher angeht. Ich habe — ich weiß nicht.

Dir in der Ordnung zu erzählen, wie's zugegangen ist, daß ich eins der liebenswürdigsten Geschöpfe habe ken-

husband's failings, that I would have to report word for word what he said if I wanted to give you a vivid picture of this man's pure affection, love, and faithfulness. In fact, I would have to possess the gifts of the greatest poet to convey to you adequately his expressive gestures, his harmonious voice, the hidden fire in his eyes. No, words cannot express the tenderness that was in his whole attitude and expression; everything that I could reproduce here would be merely crude. I was especially touched by his apprehension that I might wrongly interpret his relationship to her and doubt her good behavior. How charming it was when he spoke of her figure, her body, which drew him to her and held him captive though it lacked the charms of youth; I can only repeat it to myself in my inmost being. I have never in my life seen powerful longing and ardent yearning desire in such a pure form; indeed I might say I have never thought or dreamed that it could exist in such purity. Don't scold me if I tell you that my innermost being glows with the memory of this innocence and truth, that the image of this fidelity and tenderness pursues me everywhere, and that I pine and languish as if I myself were burning with it.

I will now try to see her too, as soon as I can, or rather, upon reflection, I will try to avoid it. It is better if I see her through the eyes of her lover; perhaps she will not appear to my own eyes as she now stands before me, and why should I spoil the lovely image?

June 16

Why don't I write to you?—You ask that and yet you are one of the learned. You should surmise that I am well, and in fact—in short, I have made an acquaintance who touches my heart closely. I have—I don't know.

To tell you in a logical way how it happened that I have come to know one of the most lovely creatures will be

55

nenlernen, wird schwer halten. Ich bin vergnügt und glücklich und also kein guter Historienschreiber.

Einen Engel! — Pfui! Das sagt jeder von der Seinigen, nicht wahr? Und doch bin ich nicht imstande, Dir zu sagen, wie sie vollkommen ist, warum sie vollkommen ist; genug, sie hat allen meinen Sinn gefangen genommen.

So viel Einfalt bei so viel Verstand, so viele Güte bei so viel Festigkeit und die Ruhe der Seele bei dem wahren Leben und der Tätigkeit. —

Das ist alles garstiges Gewäsch, was ich da von ihr sage, leidige Abstraktionen, die nicht einen Zug ihres Selbst ausdrücken. Ein andermal — nein, nicht ein andermal, jetzt gleich will ich Dir's erzählen. Tu' ich's jetzt nicht, so geschäh' es niemals. Denn, unter uns, seit ich angefangen habe zu schreiben, war ich schon dreimal im Begriffe, die Feder niederzulegen, mein Pferd satteln zu lassen und hinauszureiten. Und doch schwur ich mir heute frühe, nicht hinauszureiten, und gehe doch alle Augenblick' ans Fenster, zu sehen, wie hoch die Sonne noch steht. —

Ich hab's nicht überwinden können, ich mußte zu ihr hinaus. Da bin ich wieder, Wilhelm, will mein Butterbrot zu Nacht essen und Dir schreiben. Welch eine Wonne das für meine Seele ist, sie in dem Kreise der lieben muntern Kinder, ihrer acht Geschwister zu sehen! —

Wenn ich so fortfahre, wirst Du am Ende so klug sein wie am Anfange. Höre denn, ich will mich zwingen, ins Detail zu gehen.

Ich schrieb Dir neulich, wie ich den Amtmann S . . . habe kennenlernen, und wie er mich gebeten habe, ihn bald in seiner Einsiedelei oder vielmehr seinem kleinen Königreiche zu besuchen. Ich vernachlässigte das und wäre vielleicht nie hingekommen, hätte mir der Zufall nicht den Schatz entdeckt, der in der stllen Gegend verborgen liegt.

Unsere jungen Leute hatten einen Ball auf dem Lande angestellt, zu dem ich mich denn auch willig finden ließ. Ich bot einem hiesigen guten, schönen, übrigens unbedeutenden Mädchen die Hand, und es wurde ausgemacht, daß ich eine Kutsche nehmen, mit meiner Tänzerin und ihrer Base nach dem Orte der Lustbarkeit hinausfahren, und auf dem Wege Charlotten S . . . mitnehmen sollte.

difficult. I am contented and happy, and so I cannot be a good historian.

An angel!—Bah! Every man says that of his love, doesn't he? And yet I am unable to tell you how perfect she is, why she is perfect; enough, she has captivated all my senses.

So much simplicity with so much intelligence, so much kindness with so much firmness, and peace of mind together with true life and activity.—

All this I say about her is horrible rubbish, empty abstractions which do not express a single feature of her self. Another time—no, not another time, I will tell you about it right now. If I don't do it now, I never shall. For between ourselves, since I began to write, three times I have been at the point of putting down my pen, having my horse saddled and riding out to her. And yet I took an oath this morning not to ride out there, and yet I go to my window every minute to see how high the sun still is.—

I wasn't able to control myself, I had to go to her. Here I am again, Wilhelm, I'll sup on a slice of bread and butter and write you. What a joy it is for my soul to see her in the circle of the dear, cheerful children, her eight brothers and sisters!—

If I continue like this, you will be no wiser in the end than you were at the beginning. So listen, I will force myself to go into detail.

I wrote you recently how I made the acquaintance of S— the bailiff, and how he asked me to visit him soon in his hermitage, or rather in his little kingdom. I neglected to do so and might perhaps never have gone, if chance had not revealed to me the treasure that lies hidden in that quiet spot.

The young people here had arranged a dance in the country and I gladly agreed to attend. As my partner, I invited a local girl, nice, attractive but otherwise insignificant, and it was arranged that I would hire a carriage and ride out with my partner and her cousin to the scene of the festivities; on the way we were to pick up Charlotte S—. "You will meet a beautiful woman," said my com-

— „Sie werden ein schönes Frauenzimmer⁴⁴ kennenlernen", sagte meine Gesellschafterin, da wir durch den
weiten ausgehauenen Wald nach dem Jagdhause fuhren. —
„Nehmen Sie sich in acht", versetzte die Base, „daß Sie sich
nicht verlieben!" — „Wieso?" sagte ich. — „Sie ist schon
vergeben", antwortete jene, „an einen sehr braven Mann,
der weggereist ist, seine Sachen in Ordnung zu bringen, weil
sein Vater gestorben ist, und sich um eine ansehnliche
Versorgung zu bewerben." — Die Nachricht war mir ziemlich gleichgültig.

Die Sonne war noch eine Viertelstunde vom Gebirge,
als wir vor dem Hoftore anfuhren. Es war sehr schwül,
und die Frauenzimmer äußerten ihre Besorgnis wegen eines
Gewitters, das sich in weißgrauen dumpfichten⁴⁵ Wölkchen
rings am Horizonte zusammenzuziehen schien. Ich täuschte
ihre Furcht mit anmaßlicher Wetterkunde, ob mir gleich
selbst zu ahnen anfing, unsere Lustbarkeit werde einen
Stoß leiden.

Ich war ausgestiegen, und eine Magd, die ans Tor kam,
bat uns, einen Augenblick zu verziehen, Mamsell Lottchen
würde gleich kommen. Ich ging durch den Hof nach dem
wohlgebauten Hause, und da ich die vorliegenden Trep-
pen⁴⁶ hinaufgestiegen war und in die Tür trat, fiel mir das
reizendste Schauspiel in die Augen, das ich je gesehen
habe. In dem Vorsaale wimmelten sechs Kinder von elf zu
zwei Jahren um ein Mädchen von schöner Gestalt, mittlerer
Größe, die ein simples weißes Kleid mit blaßroten Schleifen
an Arm und Brust anhatte. Sie hielt ein schwarzes Brot
und schnitt ihren Kleinen ringsherum jedem sein Stück
nach Proportion ihres Alters und Appetits ab, gab's jedem
mit solcher Freundlichkeit, und jedes rief so ungekünstelt
sein: „Danke!" indem es mit den kleinen Händchen lange
in die Höhe gereicht hatte, ehe es noch abgeschitten war,
und nun mit seinem Abendbrote vergnügt entweder weg-
sprang oder nach seinem stillern Charakter gelassen davon-
ging nach dem Hoftore zu, um die Fremden und die
Kutsche zu sehen, darin⁴⁷ ihre Lotte wegfahren sollte. —
„Ich bitte um Vergebung", sagte sie, „daß ich Sie herein-
bemühe und die Frauenzimmer warten lasse. Über dem
Anziehen und allerlei Bestellungen fürs Haus in meiner

panion, as we drove through the broad, thinned forest toward the hunting lodge. "Take care," the cousin added, "that you don't fall in love." "What do you mean?" I said. "She's already promised," she replied, "to a very fine man, who is away on a trip to put his affairs in order because his father has died, and to apply for an important post." The information did not interest me much.

The sun was still a quarter of an hour above the mountains when we pulled up in front of the yard gate. It was very sultry and the women expressed concern about a storm that seemed to be gathering at the horizon in white-gray, hazy little clouds. I allayed their fear with a pretention of meteorological knowledge, although I myself began to fear that our entertainment would be jolted.

I had alighted and a maid who came to the gate asked us to wait a moment, Fräulein Lotte would come at once. I walked through the courtyard to the well-built house, and when I had gone up the front steps and stepped through the door, I was confronted by the most charming spectacle I have ever seen. In the anteroom six children, from eleven to two years of age, were swarming about a girl with a beautiful figure, of medium height, who wore a simple white dress, trimmed with pink bows at the arms and bosom. She was holding a loaf of dark bread, cutting for each of the little ones about her a slice proportionate to his age and appetite; she handed it to each with such kindness, and each child cried his "Thanks" so artlessly, stretching out his litle hands to her even before the bread had been cut and then either hurried away contentedly with his supper or, if he was of a quieter temperament, walked away calmly toward the courtyard gate to see the strangers and the carriage in which their Lotte was to go off.—"I beg your pardon," she said, "for troubling you to come in and for keeping the ladies waiting. But between dressing and giving all sorts of directions for the house when I am away, I forgot to give my children their supper, and they

Abwesenheit habe ich vergessen, meinen Kindern ihr Vesperbrot zu geben, und sie wollen von niemandem Brot geschnitten haben als von mir." — Ich machte ihr ein unbedeutendes Kompliment, meine ganze Seele ruhte auf der Gestalt, dem Tone, dem Betragen, und ich hatte eben Zeit, mich von der Überraschung zu erholen, als sie in die Stube lief, ihre Handschuhe und den Fächer zu holen. Die Kleinen sahen mich in einiger Entfernung so von der Seite an, und ich ging auf das jüngste los, das ein Kind von der glücklichsten Gesichtsbildung war. Es zog sich zurück, als eben Lotte zur Türe herauskam und sagte: „Louis, gib dem Herrn Vetter eine Hand." — Das tat der Knabe sehr freimütig, und ich konnte mich nicht enthalten, ihn, ungeachtet seines kleinen Rotznäschens, herzlich zu küssen. — „Vetter?" sagte ich, indem ich ihr die Hand reichte, „glauben Sie, daß ich des Glückes wert sei, mit Ihnen verwandt zu sein?" — „Oh", sagte sie mit einem leichtfertigen Lächeln, „unsere Vetterschaft ist sehr weitläufig, und es wäre mir leid, wenn Sie der schlimmste drunter sein sollten." — Im Gehen gab sie Sophien, der ältesten Schwester nach ihr, einem Mädchen von ungefähr elf Jahren, den Auftrag, wohl auf die Kinder acht zu haben und den Papa zu grüßen, wenn er vom Spazierritte nach Hause käme. Den Kleinen sagte sie, sie sollten ihrer Schwester Sophie folgen, als wenn sie's selber wäre, das[48] denn auch einige ausdrücklich versprachen. Eine kleine, naseweise Blondine aber, von ungefähr sechs Jahren, sagte: „Du bist's doch nicht, Lottchen, wir haben dich doch lieber." — Die zwei ältesten Knaben waren auf die Kutsche geklettert, und auf mein Vorbitten erlaubte sie ihnen, bis vor den Wald mitzufahren, wenn sie versprächen, sich nicht zu necken und sich recht festzuhalten.

Wir hatten uns kaum zurechtgesetzt, die Frauenzimmer sich bewillkommt, wechselsweise über den Anzug, vorzüglich über die Hüte ihre Anmerkungen gemacht und die Gesellschaft, die man erwartete, gehörig durchgezogen: als Lotte den Kutscher halten und ihre Brüder herabsteigen ließ, die noch einmal ihre Hand zu küssen begehrten, das denn der älteste mit aller Zärtlichkeit, die dem Alter von fünfzehn Jahren eigen sein kann, der andere mit viel

won't let anyone cut their bread for them except me." I paid her some insignificant compliment, by my whole mind was absorbed by the figure, the voice, the manner of the girl, and I just had time to recover from my surprise when she dashed into her room to fetch her gloves and fan. The children were giving me sidelong glances from a distance, and I walked up to the youngest one, a child with most happily formed features. He drew back just as Lotte came out of the door and said, "Louis, shake hands with your cousin." The boy did so very naturally, and I could not refrain from kissing him heartily, in spite of his runny nose. "Cousin?" I said, giving her my hand. "Do you think I deserve the good fortune of being related to you?" "Oh," she said with a sprightly smile, "I have such a number of cousins and I would feel sorry if you were the worst of them."—As she left she instructed Sophie, a girl of about eleven and the oldest sister next to Lotte, to take good care of the children and to greet papa when he came home from his ride. She told the little ones to obey their sister Sophie as if it was herself, which some of them definitely promised to do. But one saucy little blonde, about six years old, said: "But she isn't really you, Lotte, we really like you better."—The two oldest boys had climbed up on the rear of the carriage and, upon my intercession, she permitted them to ride with us to the edge of the forest if they promised not to tease each other and to hold on tight.

We had hardly settled in our seats, the ladies having welcomed each other and exchanged mutual comments about their clothes, especially their hats, and made the proper review of the company that was expected, when Lotte had the coachman stop and ordered her brothers to get down. They wanted to kiss her hand again, which the oldest one did with all the tenderness sometimes characteristic of the age of fifteen, and the other with great tempera-

61

Heftigkeit und Leichtsinn tat. Sie ließ die Kleinen noch einmal grüßen und wir fuhren weiter.

Die Base fragte, ob sie mit dem Buche fertig wäre, das sie ihr neulich geschickt hätte? — „Nein," sagte Lotte, „es gefällt mir nicht, Sie können's wieder haben. Das vorige war auch nicht besser." — Ich erstaunte, als ich fragte, was es für Bücher wären, und sie mir antwortete:* — Ich fand so viel Charakter in allem, was sie sagte, ich sah mit jedem Wort neue Reize, neue Strahlen des Geistes aus ihren Gesichtszügen hervorbrechen, die sich nach und nach vergnügt zu entfalten schienen, weil sie an mir fühlte, daß ich sie verstand.

„Wie ich jünger war", sagte sie, „liebte ich nichts so sehr als Romane. Weiß Gott, wie wohl mir's war, wenn ich mich sonntags so in ein Eckchen setzen und mit ganzem Herzen an dem Glück und Unstern einer Miß Jenny[49] teilnehmen konnte. Ich leugne auch nicht, daß die Art noch einige Reize für mich hat. Doch da ich so selten an ein Buch komme, so muß es auch recht nach meinem Geschmack sein. Und der Autor ist mir der liebste, in dem ich meine Welt wieder finde, bei dem es zugeht wie um mich, und dessen Geschichte mir doch so interessant und herzlich wird als mein eigen häuslich Leben, das freilich kein Paradies, aber doch im ganzen eine Quelle unsäglicher Glückseligkeit ist."

Ich bemühte mich, meine Bewegungen über diese Worte zu verbergen. Das ging freilich nicht weit: denn da ich sie mit solcher Wahrheit im Vorbeigehen vom Landpriester von Wakefield[50], vom † — reden hörte, kam ich ganz außer mich, sagte ihr alles, was ich wußte, und bemerkte erst nach einiger Zeit, da Lotte das Gespräch an die anderen wendete, daß diese die Zeit über mit offenen Augen, als säßen sie nicht da, dagesessen hatten. Die Base sah mich

* Man sieht sich genötigt, diese Stelle des Briefes zu unterdrücken, um niemand Gelegenheit zu einiger Beschwerde zu geben. Obgleich im Grunde jedem Autor wenig an dem Urteile eines einzelnen Mädchens, und eines jungen unsteten Menschen gelegen sein kann.

† Man hat auch hier die Namen einiger vaterländischer Autoren ausgelassen. Wer teil an Lottens Beifalle hat, wird es gewiß an seinem Herzen fühlen, wenn er diese Stelle lesen sollte, und sonst braucht es ja niemand zu wissen.

ment and joviality. She sent her greetings to the little children once more and we drove on.

The cousin asked whether she had finished the book she had recently sent her. "No," said Lotte, "I don't like it; you may have it back. The one I had before it was no better." I was astonished when, upon asking what books they were, she replied to me: *—I found so much character in everything she said. With every word she uttered I saw new charms, new rays of intelligence flash from her features which little by little seemed to take on a look of contentment, because she felt that I understood her.

"When I was younger," she said, "I liked nothing so much as novels. Heaven knows how pleasant it was when I could sit down in a corner on Sunday and enter wholeheartedly into the good and bad fortune of some Miss Jenny. And I do not deny that this type of reading still has some attraction for me; but since I so seldom get to read a book, it must really be to my taste. And the author I like best is the one in whose work I find my own world, the one who creates an environment like my own, and whose story becomes as interesting and intimate as my own domestic existence, which is, to be sure, no paradise, but on the whole a source of boundless happiness."

I tried to conceal the emotion which these words aroused in me. But I fear my efforts were not very successful; for when I heard her talk casually of *The Vicar of Wakefield,* and —— † with such truth, I completely lost control of myself, told her everything that was on my mind and noticed only after some time, when Lotte turned the conversation to the others, that they had been sitting there all this time, wide-eyed, as if they were not there. The cousin

---

* We feel compelled to suppress this passage in the letter, so that no one may be given cause for complaint. Although in reality no author can be greatly concerned about the judgment of a single girl and an unstable young man.

† Here, too, the names of some native authors have been omitted. Those who share Lotte's approval will certainly feel it in their hearts when they get to this passage; others don't need to know them.

mehr als einmal mit einem spöttischen Näschen an, daran[51] mir aber nichts gelegen war.

Das Gespräch fiel aufs Vergnügen am Tanze. — „Wenn diese Leidenschaft ein Fehler ist", sagte Lotte, „so gestehe ich Ihnen gern, ich weiß mir nichts übers Tanzen. Und wenn ich was im Kopfe habe und mir auf meinem verstimmten Klavier einen Kontretanz vortrommle, so ist alles wieder gut."

Wie ich mich unter dem Gespräche in den schwarzen Augen weidete, wie die lebendigen Lippen und die frischen muntern Wangen meine ganze Seele anzogen! wie ich, in den herrlichen Sinn ihrer Rede ganz versunken, oft gar die Worte nicht hörte, mit denen sie sich ausdrückte! — davon hast Du eine Vorstellung, weil Du mich kennst. Kurz, ich stieg aus dem Wagen wie ein Träumender, als wir vor dem Lusthause stillehielten, und war so in Träumen rings in der dämmernden[52] Welt verloren, daß ich auf die Musik kaum achtete, die uns von dem erleuchteten Saal herunter entgegenschallte.

Die zwei Herren Audran und ein gewisser N. N. — wer behält alle die Namen! —, die der Base und Lottens Tänzer waren, empfingen uns am Schlage, bemächtigten sich ihrer Frauenzimmer, und ich führte das meinige hinauf.

Wir schlangen uns in Menuetts[53] umeinander herum; ich forderte ein Frauenzimmer nach dem andern auf, und just die unleidlichsten konnten nicht dazu kommen, einem die Hand zu reichen und ein Ende zu machen. Lotte und ihr Tänzer fingen einen Englischen an, und wie wohl mir's war, als sie auch in der Reihe die Figur mit uns anfing, magst Du fühlen. Tanzen muß man sie sehen! Siehst Du, sie ist so mit ganzem Herzen und mit ganzer Seele dabei, ihr ganzer Körper e i n e Harmonie, so sorglos, so unbefangen, als wenn das eigentlich alles wäre, als wenn sie sonst nichts dächte, nichts empfände; und in dem Augenblicke gewiß schwindet alles andere vor ihr.

Ich bat sie um den zweiten Kontretanz; sie sagte mir den dritten zu und mit der liebenswürdigsten Freimütigkeit von der Welt versicherte sie mir, daß sie herzlich gern Deutsch tanze. — „Es ist hier so Mode", fuhr sie fort,

looked at me more than once with a mocking air, but I cared little about that.

The conversation turned to the pleasures of dancing. "If this passion is a fault," said Lotte, "I will gladly confess to you that I know of nothing I value more. And if there is something on my mind, I pound out a quadrille on my out-of-tune piano and at once everything is all right again."

How I feasted on those black eyes during the conversation! How those rich lips and those fresh, bright cheeks drew my whole being to her! Completely absorbed in the delightful content of her talk, often I did not even hear the words in which she expressed herself!—you can imagine that because you know me. In short, I got out of the carriage like a man in a dream when we stopped in front of the pavilion, and was so completely lost in dreams in the twilit world about me, that I scarcely heeded the music which came toward us from the brightly lit ballroom.

The two Messrs. Audran and a certain N. N.—who can keep track of all the names?—who were the dancing partners of the cousin and Lotte, received us at the carriage door, took charge of their ladies, and I escorted mine upstairs.

We circled each other in minuets; I led one lady after another, and it was precisely the most unendurable ones who could not bring themselves to give me their hand and end the dance. Lotte and her partner began an English quadrille, and you can imagine how happy I felt when it was her turn to dance a figure with us. You should see her dance! Really, she is in it with all her heart and soul, her whole body is in total harmony, so carefree, so natural, as if there were nothing else in life, as if she were thinking of nothing else, feeling nothing else; and I'm certain that in such moments everything else vanishes before her.

I asked her for the second quadrille; she promised me the third, and assured me with the most charming frankness in the world that she loved to dance an allemande. "It's the fashion here," she continued, "that every couple

„daß jedes Paar, das zusammengehört, beim Deutschen zusammenbleibt, und mein Chapeau[54] walzt schlecht und dankt mir's, wenn ich ihm die Arbeit erlasse. Ihr Frauenzimmer kann's auch nicht und mag nicht, und ich habe im Englischen gesehn, daß Sie gut walzen; wenn Sie nun mein sein wollen fürs Deutsche, so gehn Sie und bitten sich's von meinem Herrn aus, und ich will zu Ihrer Dame gehen." — Ich gab ihr die Hand darauf, und wir machten aus, daß ihr Tänzer inzwischen meine Tänzerin unterhalten sollte.

Nun ging's an, und wir ergötzten uns eine Weile an mannigfaltigen Schlingungen der Arme. Mit welchem Reize, mit welcher Flüchtigkeit bewegte sie sich! und da wir nun gar ans Walzen kamen und wie die Sphären umeinander herumrollten, ging's freilich anfangs, weil's die wenigsten können, ein bißchen bunt durcheinander. Wir waren klug und ließen sie austoben, und als die Ungeschicktesten den Plan[55] geräumt hatten, fielen wir ein und hielten mit noch einem Paare, mit Audran und seiner Tänzerin, wacker aus. Nie ist mir's so leicht vom Flecke gegangen. Ich war kein Mensch mehr. Das liebenswürdigste Geschöpf in den Armen zu haben und mit ihr herumzufliegen wie Wetter, daß alles rings umher verging, und — Wilhelm, um ehrlich zu sein, tat ich aber doch den Schwur, daß ein Mädchen, das ich liebte, auf das ich Ansprüche hätte, mir nie mit einem andern walzen sollte als mit mir, und wenn ich drüber zugrunde gehen müßte. Du verstehst mich!

Wir machten einige Touren gehend im Saale, um zu verschnaufen. Dann setzte sie sich, und die Orangen, die ich beiseite gebracht hatte, die nun die einzigen noch übrigen waren, taten vortreffliche Wirkung, nur daß mir mit jedem Schnittchen, das sie einer unbescheidenen Nachbarin ehrenhalber zuteilte, ein Stich durchs Herz ging.

Beim dritten englischen Tanz waren wir das zweite Paar. Wie wir die Reihe durchtanzten und ich, weiß Gott mit wie viel Wonne, an ihrem Arm und Auge hing, das voll vom wahrsten Ausdruck des offensten reinsten Vergnügens war, kommen wir an eine Frau, die mir wegen ihrer liebenswürdigen Miene auf einem nicht mehr ganz jungen Gesichte merkwürdig gewesen war. Sie sieht Lotten lächelnd

belonging together stays together for the allemande, but my partner waltzes badly, and will be grateful to me if I spare him the chore. Your lady can't either and doesn't like to, but I saw during the quadrille that you waltz well; if you would like to be my partner for the allemande, go and ask my escort and I'll go to your lady." We shook hands on it and agreed that her partner should entertain mine in the meantime.

Now it began, and for a while we had fun interlacing our arms in various ways. With what charm, with what lightness she moved! And when we came to the waltzing and the couples revolved about one another like the spheres, there was a bit of confusion at first, because only a few know how to do it. We were smart and let them have their fling, and when the clumsiest couples had cleared the floor, we sailed in and, together with another couple—Audran and his partner—held out bravely. I've never felt so light on my feet. I was no longer a human being. To hold the most charming creature in my arms and to fly with her like a whirlwind, so that everything around me faded away, and—Wilhelm, to tell you the truth, I nevertheless took an oath that a girl I loved, on whom I had any claim, would never waltz with another man than myself, even if it were my ruin. You know what I mean!

We walked around the ballroom a few times to recover our breath. Then she sat down, and the oranges I had put aside, the only ones now left, tasted wonderful, except that with every slice she politely gave away to an impertinent neighbor, I felt a stab in my heart.

In the third quadrille we were the second couple. As we were dancing through the line and I (Heaven knows with what bliss) clung to her arm and to her eyes, which were filled with the sincerest expression of the frankest, purest pleasure, we reached a woman whose charming expression had caught my attention, although her face was no longer young. She looked at Lotte with a smile, wagged a threat-

an, hebt einen drohenden Finger auf, und nennt den Namen Albert zweimal im Vorbeifliegen mit viel Bedeutung.

„Wer ist Albert?" sagte ich zu Lotten, „wenn's nicht Vermessenheit ist zu fragen." — Sie war im Begriff zu antworten, als wir uns scheiden mußten, um die große Achte[56] zu machen, und mich dünkte, einiges Nachdenken auf ihrer Stirn zu sehen, als wir so voreinander vorbeikreuzten. — „Was soll ich's Ihnen leugnen", sagte sie, indem sie mir die Hand zur Promenade[57] bot. „Albert ist ein braver Mensch, dem ich so gut als verlobt bin." — Nun war mir das nichts Neues (denn die Mädchen hatten mir's auf dem Wege gesagt) und war mir doch so ganz neu, weil ich es noch nicht im Verhältnis auf sie, die mir in so wenig Augenblicken so wert geworden war, gedacht hatte. Genug, ich verwirrte mich, und kam zwischen das unrechte Paar hinein, daß alles drunter und drüber ging und Lottens ganze Gegenwart und Zerren und Ziehen nötig war, um es schnell wieder in Ordnung zu bringen.

Der Tanz war noch nicht zu Ende, als die Blitze, die wir schon lange am Horizonte leuchten gesehn, und die ich immer für Wetterkühlen ausgegeben hatte, viel stärker zu werden anfingen und der Donner die Musik überstimmte. Drei Frauenzimmer liefen aus der Reihe, denen ihre Herren folgten; die Unordnung wurde allgemein, und die Musik hörte auf. Es ist natürlich, wenn uns ein Unglück oder etwas Schreckliches im Vergnügen überrascht, daß es stärkere Eindrücke auf uns macht als sonst, teils wegen des Gegensatzes, der sich so lebhaft empfinden läßt, teils und noch mehr, weil unsere Sinne einmal der Fühlbarkeit geöffnet sind und also desto schneller einen Eindruck annehmen. Diesen Ursachen muß ich die wunderbaren Grimassen zuschreiben, in die ich mehrere Frauenzimmer ausbrechen sah. Die klügste setzte sich in eine Ecke, mit dem Rücken gegen das Fenster, und hielt die Ohren zu. Eine andere kniete vor ihr nieder und verbarg den Kopf in der ersten[58] Schoß. Eine dritte schob sich zwischen beide hinein und umfaßte ihre Schwesterchen mit tausend Tränen. Einige wollten nach Hause; andere, die noch weniger wußten, was sie taten, hatten nicht so viel Besin-

ening finger at her as we flew by, and spoke the name Albert twice, with deep significance.

"Who is Albert," I said to Lotte, "if it is not presumptuous to ask?" She was on the point of answering when we had to separate to form the big eight, and it seemed to me her brow looked pensive as we crossed each other. "Why should I keep it from you?" she said, as she offered me her hand for the promenade. "Albert is a fine man, to whom I'm as good as engaged." Now this was no news to me, for the girls had told me about it on the way, and yet it seemed new to me because I hadn't yet thought of it in relation to her, who had become so precious to me in a few moments. Enough—I became confused, lost my bearing and got in with the wrong couple, so that everything was upside down, and it required all of Lotte's presence of mind, tugging and pulling, to put things quickly in order again.

The dance was not over yet when the lightning which we had seen flashing on the horizon for some time, and which I had kept explaining as heat lightning, grew more intense, and the thunder drowned out the music. Three ladies left the ranks, followed by their gentlemen; the disorder became general, and the music stopped. It is natural that, when a misfortune or some terrible event surprises us in a moment of pleasure, it makes a stronger impression on us than at other times, partly because the contrast is so keenly felt, partly—and more importantly—because our sensibility is heightened and our senses therefore more susceptible to an impression. To these causes I must ascribe the strange grimaces which I saw several ladies register. The most sensible one sat down in a corner with her back to the window and held her hands over her ears. Another knelt down before her and hid her head in the first girl's lap. A third pushed her way between them and threw her arms about her companions with a thousand tears. Some wanted to go home; others, who were even less aware of what they were doing, lacked enough presence of mind to fend off the impertinences of our young

nungskraft, den Keckheiten unserer jungen Schlucker[59] zu steuern, die sehr beschäftigt zu sein schienen, alle die ängstlichen Gebete, die dem Himmel bestimmt waren, von den Lippen der schönen Bedrängten wegzufangen. Einige unserer Herren hatten sich hinabbegeben, um ein Pfeifchen in Ruhe zu rauchen; und die übrige Gesellschaft schlug es nicht aus, als die Wirtin auf den klugen Einfall kam, uns ein Zimmer anzuweisen, das Läden und Vorhänge hätte. Kaum waren wir da angelangt, als Lotte beschäftigt war, einen Kreis von Stühlen zu stellen, und als sich die Gesellschaft auf ihre Bitte gesetzt hatte, den Vortrag[60] zu einem Spiele zu tun.

Ich sah manchen, der in Hoffnung auf ein saftiges Pfand sein Mäulchen[61] spitzte und seine Glieder reckte. — „Wir spielen Zählens",[62] sagte sie. „Nun gebt acht! Ich geh' im Kreise herum von der Rechten zur Linken, und so zählt ihr auch rings herum, jeder die Zahl, die an ihn kommt, und das muß gehen wie ein Lauffeuer, und wer stockt oder sich irrt, kriegt eine Ohrfeige, und so bis tausend." — Nun war das lustig anzusehen. Sie ging mit ausgestrecktem Arm im Kreise herum. „Eins", fing der erste an, der Nachbar „zwei", „drei" der folgende und so fort. Dann fing sie an geschwinder zu gehn, immer geschwinder; da versah's einer, patsch! eine Ohrfeige, und über das Gelächter der folgende auch patsch! Und immer geschwinder. Ich selbst kriegte zwei Maulschellen und glaubte mit innigem Vergnügen zu bemerken, daß sie stärker seien, also sie sie den übrigen zuzumessen pflegte. Ein allgemeines Gelächter und Geschwärm endigte das Spiel, ehe noch das Tausend ausgezählt war. Die Vertrautesten zogen einander beiseite, das Gewitter war vorüber, und ich folgte Lotten in den Saal. Unterwegs sagte sie: „Über die Ohrfeigen haben sie Wetter und alles vergessen!" — Ich konnte ihr nichts antworten. — „Ich war", fuhr sie fort, „eine der Furchtsamsten, und indem ich mich herzhaft stellte, um den andern Mut zu geben, bin ich mutig geworden." — Wir traten ans Fenster. Es donnerte abseitwärts, und der herrliche Regen säuselte auf das Land, und der erquickendste Wohlgeruch stieg in aller Fülle einer warmen Luft zu uns auf. Sie stand, auf ihren Ellenbogen gestützt, ihr Blick durchdrang die Gegend,

70

playboys, who seemed very busy trying to snatch all the anxious prayers which the lips of the pretty ladies in distress had intended for Heaven. Some of our gentlemen had gone down to smoke a pipe in peace; the rest of the company did not refuse when the landlady hit upon the clever idea of showing us to a room that had shutters and drapes. We had scarcely arrived in it when Lotte was busy setting up a circle of chairs, and when, at her invitation, the company had sat down, she proposed that we play a game.

I saw more than one man purse his lips and stretch his limbs in anticipation of a juicy forfeit. "We'll play counting," said Lotte. "Now pay attention. I'll go around a circle from right to left, and you count off in turn, each saying the number that follows; it must go like wildfire; and anyone who gets stuck or makes a mistake gets his ears boxed, and so on to a thousand." It was fun to watch. She went around the circle with outstretched arm. "One," the first began, his neighbor said, "two," the next, "three," and so on. Then she began to walk faster and faster; then someone missed, and whack! A slap. And in the midst of the laughter the next man too, whack! And faster still. I myself was slapped twice and I thought I noticed, with deep satisfaction, that she slapped me harder than she did the others. General laughter and confusion ended the game before we had reached one thousand. Intimate groups went off together; the storm was over and I followed Lotte into the ballroom. On the way she said: "The slaps made them forget the storm and everything else."—I was unable to say anything in reply. "I was one of the most anxious," she continued, "and by pretending to be brave so as to inspire courage in the others, I did become brave." We went to the window. There was thunder off to one side, the glorious rain was pouring down on the land, and the most refreshing fragrance rose up to us with the fullness of a warm breeze. She stood leaning on her elbows, her eyes gazing out into the country; she looked up at the sky, and at me; I saw her eyes fill with tears; she laid her hand on

sie sah gen[63] Himmel und auf mich, ich sah ihr Auge
tränenvoll, sie legte ihre Hand auf die meinige und sagte —
„Klopstock!" — Ich erinnerte mich sogleich der[64] herrlichen Ode[65], die ihr in Gedanken lag, und versank in dem
Strome von Empfindungen, den sie in dieser Losung über
mich ausgoß. Ich ertrug's nicht, neigte mich auf ihre Hand
und küßte sie unter den wonnevollsten Tränen. Und sah
nach ihrem Auge wieder — Edler! Hättest Du Deine Vergötterung in diesem Blicke gesehen, und möcht' ich nun
Deinen so oft entweihten Namen nie wieder nennen hören!

Am 19. Junius

Wo ich neulich mit meiner Erzählung geblieben bin,
weiß ich nicht mehr; das weiß ich, daß es zwei Uhr des
Nachts war, als ich zu Bette kam, und daß, wenn ich Dir
hätte vorschwatzen können, statt zu schreiben, ich Dich
vielleicht bis an den Morgen aufgehalten hätte.

Was auf unserer Hereinfahrt vom Balle geschehen ist,
habe ich noch nicht erzählt, habe auch heute keinen Tag[66]
dazu.

Es war der herrlichste Sonnenaufgang. Der tröpfelnde
Wald und das erfrischte Feld umher! Unsere Gesell-
schafterinnen nickten ein. Sie fragte mich, ob ich nicht
auch von der Partie sein wollte? Ihretwegen sollt' ich unbekümmert sein. — „Solange ich diese Augen offen sehe",
sagte ich und sah sie fest an, „solange hat's keine Gefahr."
— Und wir haben beide ausgehalten bis an ihr Tor, da ihr
die Magd leise aufmachte und auf ihr Fragen versicherte,
daß Vater und Kleine wohl seien und alle noch schliefen.
Da verließ ich sie mit der Bitte: sie selbigen Tags noch
sehen zu dürfen, sie gestand mir's zu, und ich bin gekommen; und seit der Zeit können Sonne, Mond und Sterne
geruhig ihre Wirtschaft treiben, ich weiß weder daß Tag
noch daß Nacht ist, und die ganze Welt verliert sich um
mich her.

Am 21. Junius

Ich lebe so glückliche Tage, wie sie Gott seinen Heiligen
ausspart; und mit mir mag werden was will, so darf ich

72

mine and said, "Klopstock!" I recalled at once the splendid ode she had in mind and sank into the stream of emotions which she poured out over me with this keyword. I could not bear it, bent down over her hand and kissed it amid tears of deepest rapture. And I looked into her eyes again. —Noble man! If you had seen your apotheosis in those eyes! And may I never again hear your name, so often desecrated!

June 19

I can no longer remember where I recently left off in my tale; this much I know: that it was two o'clock in the morning when I got to bed, and that if I could have chatted with you instead of writing, I would probably have kept you up till morning.

I haven't told you yet what happened on our return trip from the ball, and I have no time to do so today.

It was a most glorious sunrise. The dripping forest, and the refreshed fields all around! Our companions were falling asleep. She asked me if I didn't want to join them. I need not worry about her. "As long as I see those eyes open," I said, looking steadily at her, "there is no danger." And we held out, both of us, to her very gateway, which the maid quietly opened for her, assuring her, in answer to her questions, that her father and the little ones were well and that they were all still sleeping. I left her, asking permission to see her again that same day; she granted it and I came; and since that time sun, moon, and stars may calmly carry on their commerce, I don't know whether it is day or night, and the whole world around me is vanishing.

June 21

I spend days as happy as those God reserves for His saints; and no matter what may happen to me, I cannot

73

nicht sagen, daß ich die Freuden, die reinsten Freuden des Lebens nicht genossen habe. — Du kennst mein Wahlheim; dort bin ich völlig etabliert, von da habe ich nur eine halbe Stunde zu Lotten, dort fühl' ich mich selbst und alles Glück, das dem Menschen gegeben ist.

Hätt' ich gedacht, als ich mir Wahlheim zum Zwecke meiner Spaziergänge wählte, daß es so nahe am Himmel läge! Wie oft habe ich das Jagdhaus, das nun alle meine Wünsche einschließt, auf meinen weiten Wanderungen, bald vom Berge, bald von der Ebne über den Fluß, gesehn!

Lieber Wilhelm, ich habe allerlei nachgedacht, über die Begier im Menschen, sich auszubreiten, neue Entdeckungen zu machen, herumzuschweifen; und dann wieder über den inneren Trieb, sich der Einschränkung willig zu ergeben, in dem Gleise der Gewohnheit so hinzufahren und sich weder um rechts noch um links zu bekümmern.

Es ist wunderbar: wie ich hierhar kam und vom Hügel in das schöne Tal schaute, wie es mich rings umher anzog. — Dort das Wäldchen! — Ach, könntest Du Dich in seine Schatten mischen! — Dort die Spitze des Berges! — Ach, könntest Du von da die weite Gegend überschauen! — Die ineinandergeketteten Hügel und vertraulichen Täler! — O könnte ich mich in ihnen verlieren! — — Ich eilte hin und kehrte zurück und hatte nicht gefunden, was ich hoffte. Oh, es ist mit der Ferne, wie mit der Zukunft! Ein großes dämmerndes Ganzes ruht vor unserer Seele, unsere Empfindung verschwimmt darin wie unser Auge, und wir sehnen uns, ach! unser ganzes Wesen hinzugeben, uns mit aller Wonne eines einzigen, großen, herrlichen Gefühls ausfüllen zu lassen. — Und ach! wenn wir hinzueilen, wenn das Dort nun Hier wird, ist alles vor wie nach, und wir stehen in unserer Armut, in unserer Eingeschränktheit, und unsere Seele lechzt nach entschlüpftem Labsale.

So sehnt sich der unruhigste Vagabund zuletzt wieder nach seinem Vaterlande und findet in seiner Hütte, an der Brust seiner Gattin, in dem Kreise seiner Kinder, in den Geschäften zu ihrer Erhaltung die Wonne, die er in der weiten Welt vergebens suchte.

Wenn ich des Morgens mit Sonnenaufgange hinausgehe nach meinem Wahlheim, und dort im Wirtsgarten mir meine

say that I have not experienced the joys, the purest joys of life.—You know my Wahlheim; I am completely settled in it; from there it is only half an hour's walk to Lotte; there I feel that I am myself, and taste all the happiness that is given to man.

Could I have known, when I chose Wahlheim as the goal of my walks, that it was so close to Heaven? How often, on my lengthy walks, have I seen, from the mountain or the plain across the river, the hunting lodge which encloses all that I now wish.

My dear Wilhelm, I have made all sorts of reflections about man's desire to extend himself, to make new discoveries, to roam about; and then again about his inner impulse willingly to accept limitation, to travel along in the groove of habit and to look neither right nor left.

It is remarkable, when I came here and looked from the hill down on the beautiful valley, how I was attracted by the prospect round about me.—There, the grove! Oh, if only you could mingle with its shade.—Over there, the mountain peak.—Oh, if only you could survey the wide expanse from that spot! The chain of hills and the cozy valleys.—Oh, if only I could lose myself in them!—I hurried there, and I returned, and had not found what I hoped for. Oh, distance is like the future: a great, dim whole lies before the mind. Our feelings are submerged in it like our vision and we yearn, alas, to surrender our whole being, to let ourselves be filled with all the bliss of a single, great, glorious emotion.—But alas! when we hurry to it, when There becomes Here, everything is as it was, and we stand in our poverty, in our limitation, and our soul pines for the comfort that has eluded it.

So the most restless vagabond finally yearns to return to his native land and finds in his little cottage, on the breast of his wife, in the circle of his children, in the business of supporting them, the bliss which he sought in vain in the big world.

When I go out to my Wahlheim in the morning at sunrise and there pick my own sugar peas in the garden of

Zuckererbsen selbst pflücke, mich hinsetze, sie abfädne und dazwischen in meinem Homer lese; wenn ich dann in der kleinen Küche mir einen Topf wähle, mir Butter aussteche, Schoten ans Feuer stelle, zudecke und mich dazusetze, sie manchmal umzuschütteln: da fühl' ich so lebhaft, wie die übermütigen Freier der Penelope[67] Ochsen und Schweine schlachten, zerlegen und braten. Es ist nichts, das mich so mit einer stillen, wahren Empfindung ausfüllte als die Züge patriarchalischen Lebens, die ich, Gott sei Dank, ohne Affektation in meine Lebensart verweben kann.

Wie wohl ist mir's, daß mein Herz die simple harmlose Wonne des Menschen fühlen kann, der ein Krauthaupt auf seinen Tisch bringt, das er selbst gezogen, und nun nicht den Kohl allein, sondern all die guten Tage, den schönen Morgen, da er ihn pflanzte, die lieblichen Abende, da er ihn begoß, und da er an dem fortschreitenden Wachstum seine Freude hatte, alle in *einem* Augenblicke wieder mitgenießt.

Am 29. Junius

Vorgestern kam der Medikus hier aus der Stadt hinaus zum Amtmann und fand mich auf der Erde unter Lottens Kindern, wie einige auf mir herumkrabbelten, andere mich neckten, und wie ich sie kitzelte und ein großes Geschrei mit ihnen erregte. Der Doktor, der eine sehr dogmatische Drahtpuppe ist, unterm Reden seine Manschetten in Falten legt und einen Kräusel[68] ohne Ende herauszupft, fand dieses unter der Würde eines gescheiten Menschen; das merkte ich an seiner Nase. Ich ließ mich aber in nichts stören, ließ ihn sehr vernünftige Sachen abhandeln und baute den Kindern ihre Kartenhäuser wieder, die sie zerschlagen hatten. Auch ging er darauf in der Stadt herum und beklagte: des Amtmanns Kinder wären so schon ungezogen genug, der[69] Werther verderbe sie nun völlig.

Ja, lieber Wilhelm, meinem Herzen sind die Kinder am nächsten auf der Erde. Wenn ich ihnen zusehe und in dem kleinen Dinge die Keime aller Tugenden, aller Kräfte sehe, die sie einmal so nötig brauchen werden; wenn ich in dem Eigensinne künftige Standhaftigkeit und Festigkeit des

the inn, sit down to shell them, reading my Homer in between; when I then select a pot in the little kitchen, dig out a piece of butter, put the peas on the fire, cover them and sit down nearby to stir them now and then—then I vividly imagine the arrogant suitors of Penelope slaughtering oxen and pigs, cutting them up and roasting them. Nothing fills me with such quiet, genuine emotion as the features of patriarchal life which, thank Heaven, I can weave into my existence without affectation.

How happy I am that I can feel in my heart the simple, innocent joy of the man who brings to his table a head of cabbage which he has grown himself and who now enjoys not only the cabbage, but all the good days, the beautiful morning on which he planted it, the lovely evenings on which he watered it and found pleasure in seeing it steadily grow—enjoying it all once more in that one moment.

June 29

The day before yesterday the town physician came out here to see the bailiff and found me sitting on the floor among Lotte's children, some of them crawling over me, others teasing me, I tickling them and raising a great uproar with them. The doctor, who is an extremely dogmatic puppet, who folds his cuffs and tugs at his frills as he talks, found this to be beneath the dignity of an intelligent man; I noticed it from the angle of his nose. But I did not let him disturb me in the least, and allowed him to continue talking about sensible matters while I rebuilt the children's card houses, which they had demolished. Afterwards he went about town complaining that the bailiff's children were spoiled enough in any case, but that Werther was ruining them completely.

Yes, my dear Wilhelm, children are closer to my heart than anything else on earth. When I watch them, and see in these tiny creatures the germ of all virtues and all the resources which they will one day need so sorely; when I glimpse in their stubbornness a future steadfastness and

77

Charakters, in dem Mutwillen guten Humor und Leichtigkeit, über die Gefahren der Welt hinzuschlüpfen, erblicke,
alles so unverdorben, so ganz! — immer, immer wiederhole
ich dann die goldenen Worte des Lehrers der Menschen:
„Wenn ihr nicht werdet wie eines von diesen[70]!" Und nun,
mein Bester, sie, die unseresgleichen sind, die wir als unsere Muster ansehen sollten, behandeln wir als Untertanen.
Sie sollen keinen Willen haben! — Haben wir denn keinen?
Und wo liegt das Vorrecht? — Weil wir älter sind und
gescheiter! — Guter Gott von deinem Himmel, alte Kinder
siehst du und junge Kinder und nichts weiter; und an
welchen du mehr Freude hast, das hat dein Sohn schon
lange verkündigt. Aber sie glauben an ihn und hören ihn
nicht, — das ist auch was Altes! — und bilden ihre Kinder
nach sich und — Adieu, Wilhelm! Ich mag darüber nicht
weiter radotieren.

Am 1. Julius

Was Lotte einem Kranken sein muß, fühl' ich an meinem
eigenen armen Herzen, das übler dran ist als manches, das
auf dem Siechbette verschmachtet. Sie wird einige Tage in
der Stadt bei einer rechtschaffnen Frau zubringen, die sich
nach der Aussage der Ärzte ihrem Ende naht und in diesen
letzten Augenblicken Lotten um sich haben will. Ich war
vorige Woche mit ihr den Pfarrer von St . . . zu besuchen;
ein Örtchen, das eine Stunde seitwärts im Gebirge liegt.
Wir kamen gegen vier dahin. Lotte hatte ihre zweite
Schwester mitgenommen. Als wir in den mit zwei hohen
Nußbäumen überschatteten Pfarrhof traten, saß der gute
alte Mann auf einer Bank vor der Haustür, und da er Lotten sah, ward er wie neu belebt, vergaß seinen Knotenstock
und wagte sich auf, ihr entgegen. Sie lief hin zu ihm, nötigte
ihn, sich niederzulassen, indem sie sich zu ihm setzte,
brachte viele Grüße von ihrem Vater, herzte seinen garstigen, schmutzigen, jüngsten Buben, das Quakelchen[71] seines
Alters. Du hättest sie sehen sollen, wie sie den Alten
beschäftigte, wie sie ihre Stimme erhob, um seinen halb
tauben Ohren vernehmlich zu werden, wie sie ihm von
jungen robusten Leuten erzählte, die unvermutet gestorben

firmness of character, in their mischievousness good humor and the facility to slide across the dangers of the world, and all that so unspoiled, so complete!—always, always at such times I repeat the golden words of the Teacher of men: "Except ye become as one of these!" And now, my dear friend, they who are like us, whom we should look on as our models, we treat as subjects. They are supposed to have no will. But have we none ourselves? Wherein our superiority? Is it because we are older and more sensible! Good Lord, from your Heaven You see old children and young children and nothing else; and Your Son told us long ago which of the two gives You greater joy. But they believe in Him and do not hear Him; that's an old story too, and they form their children in their own image and—good-by, Wilhelm. I don't want to ramble on about it any more.

July 1

What Lotte must mean to a sick man I feel in my own poor heart, which is worse off than that of many a person who languishes on his sickbed. She will spend a few days in town at the bedside of some good woman who, in the view of the doctors, is approaching her end and wishes to have Lotte beside her in her last moments. I went with her last week to visit the pastor of St. —, a village situated about an hour's walk away in the mountains. We got there at about four o'clock. Lotte had taken her second sister along. When we entered the parsonage, shaded by two tall nut trees, the good old man was sitting on a bench before the front door, and when he saw Lotte, he seemed to revive, forgot his knotty stick and risked standing up to meet her. She ran up to him, urged him to sit down and, sitting down beside him, brought many greetings from her father; she embraced his youngest boy, horribly dirty but the darling of his old age. You should have seen her keeping the old man occupied, raising her voice so that she might be audible to his half-deaf ears, telling him stories about robust young people who had died unexpectedly, about the excellence of Karlsbad, praising his resolve to go there

wären, von der Vortrefflichkeit des Karlsbades[72], und wie
sie seinen Entschluß lobte, künftigen Sommer hinzugehen,
wie sie fand, daß er viel besser aussähe, viel munterer sei
als das letztemal, da sie ihn gesehn. — Ich hatte indes
der Frau Pfarrerin meine Höflichkeiten gemacht. Der Alte
wurde ganz munter, und da ich nicht umhin konnte, die
schönen Nußbäume zu loben, die uns so lieblich beschat-
teten, fing er an, uns, wiewohl mit einiger Beschwerlichkeit,
die Geschichte davon zu geben. — „Den alten“, sagte er,
„wissen wir nicht, wer den gepflanzt hat: einige sagen dieser,
andere jener Pfarrer. Der jüngere aber dort hinten ist so alt
als meine Frau, im Oktober fünfzig Jahr'. Ihr Vater pflanzte
ihn des Morgens, als sie gegen Abend geboren wurde. Er
war mein Vorfahr im Amt, und wie lieb ihm der Baum war,
ist nicht zu sagen; mir ist er's gewiß nicht weniger. Meine
Frau saß darunter auf einem Balken und strickte, da ich
vor siebenundzwanzig Jahren als ein armer Student zum
ersten Male hier in den Hof kam.“ — Lotte fragte nach
seiner Tochter: es hieß[73], sie sei mit Herrn Schmidt auf die
Wiese hinaus zu den Arbeitern, und der Alte fuhr in seiner
Erzählung fort: wie sein Vorfahr ihn lieb gewonnen und die
Tochter dazu, und wie er erst sein Vikar und dann sein
Nachfolger geworden. Die Geschichte war nicht lange zu
Ende, als die Jungfer[74] Pfarrerin mit dem sogenannten
Herrn Schmidt durch den Garten herkam: sie bewill-
kommte Lotten mit herzlicher Wärme, und ich muß sagen,
sie gefiel mir nicht übel; eine rasche, wohlgewachsene
Brünette, die einen die kurze Zeit über[75] auf dem Lande
wohl unterhalten hätte. Ihr Liebhaber (denn als solchen
stellte sich Herr Schmidt gleich dar), ein feiner, doch stiller
Mensch, der sich nicht in unsere Gespräche mischen wollte,
ob ihn gleich Lotte immer hereinzog. Was mich am meisten
betrübte, war, daß ich an seinen Gesichtszügen zu bemerken schien, es sei mehr Eigensinn und übler Humor als
Eingeschränktheit des Verstandes, der ihn sich mitzuteilen
hinderte. In der Folge war dies leider nur zu deutlich; denn
als Friederike beim Spazierengehen mit Lotten und ge-
legentlich auch mit mir ging, wurde des Herrn Angesicht,
das ohnedies einer bräunlichen Farbe war, so sichtlich ver-
dunkelt, daß es Zeit war, daß Lotte mich beim Ärmel

next summer, saying she found that he looked much better and was much more lively than the last time she had seen him. Meanwhile I had paid my respects to the pastor's wife. The old man became quite gay and, as I could not help praising the beautiful nut trees, which were casting such a pleasant shade over us, he began to tell us their history, though with some difficulty.—"That old one," he said, "we don't know who planted that one: some say this pastor, some say another. But the younger one back there is as old as my wife, fifty years in October. Her father planted it on the morning of the day on which she was born in the evening. He was my predecessor in office, and it is impossible to say how precious the tree was to him, and it is certainly no less so to me. My wife was sitting under it on a log, knitting, when I first came into this yard as a poor student twenty-seven years ago."—Lotte asked about his daughter and learned that she had gone out with Herr Schmidt to the meadow where the workers were; the old man continued his story and told how both his predecessor and his daughter had come to like him, and how he had become first his vicar and then his successor. Not long after he had finished the story the pastor's daughter came walking through the garden with the aforesaid Herr Schmidt; she welcomed Lotte with cordial warmth, and I must say I liked her more than a little: a lively, well-formed brunette, who would have been good company for a short stay in the country. Her suitor (for Herr Schmidt at once presented himself in this role), was a gentle, quiet person, who did not want to mix in our conversation, although Lotte kept drawing him into it. What distressed me most was the fact that I seemed to notice in his features that it was obstinacy and ill-humor rather than limited intelligence which prevented him from speaking. Unfortunately this soon became only too plain, for during our walk, when Friederike walked with Lotte and occasionally with me too, the gentleman's face, which was of a brownish color even normally, darkened so visibly that it was time for Lotte to tug at my sleeve and indicate to me that I had been too attentive to Friederike. Now there is nothing that annoys me more than when people torment each other,

81

zupfte und mir zu verstehen gab, daß ich mit Friederiken zu artig getan. Nun verdrießt mich nichts mehr, als wenn die Menschen einander plagen, am meisten, wenn junge Leute in der Blüte des Lebens, da sie am offensten für alle Freuden sein könnten, einander die paar guten Tage mit Fratzen verderben und nur erst zu spät das Unersetzliche ihrer Verschwendung einsehen. Mich wurmte das, und ich konnte nicht umhin, da wir gegen Abend in den Pfarrhof zurückkehrten und an einem Tische Milch aßen[76] und das Gespräch auf Freude und Leid der Welt sich wendete, den Faden zu ergreifen und recht herzlich gegen die üble Laune zu reden. — „Wir Menschen beklagen uns oft", fing ich an, „daß der[77] guten Tage so wenig sind und der schlimmen so viel, und wie mich dünkt, meist mit Unrecht. Wenn wir immer ein offenes Herz hätten, das Gute zu genießen, das uns Gott für jeden Tag bereitet, wir würden alsdann auch Kraft genug haben, das Übel zu tragen, wenn es kommt." — „Wir haben aber unser Gemüt nicht in unserer Gewalt", versetzte die Pfarrerin: „wie viel hängt vom Körper ab; wenn einem nicht wohl ist, ist's einem überall nicht recht." — Ich gestand ihr das ein. — „Wir wollen es also", fuhr ich fort, „als eine Krankheit ansehen und fragen, ob dafür kein Mittel ist?" — „Das läßt sich hören", sagte Lotte, „ich glaube wenigstens, daß viel von uns abhängt. Ich weiß es an mir. Wenn mich etwas neckt und mich verdrießlich machen will, spring' ich auf und sing' ein paar Kontretänze den Garten auf und ab, gleich ist's weg." — „Das war's, was ich sagen wollte", versetzte ich; „es ist mit der üblen Laune völlig wie mit der Trägheit, denn es ist eine Art von Trägheit. Unsere Natur hängt sehr dahin, und doch, wenn wir nur einmal die Kraft haben, uns zu ermannen, geht uns die Arbeit frisch von der Hand, und wir finden in der Tätigkeit ein wahres Vergnügen." — Friederike war sehr aufmerksam, und der junge Mensch wandte mir ein: daß man nicht Herr über sich selbst sei, und am wenigsten über seine Empfindungen gebieten könne. — „Es ist hier die Frage von einer unangenehmen Empfindung", versetzte ich, „die doch jedermann gerne los ist; und niemand weiß, wie weit seine

most of all when young people in the flower of life, when they could be most responsive to all the joys of life, spoil those few good days with nonsense and realize only too late that what they have squandered is irretrievable. This galled me, and toward evening when we returned to the parsonage and sat at a table over our sour milk, and the conversation turned to the joys and sorrows of the world, I could not help picking up the thread and making a heart-felt speech against ill-humor. "We human beings," I began, "often complain that there are so few good days and so many bad ones, but it seems to me we are mostly wrong to complain. If our hearts were always disposed to enjoy the good that God prepares for us every day, we would also have enough strength to endure evil when it comes." —"But we cannot control our feelings," the parson's wife replied, "how much depends on our physical condition! When one doesn't feel well, nothing goes right."—I conceded this.—"So let's regard it as a disease," I continued, "and ask if there is no remedy for it."—"That sounds like a good idea," said Lotte, "at least I believe that a lot depends on ourselves. I know it from my own experience. Where something annoys me and makes me peevish, I jump up and sing a few country dance tunes up and down the garden, and in a jiffy it's gone."—"That's exactly what I wanted to say," I continued, "ill-humor is just like sluggishness, for it is a type of sluggishness. We are naturally prone to it, and yet if we once have the strength to pull ourselves together, we do our work quickly and we find true pleasure in our activity."—Friederike was very attentive and the young man objected that one is not master of himself and has command least of all over his emotions. "We are dealing here," I replied, "with an unpleasant emotion, of which everyone, after all, wants to rid himself, and no one knows how far his powers extend until he has tried them. Of course, anyone who is sick will ask around among all the doctors and he will not reject the most demanding deprivations or the bitterest medicines to recover his valued health."—I noticed that the good old man was straining his ears to hear; so that he might take part in our con-

Kräfte gehen, bis er sie versucht hat. Gewiß, wer krank ist, wird bei allen Ärzten herumfragen, und die größten Resignationen, die bittersten Arzneien wird er nicht abweisen, um seine gewünschte Gesundheit zu erhalten." — Ich bemerkte, daß der ehrliche Alte sein Gehör anstrengte, um an userm Diskurse teilzunehmen, ich erhob die Stimme, indem ich die Rede gegen ihn wandte: „Man predigt gegen so viele Laster", sagte ich; „ich habe noch nie gehört, daß man gegen die üble Laune vom Predigtstuhle gearbeitet hätte*." — „Das müssen die Stadtpfarrer tun", sagte er, „die Bauern haben keinen bösen Humor; doch könnte es auch zuweilen nicht schaden, es wäre eine Lektion für seine[79] Frau wenigstens und für den Herrn Amtmann." — Die Gesellschaft lachte und er herzlich mit, bis er in einen Husten verfiel, der unsern Diskurs eine Zeitlang unterbrach; darauf denn der junge Mensch wieder das Wort nahm: „Sie nannten den bösen Humor ein Laster; mich deucht[80], das ist übertrieben." — „Mitnichten", gab ich zur Antwort, „wenn das, womit man sich selbst und seinem Nächsten schadet, diesen Namen verdient. Ist es nicht genug, daß wir einander nicht glücklich machen können, müssen wir auch noch einander das Vergnügen rauben, das jedes Herz sich noch manchmal selbst gewähren kann? Und nennen Sie mir den Menschen, der übler Laune ist und so brav dabei, sie zu verbergen, sie allein zu tragen, ohne die Freude um sich her zu zerstören! Oder ist sie nicht vielmehr ein innerer Unmut über unsere eigene Unwürdigkeit, ein Mißfallen an uns selbst, das immer mit einem Neide verknüpft ist, der durch eine törichte Eitelkeit aufgehetzt wird? Wir sehen glückliche Menschen, die wir nicht glücklich machen, und das ist unerträglich." — Lotte lächelte mich an, da sie die Bewegung sah, mit der ich redete, und eine Träne in Friederikens Auge spornte mich fortzufahren. — „Wehe denen", sagte ich, „die sich der Gewalt bedienen, die sie über ein Herz haben, um ihm die einfachen Freuden zu rauben, die aus ihm selbst hervorkeimen. Alle Geschenke, alle Gefälligkeiten der Welt ersetzen nicht einen Augenblick Vergnügen

* Wir haben nun von Lavatern eine treffliche Predigt hierüber, unter denen über das Buch Jonas[78].

versation, I turned toward him and raised my voice. "We preach against so many vices," I said, "but I've never yet heard of an attack on ill-humor from the pulpit." *—"The city parsons would have to do that," he said, "farm folk are never ill-humored. However, it wouldn't hurt occasionally; it would at least be a lesson for his wife and for the bailiff." The company laughed and he laughed heartily with them, till he fell into a fit of coughing which interrupted our conversation for a while; then the young man resumed: "You called ill-humor a vice; it seems to me that that's an exaggeration."—"Not at all," I replied, "if that which causes harm to oneself and one's neighbor deserves that name. Is it not enough that we cannot make one another happy? Must we also rob one another of the pleasure which every heart can still grant itself at times? And name me a man who is ill-humored and yet decent enough to conceal it, to bear it alone, without disturbing the happiness of those around him. Or isn't it rather an inner displeasure at our own unworthiness, a dissatisfaction with ourselves which is always bound up with envy, which is stirred by foolish vanity? We see happy people whom we have not made happy and find this unendurable."—Lotte smiled at me when she noticed with what emotion I was speaking, and a tear in Friederike's eye spurred me on to continue. "Woe to those," I said, "who make use of their power over someone else's heart to destroy the simple joys which grow out of it naturally. All the gifts, all the kindness in the world will not for a moment compensate for the loss of that inner happiness which our tyrant's envy and discomfort have turned to bitterness."

---

* We now have an excellent sermon by Lavater on this theme, among the ones on the Book of Jonah.

an sich selbst, den uns eine neidische Unbehaglichkeit unsers Tyrannen vergällt hat."

Mein ganzes Herz war voll in diesem Augenblicke; die Erinnerung so manches Vergangenen drängte sich an meine Seele, und die Tränen kamen mir in die Augen.

„Wer sich das nur täglich sagte", rief ich aus, „du vermagst nichts auf deine Freunde, als ihnen ihre Freuden zu lassen und ihr Glück zu vermehren, indem du es mit ihnen genießest. Vermagst du, wenn ihre innere Seele von einer ängstigenden Leidenschaft gequält, vom Kummer zerrüttet ist, ihnen einen Tropfen Linderung zu geben?"

„Und wenn die letzte bangste Krankheit dann über das Geschöpf herfällt, das du in blühenden Tagen untergraben hast, und sie nun daliegt in dem erbärmlichen Ermatten, das Auge gefühllos gen Himmel sieht, der Todesschweiß auf der blassen Stirne abwechselt und du vor dem Bette stehst wie ein Verdammter, in dem innigsten Gefühl, daß du nichts vermagst mit deinem ganzen Vermögen, und die Angst dich inwendig krampft, daß du alles hingeben möchtest, dem untergehenden Geschöpfe einen Tropfen Stärkung, einen Funken Mut einflößen zu können."

Die Erinnerung einer solchen Szene, wobei ich gegenwärtig war, fiel mit ganzer Gewalt bei diesen Worten über mich. Ich nahm das Schnupftuch vor die Augen und verließ die Gesellschaft, und nur Lottens Stimme, die mir rief, wir wollten fort, brachte mich zu mir selbst. Und wie sie mich auf dem Wege schalt über den zu warmen Anteil an allem, und daß ich drüber zugrunde gehen würde! daß ich mich schonen sollte! — Oh, der Engel! Um deinetwillen muß ich leben!

Am 6. Julius

Sie ist immer um ihre sterbende Freundin und ist immer dieselbe, immer das gegenwärtige[81], holde Geschöpf, das, wo sie hinsieht, Schmerzen lindert und Glückliche macht. Sie ging gestern abend mit Mariannen und dem kleinen Malchen spazieren, ich wußte es und traf sie an, und wir gingen zusammen. Nach einem Wege von anderthalb Stunden kamen wir gegen die Stadt zurück, an den Brun-

My heart was full at this moment; the memory of so many past events forced itself into my mind, and tears came to my eyes.

"If only a man said to himself every day," I exclaimed, "you can do nothing better for your friends than to leave them their joys and increase their happiness by enjoying it with them. Can you give them one drop of comfort when their minds are tormented by a disturbing passion, shaken by grief?

"And when the last, most harrowing illness befalls the being whom you have undermined in her flower, when she lies there in wretched weakness, her unseeing eye turned toward heaven, the sweat of death appearing at intervals on her pale brow, and you stand beside her bed like a man condemned, with the most profound conviction that all your powers are powerless, and anxiety convulses you within, so that you would give anything to be able to instill a drop of strength, a spark of courage into the perishing being."

The recollection of such a scene at which I had been present overcame me with all its force as I uttered these words. I put my handkerchief to my eyes and left the company; and only Lotte's voice calling to me that we were leaving brought me back to myself. And how she scolded me on the way because I took everything too much to heart and that it would destroy me, and that I must spare myself.—Oh, you angel! For your sake I must live on.

July 6

She is always with her dying friend, and she is always the same, always there, always sweet, easing pain and bringing happiness wherever she turns her eyes. Last night she went for a walk with Marianne and little Malchen; I knew of it and met them and we walked together. After walking for an hour and a half we came back toward the town, to the well which is so precious to me and is now a thousand

nen, der mir so wert und nun tausendmal werter ist. Lotte setzte sich aufs Mäuerchen, wir standen vor ihr. Ich sah umher, ach, und die Zeit, da mein Herz so allein war, lebte wieder vor mir auf. — „Lieber Brunnen", sagte ich, „seither hab' ich nicht mehr an deiner Kühle geruht, hab' in eilendem Vorübergehn dich manchmal nicht angesehen." — Ich blickte hinab und sah, daß Malchen mit einem Glase Wasser sehr beschäftigt heraufstieg. — Ich sah Lotten an und fühlte alles, was ich an ihr habe. Indem kommt Malchen mit einem Glase. Marianne wollt' es ihr abnehmen. — „Nein!" rief das Kind mit dem süßesten Ausdrucke, „nein, Lottchen, du sollst zuerst trinken!" — Ich ward über die Wahrheit, über die Güte, womit sie das ausrief, so entzückt, daß ich meine Empfindung mit nichts ausdrücken konnte, als ich nahm das Kind von der Erde und küßte es lebhaft, das sogleich zu schreien und zu weinen anfing. — „Sie haben übel getan", sagte Lotte. — Ich war betroffen. — „Komm, Malchen", fuhr sie fort, indem sie es bei der Hand nahm und die Stufen hinabführte, „da wasche dich aus der frischen Quelle geschwind, geschwind, da tut's nichts." — Wie ich so dastand und zusah, mit welcher Emsigkeit das Kleine mit seinen nassen Händchen die Backen rieb, mit welchem Glauben, daß durch die Wunderquelle alle Verunreinigung abgespült und die Schmach abgetan würde, einen häßlichen Bart zu kriegen; wie Lotte sagte: „es ist genug", und das Kind doch immer eifrig fortwusch, als wenn viel mehr täte als wenig. — Ich sage Dir, Wilhelm, ich habe mit mehr Respekt nie einer Taufhandlung beigewohnt — und als Lotte heraufkam, hätte ich mich gern vor ihr niedergeworfen wie vor einem Propheten, der die Schulden[82] einer Nation weggeweiht hat.

Des Abends konnte ich nicht umhin, in der Freude meines Herzens den Vorfall einem Manne zu erzählen, dem ich Menschensinn zutraute, weil er Verstand hat; aber wie kam ich an! Er sagte, das sei sehr übel von Lotten gewesen; man solle den Kindern nichts weismachen[83]; dergleichen gebe zu unzähligen Irrtümern und Aberglauben Anlaß, wovor man die Kinder frühzeitig bewahren müsse. — Nun fiel mir ein, daß der Mann vor acht Tagen hatte

times more precious. Lotte sat down on the little wall, and we stood before her. I looked about me, alas, and the time when my heart was so alone came back to me. "Dear well," I said, "since then I have not rested beside your cool waters; sometimes I did not even look at you as I hurried past." I looked down and saw little Malchen busily climbing up the steps with a glass of water in her hand.—I looked at Lotte and felt all that she means to me. Meanwhile Malchen arrived with a glass. Marianne wanted to take it from her. "No," the child cried with the sweetest expression on her face, "no, Lotte, you must drink first." This disingenuousness, the sweetness with which she said this, so delighted me that I could express my emotion in no other way than to lift the child off the ground and kiss it warmly; she began to cry and scream at once. "You did a bad thing," said Lotte.—I was taken aback. "Come, Malchen," she continued, taking her by the hand and leading her down the steps, "wash it off there with the fresh water—quick, quick, then it won't matter."—As I stood there and watched how zealously the little girl rubbed her cheeks with her wet little hands, with what faith that the miraculous spring would wash away all contamination and save her from the disgrace of getting an ugly beard, and how, even after Lotte said, "That's enough," the child still kept washing busily, as if much could do more than little, —I tell you, Wilhelm, I have never witnessed a baptismal ceremony with more respect, and when Lotte came up, I would gladly have thrown myself at her feet as before a prophet who had washed away the sins of a nation with holy water.

That evening, in the joy of my heart, I could not refrain from relating the incident to a man whom I expected to have some human feeling because he is intelligent; but what a reception I got from him! He said Lotte had done a very bad thing; children should not be deceived; such things caused an incredible amount of error and superstition against which children should be protected from an early age.—I now remembered that the man had had his

taufen lassen, drum ließ ich's vorbeigehen und blieb in meinem Herzen der Wahrheit getreu: Wir sollen es mit den Kindern machen wie Gott mit uns, der uns am glücklichsten macht, wenn er uns in freundlichem Wahne so hintaumeln läßt.

Am 8. Julius

Was man ein Kind ist! Was man nach so einem Blicke geizt! Was man ein Kind ist! — Wir waren nach Wahlheim gegangen. Die Frauenzimmer fuhren hinaus, und während unserer Spaziergänge glaubte ich in Lottens schwarzen Augen — ich bin ein Tor, verzeih mir's! Du solltest sie sehen, diese Augen. — Daß ich kurz bin[84] (denn die Augen fallen mir zu vor Schlaf), siehe, die Frauenzimmer stiegen ein, da standen um die Kutsche der junge W . . ., Selstadt und Audran und ich. Da ward aus dem Schlage geplaudert mit den Kerlchen, die freilich leicht und luftig genug waren. — Ich suchte Lottens Augen; ach, sie gingen von einem zum andern! Aber auf mich! mich! mich!, der ganz allein auf sie resigniert[85] dastand, fielen sie nicht! — Mein Herz sagte ihr tausend Adieu! Und sie sah mich nicht! Die Kutsche fuhr vorbei, und eine Träne stand mir im Auge. Ich sah ihr nach und sah Lottens Kopfputz sich zum Schlage herauslehnen, und sie wandte sich um zu sehen, ach! nach mir? — Lieber! In dieser Ungewißheit schwebe ich; das ist mein Trost: vielleicht hat sie sich nach mir umgesehen! Vielleicht! — Gute Nacht! Oh, was ich ein Kind bin!

Am 10. Julius

Die alberne Figur, die ich mache, wenn in Gesellschaft von ihr gesprochen wird, solltest Du sehen! Wenn man mich nun gar fragt, wie sie mir gefällt? — Gefällt! das Wort hasse ich auf den Tod. Was muß das für ein Mensch sein, dem Lotte gefällt, dem sie nicht alle Sinne, alle Empfindungen ausfüllt! Gefällt! Neulich fragte mich einer, wie mir Ossian[86] gefiele!

child baptized a week before, so I let the matter pass and in my heart remained loyal to the truth that we should behave toward children as God behaves toward us, making us happiest when He allows us to stagger about in a pleasant illusion.

July 8

What a child I am! How greedy I am for a look from her! What a child I am!—We had gone to Wahlheim. The ladies drove out and during our walks I thought that Lotte's black eyes—pardon me, I'm a fool, you ought to see those eyes. To be brief (I can't keep my eyes open), the ladies got into the carriage, young W——, Selstadt, and Audran and I stood around them. They chatted through the carriage door with the fellows, who were a gay and merry lot to be sure.—I sought Lotte's eyes; alas, they were going from one person to the next! But they did not fall on me, me, me, who stood there devoted only to them.— My heart said a thousand farewells to her. And she did not see me! The carriage drove off and tears came to my eyes. I looked after her, and saw Lotte's bonnet lean out of the carriage door, and she turned to look—ah, at me?—My dear friend! I am suspended in uncertainty; that is my consolation: perhaps she turned to look at me. Perhaps!— Good night! Oh, what a child I am!

July 10

You should see the silly figure I cut when she is mentioned in company! And particularly when I am asked how I like her—like her! I hate the word as I hate death. What kind of person must he be who *likes* Lotte, whose every sense and every emotion she does not occupy? Like! Someone asked me recently how I liked Ossian!

Frau M . . . ist sehr schlecht; ich bete für ihr Leben, weil ich mit Lotten dulde. Ich sehe sie selten bei meiner Freundin[87], und heute hat sie mir einen wunderbaren Vorfall erzählt. — Der alte M . . . ist ein geiziger rangiger[88] Filz, der seine Frau im Leben was rechts[89] geplagt und eingeschränkt hat; doch hat sich die Frau immer durchzuhelfen gewußt. Vor wenigen Tagen, als der Arzt ihr das Leben abgesprochen hatte, ließ sie ihren Mann kommen (Lotte war im Zimmer) und redete ihn also an: „Ich muß dir eine Sache gestehen, die nach meinem Tode Verwirrung und Verdruß machen könnte. Ich habe bisher die Haushaltung geführt, so ordentlich und sparsam als möglich; allein du wirst mir verzeihen, daß ich dich diese dreißig Jahre her hintergangen habe. Du bestimmtest im Anfange unserer Heirat ein Geringes für die Bestreitung der Küche und anderer häuslicher Ausgaben. Als unsere Haushaltung stärker wurde, unser Gewerbe größer, warst du nicht zu bewegen, mein Wochengeld nach dem Verhältnisse zu vermehren; kurz, du weißt, daß du in den Zeiten, da sie am größten war, verlangtest, ich solle mit sieben Gulden[90] die Woche auskommen. Die habe ich denn ohne Widerrede genommen und mir den Überschuß wöchentlich aus der Losung geholt, da niemand vermutete, daß die Frau die Kasse bestehlen würde. Ich habe nichts verschwendet und wäre auch, ohne es zu bekennen, getrost der Ewigkeit entgegengegangen, wenn nicht diejenige, die nach mir das Hauswesen zu führen hat, sich nicht zu helfen wissen würde und du doch immer darauf bestehen könntest, deine erste Frau sei damit ausgekommen."

Ich redete mit Lotten über die unglaubliche Verblendung des Menschensinns, daß einer nicht argwöhnen soll, dahinter müsse was anders stecken, wenn eins[91] mit sieben Gulden hinreicht, wo man den Aufwand vielleicht um zweimal so viel sieht. Aber ich habe selbst Leute gekannt, die des Propheten ewiges Ölkrüglein[92] ohne Verwunderung in ihrem Hause angenommen hätten.

Frau M— is very bad; I pray for her life because I endure with Lotte. I rarely see her at the home of my friend, and today she told me of a remarkable incident.—Old M— is a greedy, nasty skinflint, who horribly tormented and restricted his wife all her life, but she has always been able to get by. A few days ago, when the doctor had given her up, she sent for her husband—Lotte was in the room— and addressed him as follows: "I must confess a matter to you which might cause confusion and vexation after my death. I have until now kept house as neatly and economically as possible, but you must pardon me for having cheated you these thirty years. At the beginning of our marriage you fixed a small amount of money for the kitchen and other domestic expenses. When our household and our property grew larger, you could not be persuaded to increase my allowance proportionately; in short, you know that at a time when you knew our expenses were greatest, you demanded that I get along with seven gulden a week. So without contradicting you I took the money and got the supplement every week from the receipts, since no one would suspect that your wife was robbing the till. I have squandered nothing and would have confidently faced eternity without making this confession to you, except that the person who will have to keep house after me would not know how to do it on this sum and you could always insist that your first wife had been able to get along on it."

I discussed with Lotte man's incredible blindness; how can a person not suspect that something is amiss when his wife makes out with seven gulden and he sees that the expenditure amounts to about double that? But I myself have known people who would have accepted the prophet's perpetual little oil jug in their home without astonishment.

Nein, ich betrüge mich nicht! Ich lese in ihren schwarzen Augen wahre Teilnehmung an mir und meinem Schicksal. Ja ich fühle, und darin darf ich meinem Herzen trauen, daß sie — o darf ich, kann ich den Himmel in diesen Worten aussprechen? — daß sie mich liebt!

Mich liebt! — Und wie wert ich mir selbst werde, wie ich — Dir darf ich's wohl sagen, Du hast Sinn für so etwas — wie ich mich selbst anbete, seitdem sie mich liebt!

Ob das Vermessenheit ist oder Gefühl des wahren Verhältnisses? — Ich kenne den Menschen nicht, von dem ich etwas in Lottens Herzen fürchtete. Und doch — wenn sie von ihrem Bräutigam spricht, mit solcher Wärme, solcher Liebe von ihm spricht — da ist mir's wie einem, der aller seiner Ehren und Würden entsetzt und dem der Degen genommen wird.

Ach, wie mir das durch alle Adern läuft, wenn mein Finger unversehens den ihrigen berührt, wenn unsere Füße sich unter dem Tische begegnen! Ich ziehe zurück wie vom Feuer, und eine geheime Kraft zieht mich wieder vorwärts — mir wird's so schwindelig vor allen Sinnen. — Oh, und ihre Unschuld, ihre unbefangene Seele fühlt nicht, wie sehr mich die kleinen Vertraulichkeiten peinigen. Wenn sie gar im Gespräch ihre Hand auf die meinige legt und im Interesse der Unterredung näher zu mir rückt, daß der himmlische Atem ihres Mundes meine Lippen erreichen kann —: ich glaube zu versinken, wie vom Wetter gerührt. — Und, Wilhelm! wenn ich mich jemals unterstehe, diesen Himmel, dieses Vertrauen —! Du verstehst mich. Nein, mein Herz ist so verderbt nicht! Schwach! schwach genug! — Und ist das nicht Verderben? —

Sie ist mir heilig. Alle Begier schweigt in ihrer Gegenwart. Ich weiß nie, wie mir ist, wenn ich bei ihr bin; es ist, als wenn die Seele sich mir in allen Nerven umkehrte. — Sie hat eine Melodie, die sie auf dem Klavier spielt mit der Kraft[93] eines Engels, so simpel und so geistvoll[94]! Es

No, I am not deceiving myself. I read in her black eyes genuine interest in me and my fate. Yes, I feel, and in this I may trust my heart, that she—oh, may I, can I express the heaven that is in these words?—that she loves me!

Loves me!—And how precious I become to myself when I—I suppose I may say it to you, you understand such things—how I worship myself since she loves me!

I wonder whether this is presumptuousness or true understanding of our relationship?—I don't know the man I could fear as a rival for Lotte's heart. And yet—when she speaks of her fiancé with such warmth, with such love —I feel like a man who has been stripped of all his honors and titles, and whose sword is taken away.

Oh, what a thrill courses through my veins when my finger accidentally touches hers, when our feet meet under the table. I withdraw as if I had touched fire, and a mysterious force draws me forward again—all my senses begin to reel.—Oh! and her innocence, her naïve heart does not feel what a torment these little intimacies are to me. When she actually puts her hand on mine during one of our conversations and moves closer to me for the sake of communication, so that the heavenly breath of her mouth can reach my lips—I think I shall fall to the ground as if struck by lightning.—And Wilhelm, if ever I dare to—this heaven, this trust!—You understand me. No, my heart is not that depraved! Weak, weak enough!—And isn't that depravity?—

She is sacred to me. All desire subsides in her presence. I never know how I feel when I am with her; it is as if my soul were whirling in every nerve. She has a tune which she plays on the piano with the touch of an angel, so simple and so spiritual. It is her favorite song and it cures me of

ist ihr Leiblied, und mich stellt es von aller Pein, Verwirrung und Grillen her, wenn sie nur die erste Note davon greift.

Kein Wort von der alten Zauberkraft der Musik ist mir unwahrscheinlich. Wie mich der einfache Gesang angreift! Und wie sie ihn anzubringen weiß, oft zur Zeit, wo ich mir eine Kugel vor den Kopf schießen möchte! Die Irrung und Finsternis meiner Seele zerstreut sich, und ich atme wieder freier.

Am 18. Julius

Wilhelm, was ist unserem Herzen die Welt ohne Liebe! Was eine Zauberlaterne[95] ist ohne Licht! Kaum bringst du das Lämpchen hinein, so scheinen dir die buntesten Bilder an deine weiße Wand! Und wenn's nichts wäre als das, als vorübergehende Phantome, so macht's doch immer unser Glück, wenn wir wie frische Jungen davor stehen und uns über die Wundererscheinungen entzücken. Heute konnte ich nicht zu Lotten, eine unvermeidliche Gesellschaft hielt mich ab. Was war zu tun? Ich schickte meinen Diener hinaus, nur um einen Menschen um mich zu haben, der ihr heute nahegekommen wäre. Mit welcher Ungeduld ich ihn erwartete, mit welcher Freude ich ihn wieder sah! Ich hätte ihn gern beim Kopf genommen und geküßt, wenn ich mich nicht geschämt hätte.

Man erzählt von dem Bononischen[96] Steine, daß er, wenn man ihn in die Sonne legt, ihre Strahlen anzieht und eine Weile bei Nacht leuchtet. So war mir's mit dem Burschen. Das Gefühl, daß ihre Augen auf seinem Gesichte, seinen Backen, seinen Rockknöpfen und dem Kragen am Surtout geruht hatten, machte mir das alles so heilig, so wert! Ich hätte in dem Augenblick den Jungen nicht um[97] tausend Taler[98] gegeben. Es war mir so wohl in seiner Gegenwart. — Bewahre Dich Gott, daß Du darüber lachest. Wilhelm, sind das Phantome, wenn es uns wohl ist?

Den 19. Julius

„Ich werde sie sehen!" ruf' ich morgens aus, wenn ich

all my anguish, confusion, and whims when she strikes its first note.

Not a word about the magic power of ancient music appears improbable to me. How the simple song affects me! And how she knows when to play it, often when I would like to put a bullet through my head. The confusion and darkness in my mind are dispersed and I breathe more freely once more.

July 18

Wilhelm, what is the world without love to our hearts? What a magic lantern is without light. But as soon as you put the little lamp inside, the most colorful pictures shine on your white wall. And even if it were no more than that, transitory phantoms, still it always makes us happy to stand before them like eager boys and delight in these marvelous sights. Today I was unable to go to Lotte. A party I could not avoid detained me. What was I to do? I sent out my man, just to have someone about me who had been close to her today. How impatiently I waited for him, and with what joy I welcomed him back. I would have liked to take his head and kiss him if I hadn't felt ashamed to do so.

They say of Bologna stone that, when placed in the sun, it attracts the rays and shines for a while at night. That's the way I felt about the boy. The idea that her eyes had rested on his face, his cheeks, the buttons of his jacket, and the collar of his overcoat, made them all so sacred, so dear to me! At that moment I wouldn't have parted with the boy for a thousand thalers. I felt so happy in his presence.—God keep you from laughing at me. Wilhelm, is it a delusion when we feel happy?

July 19

"I shall see her!" I exclaim in the morning when I'm

mich ermuntere und mit aller Heiterkeit der schönen Sonne entgegenblicke; „ich werde sie sehen!" Und da habe ich für den ganzen Tag keinen Wunsch weiter. Alles, alles verschlingt sich in dieser Aussicht.

Den 20. Julius

Eure Idee will noch nicht die meinige werden, daß ich mit dem Gesandten nach * * * gehen soll. Ich liebe die Subordination nicht sehr, und wir wissen alle, daß der Mann noch dazu ein widriger Mensch ist. Meine Mutter möchte mich gern in Aktivität haben, sagst Du; das hat mich zu[99] lachen gemacht. Bin ich jetzt nicht auch aktiv? und ist's im Grunde nicht einerlei, ob ich Erbsen zähle oder Linsen? Alles in der Welt läuft doch auf eine Lumperei hinaus, und ein Mensch, der um anderer willen, ohne daß es seine eigene Leidenschaft, sein eigenes Bedürfnis ist, sich um Geld oder Ehre oder sonst was abarbeitet, ist immer ein Tor.

Am 24. Julius

Da Dir so sehr daran gelegen ist, daß ich mein Zeichnen nicht vernachlässige, möchte ich lieber die ganze Sache übergehen, als Dir sagen, daß zeither wenig getan wird.
Noch nie war ich glücklicher, noch nie war meine Empfindung an der Natur, bis aufs Steinchen, aufs Gräschen herunter, voller und inniger, und doch — Ich weiß nicht, wie ich mich ausdrücken soll, meine vorstellende Kraft ist so schwach, alles schwimmt und schwankt so vor meiner Seele, daß ich keinen Umriß packen kann; aber ich bilde mir ein, wenn ich Ton hätte oder Wachs, so wollte ich's wohl herausbilden. Ich werde auch Ton nehmen, wenn's länger währt, und kneten, und sollten's Kuchen werden!
Lottens Porträt habe ich dreimal angefangen und habe mich dreimal prostituiert[100]; das[101] mich um so mehr verdrießt, weil ich vor einiger Zeit sehr glücklich im Treffen[102] war. Darauf habe ich denn ihren Schattenriß gemacht und damit soll mir genügen.

fully awake and look at the beautiful sun with the utmost joy, "I shall see her!" And I have no other wish all day. Everything, everything is swallowed up by this prospect.

July 20

I cannot yet accept your notion that I should go with the ambassador to ———. I am not fond of being a subordinate, and we all know that the man is unpleasant to boot. You say my mother would like to see me active; that made me laugh. Am I not active now? And does it make any real difference whether I count peas or lentils? After all, everything in the world ends in the same triviality, and a person who works himself to the bone for others, for money or honor or anything else without a passion or need for doing it, is always a fool.

July 24

Since you are so concerned that I should not neglect my drawing, I would rather skip the whole matter than tell you that for the present little is being accomplished.

I've never been happier, my feeling for nature, down to a little stone, a blade of grass, has never been richer and deeper, and yet—I don't know how to express myself, my imagination is so feeble, everything swims and floats before my mind in such a way that I cannot capture a clear outline; but I tell myself if I had clay or wax I would give it proper form. If this lasts any longer I will actually take clay and knead it, even if I produce only cakes.

I've begun Lotte's portrait three times and three times made a fool of myself, which is all the more annoying because a while ago I was able to do very good likenesses. I have since made her silhouette, and this will have to do.

Ja, liebe Lotte, ich will alles besorgen und bestellen; geben Sie mir nur mehr Aufträge, nur recht oft. Um eins bitte ich Sie: keinen Sand[103] mehr auf die Zettelchen, die Sie mir schreiben. Heute führte ich es schnell nach der Lippe, und die Zähne knisterten mir.

Ich habe mir schon manchmal vorgenommen, sie nicht so oft zu sehn. Ja, wer das halten könnte! Alle Tage unterliege ich der Versuchung und verspreche mir heilig: morgen willst du einmal[104] wegbleiben, und wenn der Morgen kommt, finde ich doch wieder eine unwiderstehliche Ursache, und ehe ich mich's versehe, bin ich bei ihr. Entweder sie hat des Abends gesagt: „Sie kommen doch morgen?" — wer könnte da wegbleiben? — oder sie gibt mir einen Auftrag, und ich finde schicklich, ihr selbst die Antwort zu bringen; oder der Tag ist gar zu schön, ich gehe nach Wahlheim, und wenn ich nun da bin, ist's nur noch eine halbe Stunde zu ihr! — Ich bin zu nah in der Atmosphäre — Zuck! so bin ich dort. Meine Großmutter hatte ein Märchen vom Magnetenberg: die Schiffe, die zu nahe kamen, wurden auf einmal alles Eisenwerks beraubt, die Nägel flogen dem Berge zu, und die armen Elenden scheiterten zwischen den übereinander stürzenden Brettern.

Albert ist angekommen, und ich werde gehen; und wenn er der beste, der edelste Mensch wäre, unter den ich mich in jeder Betrachtung zu stellen bereit wäre, so wär's unerträglich, ihn vor meinem Angesicht im Besitz so vieler Vollkommenheiten zu sehen. — Besitz! — Genug, Wilhelm, der Bräutigam ist da! Ein braver lieber Mann, dem man gut sein muß. Glücklicherweise war ich nicht beim Empfange! Das hätte mir das Herz zerrissen. Auch ist er so ehrlich und hat Lotten in meiner Gegenwart noch nicht ein einzigmal geküßt. Das lohn' ihm Gott! Um des Res-

Yes, dear Lotte, I will attend to and order everything; just give me more commissions to carry out, and very often. But one thing I beg of you: no more sand on the little notes you write me. Today I raised it swiftly to my lips and the sand gritted on my teeth.

I have already resolved more than once not to see her so often. If one could only stick to such a resolution! Every day I succumb to temptation and make a sacred promise to myself: tomorrow you will stay away; and when tomorrow comes I find one more irresistible reason for going, and before I realize it I'm with her. Either she said the evening before: "You're coming tomorrow, aren't you?" —who could stay away after that?—or she gives me an errand to do and I find it proper to bring her the answer myself, or the day is altogether too beautiful, so I walk to Wahlheim and when I have got that far, it's only another half hour to her! I am too close to her atmosphere—zoom, I'm there. My grandmother used to tell a fairy tale about the Magnetic Mountain. Ships that came too close to it suddenly lost all their iron; the nails flew to the mountain and the poor wretches perished amid the collapsing boards.

Albert has arrived and I shall go. Even if he were the best, the noblest man, whom I could accept as my superior in every respect, it would be intolerable to see him before me in possession of such perfection.—Possession!— Enough, Wilhelm, the fiancé is here. A nice, dear man, whom one cannot help liking. Fortunately I was not present when they met. That would have rent my heart. And he's so respectable he hasn't kissed Lotte in my presence a single time. May God reward him for it. I must love him because of the respect he feels for the girl. He's

pekts willen, den er vor dem Mädchen hat, muß ich ihn lieben. Er will mir wohl, und ich vermute, das ist Lottens Werk mehr als seiner eigenen Empfindung: denn darin sind die Weiber fein und haben recht; wenn sie zwei Verehrer in gutem Vernehmen miteinander erhalten können, ist der Vorteil immer ihr, so selten es auch angeht.

Indes kann ich Alberten meine Achtung nicht versagen. Seine gelassene Außenseite sticht gegen die Unruhe meines Charakters sehr lebhaft ab, die sich nicht verbergen läßt. Er hat viel Gefühl und weiß, was er an Lotten hat. Er scheint wenig üble Laune zu haben, und Du weißt, das ist die Sünde[105], die ich ärger hasse am Menschen als alle andren.

Er hält mich für einen Menschen von Sinn; und meine Anhänglichkeit an Lotten, meine warme Freude, die ich an allen ihren Handlungen habe, vermehrt seinen Triumph, und er liebt sie nur desto mehr. Ob er sie nicht manchmal mit kleiner Eifersüchtelei peinigt, das lasse ich dahingestellt sein, wenigstens würd' ich an seinem Platze nicht ganz sicher vor diesem Teufel bleiben.

Dem sei nun wie ihm wolle! Meine Freude, bei Lotten zu sein, ist hin. Soll ich das Torheit nennen oder Verblendung? — Was braucht's Namen! Erzählt die Sache an sich[106]! — Ich wußte alles, was ich jetzt weiß, ehe Albert kam; ich wußte, daß ich keine Prätension auf sie zu machen hatte, machte auch keine — das heißt, insofern es möglich ist, bei so viel Liebenswürdigkeit nicht zu begehren. — Und jetzt macht der Fratze große Augen, da der andre nun wirklich kommt und ihm das Mädchen wegnimmt.

Ich beiße die Zähne aufeinander und spotte über mein Elend und spottete derer doppelt und dreifach, die sagen könnten, ich sollte mich resignieren, und weil es nun einmal nicht anders sein könnte. — Schafft mir diese Strohmänner[107] vom Halse! — Ich laufe in den Wäldern herum, und wenn ich zu Lotten komme und Albert bei ihr sitzt im Gärtchen unter der Laube und ich nicht weiter kann, so bin ich ausgelassen närrisch und fange viel Possen, viel verwirrtes Zeug an. — „Um Gottes willen", sagte mir Lotte heut', „ich bitte Sie, keine Szene wie die von gestern abend! Sie sind fürchterlich, wenn Sie so lustig sind." — Unter

friendly toward me, and I suspect that this is Lotte's work rather than his own sentiment; for women are subtle in these matters and they are right: if they can keep two admirers on good terms with each other, the advantage is always on their side, though it rarely works out.

However I can't deny Albert my esteem. His calm exterior contrasts sharply with the restlessness of my character, which I cannot hide. He is a very sensitive person and knows what he has in Lotte. He seems to have little ill-humor, and you know that is the sin I hate in people more than any other.

He regards me as a man of sensibility; my attachment to Lotte, my warm joy in all her actions increases his triumph and he loves her all the more for it. I shall not inquire whether he torments her occasionally with petty jealousies, but if I were in his place, I would not be altogether safe from this devil.

Be that as it may, my joy at being with Lotte is gone. Call it foolishness or delusion—what need is there of finding a name for it? The thing speaks for itself.—I knew everything I know now before Albert came; I knew that I could make no claims on her, and made none—that is, insofar as it is possible not to desire so much charm.—And now the fool is astonished when the other man really appears and takes the girl away from him.

I grind my teeth and mock my misery and would be doubly and triply scornful of those who could say I ought to resign myself, because it simply couldn't be any different.—Get these scarecrows off my back!—I ramble in the woods and, when I return to Lotte and find Albert sitting beside her in the little garden under the arbor, I can't bear it any longer, I am wild and foolish, and do absurd and confused things.—"For Heaven's sake," Lotte said to me today, "I beg of you, not another scene like that of last night. You frighten me when you are so merry."—Between you and me, I watch for the time when he's busy else-

uns, ich passe die Zeit ab, wenn er zu tun hat; wutsch! bin ich drauß, und da ist mir's immer wohl, wenn ich sie allein finde.

Am 8. August

Ich bitte Dich, lieber Wilhelm, es war gewiß nicht auf Dich geredet, wenn ich die Menschen unerträglich schalt, die von uns Ergebung in unvermeidliche Schicksale fordern. Ich dachte wahrlich nicht daran, daß Du von ähnlicher Meinung sein könntest. Und im Grunde hast Du recht. Nur eins, mein Bester, in der Welt ist es sehr selten mit dem Entweder—Oder getan[108]; die Empfindungen und Handlungsweisen schattieren sich so mannigfaltig, als Abfälle zwischen einer Habichts- und Stumpfnase sind.

Du wirst mir also nicht übel nehmen, wenn ich Dir Dein ganzes Argument einräume, und mich doch zwischen dem Entweder—Oder durchzustehlen suche.

Entweder, sagst Du, hast du Hoffnung auf Lotten, oder du hast keine. Gut, im ersten Falle suche sie durchzutreiben, suche die Erfüllung deiner Wünsche zu umfassen: im anderen Fall ermanne dich und suche einer elenden Empfindung loszuwerden, die alle deine Kräfte verzehen muß. — Bester! das ist wohl gesagt, und — bald gesagt.

Und kannst Du von dem Unglücklichen, dessen Leben unter einer schleichenden Krankheit unaufhaltsam allmählich abstirbt, kannst Du von ihm verlangen, er solle durch einen Dolchstoß der Qual auf einmal ein Ende machen? Und raubt das Übel, das ihm die Kräfte verzehrt, ihm nicht auch zugleich den Mut, sich davon zu befreien?

Zwar könntest Du mir mit einem verwandten Gleichnisse antworten: Wer ließe sich nicht lieber den Arm abnehmen, also daß er durch Zaudern und Zagen sein Leben aufs Spiel setzte? — Ich weiß nicht! — und wir wollen uns nicht in Gleichnissen herumbeißen. Genug — Ja, Wilhelm, ich habe manchmal so einen Augenblick aufspringenden, abschüttelnden Muts, und da — wenn ich nur wüßte wohin, ich ginge wohl.

where; zoom! I am out there, and I'm always happy when I find her alone.

Please, dear Wilhelm, I certainly did not mean you when I called those people unbearable who demand submission to inevitable destiny. I really did not think that you would share this opinion. Basically you are right. But just remember this, my dear fellow: in this world it is rarely an either-or decision; sentiments and deeds take on as many different shadings as there are gradations between an aquiline and a pug nose.

So you will not be angry with me if I grant you your whole argument and yet try to thread my way through the either-or.

Either, you say, you have hopes of winning Lotte, or you have none. Good. In the first case try to realize them, try to encompass the fulfillment of your wishes; in the other case, show yourself to be a man and try to rid yourself of a wretched feeling which must consume all your energies. —My dear fellow, that is well put and—easy to say.

But can you demand of the unhappy man, whose life is gradually, inevitably withering from a lingering disease, can you demand of him that he abruptly bring an end to his torture with the thrust of a dagger? Does not the ailment which is consuming his energies at the same time rob him of the courage to free himself?

True, you could reply to me with a related analogy: who would not rather lose an arm than risk his whole life by hesitating and wavering?—I don't know!—Let us not bite each other with similes. Enough—yes, Wilhelm, at times I experience moments of courage when I leap up and shake it off, and then—I would gladly go away, if I only knew where.

Mein Tagebuch, das ich seit einiger Zeit vernachlässiget[109], fiel mir heut' wieder in die Hände, und ich bin erstaunt, wie ich so wissentlich in das alles, Schritt vor Schritt, hineingegangen bin! Wie ich über meinen Zustand immer so klar gesehen und doch gehandelt habe wie ein Kind, jetzt noch so klar sehe und es noch keinen Anschein zur Besserung hat.

Am 10. August

Ich könnte das beste, glücklichste Leben führen, wenn ich nicht ein Tor wäre. So schöne Umstände vereinigen sich nicht leicht, eines Menschen Seele zu ergötzen, als die sind, in denen ich mich jetzt befinde. Ach so gewiß ist's, daß unser Herz allein sein Glück macht. — Ein Glied der liebenswürdigen Familie zu sein, von dem Alten geliebt zu werden wie ein Sohn, von den Kleinen wie ein Vater und von Lotten! — dann der ehrliche[110] Albert, der durch keine launische Unart mein Glück stört; der mich mit herzlicher Freundschaft umfaßt; dem ich nach Lotten das Liebste auf der Welt bin! — Wilhelm, es ist eine Freude, uns zu hören, wenn wir spazierengehen und uns einander von Lotten unterhalten: es ist in der Welt nichts Lächerlichers erfunden worden als dieses Verhältnis, und doch kommen mir oft darüber die Tränen in die Augen.

Wenn er mir von ihrer rechtschaffenen Mutter erzählt: wie sie auf ihrem Todbette Lotten ihr Haus und ihre Kinder übergeben und ihm Lotten anbefohlen habe, wie seit der Zeit ein ganz anderer Geist Lotten belebt habe, wie sie, in der Sorge für ihre Wirtschaft und in dem Ernste eine wahre Mutter geworden, wie kein Augenblick ihrer Zeit ohne tätige Liebe, ohne Arbeit verstrichen, und dennoch ihre Munterkeit, ihr leichter Sinn sie nie dabei verlassen habe. — Ich gehe so neben ihm hin und pflücke Blumen am Wege, füge sie sehr sorgfältig in einen Strauß und — werfe sie in den vorüberfließenden Strom und sehe ihnen nach, wie sie leise hinunterwallen. — Ich weiß nicht, ob ich Dir geschrieben habe, daß Albert hierbleiben und ein Amt

My diary, which I have neglected for some time, fell into my hands again today, and I am astonished how deliberately I have walked into the whole situation step by step. How clearly I have always seen my situation, and yet have acted like a child; even now I see it so clearly and yet there is no sign of a turn for the better.

August 10

I could live the best and happiest life here if I weren't a fool. It is not often that one finds such a beautiful conjunction of circumstances designed to delight the heart as those in which I find myself now. Oh, it is so certain that our hearts alone make us happy.—To be a member of this charming family, loved like a son by the old man, like a father by the children, and by Lotte!—And then honest Albert, who does not disturb my happiness with ill-humor; who receives me with cordial friendship; for whom I am, after Lotte, the person he holds dearest in this world—Wilhelm, it is a joy to hear us when we go for a walk and talk about Lotte; there is nothing more ridiculous in the world than this relationship, and yet it often brings tears to my eyes.

When he tells me about her fine mother; how, on her deathbed, she turned over her house and her children to Lotte, how she commended Lotte to his care, how Lotte had been inspired by a wholly different spirit since that time, how care for the household and the seriousness of the situation had made a true mother out of her, how not a moment of her time had passed without active love or work and yet her cheerfulness, her gaiety had never left her.—I walk along beside him, picking flowers by the roadside, weave them very carefully into a nosegay—and throw them into the stream that flows past us, looking after them as they float gently downstream.—I don't know whether I've written you that Albert is going to stay here

107

mit einem artigen Auskommen vom Hofe erhalten wird, wo er sehr beliebt ist. In Ordnung und Emsigkeit in Geschäften habe ich wenig seinesgleichen gesehen.

Am 12. August

Gewiß, Albert ist der beste Mensch unter dem Himmel. Ich habe gestern eine wunderbare Szene mit ihm gehabt. Ich kam zu ihm, um Abschied von ihm zu nehmen; denn mich wandelte die Lust an, ins Gebirge zu reiten, von woher ich Dir auch jetzt schreibe, und wie ich in der Stube auf und ab gehe, fallen mir seine Pistolen in die Augen. — „Borge mir die Pistolen“, sagte ich, „zu meiner Reise.“ — „Meinetwegen“, sagte er, „wenn du dir die Mühe nehmen willst, sie zu laden; bei mir hängen sie nur pro forma.“ — Ich nahm eine herunter, und er fuhr fort: „Seit mir meine Vorsicht einen so unartigen Streich gespielt hat, mag ich mit dem Zeuge nichts mehr zu tun haben.“ — Ich war neugierig, die Geschichte zu wissen. — „Ich hielt mich“, erzählte er, „wohl ein Vierteljahr auf dem Lande bei einem Freunde auf, hatte ein paar Terzerolen[111], ungeladen, und schlief ruhig. Einmal an einem regnerischen Nachmittage, da ich müßig sitze[112], weiß ich nicht, wie mir einfällt: wir könnten überfallen werden, wir könnten die Terzerolen nötig haben und könnten — du weißt ja, wie das ist. — Ich gab sie dem Bedienten, sie zu putzen und zu laden; und der dahlt mit den Mädchen, will sie erschrecken, und Gott weiß wie, das Gewehr geht los, da der Ladstock noch drinsteckt, und schießt den Ladstock einem Mädchen zur Maus herein an der rechten Hand und zerschlägt ihr den Daumen. Da hatte ich das Lamentieren und die Kur zu bezahlen obendrein, und seit der Zeit lass’[113] ich alles Gewehr ungeladen. Lieber Schatz, was ist Vorsicht? Die Gefahr läßt sich nicht[114] auslernen! Zwar“ — Nun weißt Du, daß ich den Menschen sehr lieb habe bis auf seine Zwar; denn versteht sich’s nicht von selbst, daß jeder allgemeine Satz Ausnahmen leidet? Aber so rechtfertig ist der Mensch! wenn er glaubt, etwas Übereiltes, Allgemeines, Halbwahres gesagt zu haben: so hört er dir[115] nicht auf zu limitieren, zu modifizieren und ab- und zuzutun, bis

and will be given an office and a tidy income by the Court, where he is in high favor. I have met few people who are his equal in the orderly and diligent conduct of affairs.

August 12

Certainly, Albert is the best person beneath the sky. I had a remarkable scene with him yesterday. I went to him to take leave of him, for I had a sudden wish to ride into the mountains, from which place I am writing to you now; as I was walking up and down the room, his pistols caught my eye.—"Lend me your pistols," I said, "for my trip." "It's all right with me," he said, "if you want to go to the trouble of loading them. They hang in my room only pro forma."—I took one down and he continued: "Ever since my caution played me a mean trick, I don't want to have anything more to do with the things." I was curious to hear the story. "I was staying," he related, "at the house of a friend in the country for some three months. I had a pair of unloaded pistols, and I slept in peace. Once on a rainy afternoon, as I was sitting there idly, I don't know what gave me the idea that we might be attacked, we might need the pistols, and could—you know how these things are.— I gave them to my servant to clean and load. He was dallying with the maids, trying to frighten them, when, Lord knows how it happened, the weapon went off. The ramrod was still in the barrel, and it went right through the ball of one girl's thumb, smashing it. I had to stand all her wailing and pay the costs of her cure as well, and since that time I have left all my weapons unloaded. My dear fellow! What is caution? You can never anticipate every danger. Of course—" Now, you know, I like the man very much except for his "of courses"; for is it not obvious that every general statement has its exceptions? But the man is so anxious to be exactly right, that if he thinks he has said something overhasty, general, or half-true, he won't stop limiting, modifying, adding, and subtracting, until finally there is nothing left of the statement. And on this occasion he got very deeply into his subject; at last I stopped listening to him altogether, fell into an irritated mood and

zuletzt gar nichts mehr an der Sache ist. Und bei diesem Anlaß kam er sehr tief in den Text: ich hörte endlich gar nicht weiter auf ihn, verfiel in Grillen, und mit einer auffahrenden Gebärde drückte ich mir die Mündung der Pistole übers rechte Aug' an die Stirn. — „Pfui!" sagte Albert, indem er mir die Pistole herabzog, „was soll das[116]?" — „Sie ist nicht geladen", sagte ich. — „Und auch so, was soll's?" versetzte er ungeduldig. „Ich kann mir nicht vorstellen, wie ein Mensch so töricht sein kann, sich zu erschießen; der bloße Gedanke erregt mir Widerwillen."

„Daß ihr Menschen", rief ich aus, „um von einer Sache zu reden, gleich sprechen müßt: das ist töricht, das ist klug, das ist gut, das ist bös! Und was will das alles heißen? Habt ihr deswegen die inneren Verhältnisse einer Handlung erforscht? Wißt ihr mit Bestimmtheit die Ursachen zu entwickeln, warum sie geschah, warum sie geschehen mußte? Hättet ihr das, ihr würdet nicht so eilfertig mit euren Urteilen sein."

„Du wirst mir zugeben", sagte Albert, „daß gewisse Handlungen lasterhaft bleiben, sie mögen geschehen, aus welchem Beweggrunde sie wollen."

Ich zuckte die Achseln und gab's ihm zu. — „Doch, mein Lieber", fuhr ich fort, „finden sich auch hier einige Ausnahmen. Es ist wahr, der Diebstahl ist ein Laster; aber der Mensch, der, um sich und die Seinigen vom gegenwärtigen Hungertode zu erretten, auf Raub ausgeht, verdient der Mitleiden oder Strafe? Wer hebt den ersten Stein auf gegen den Ehemann, der im gerechten Zorne sein untreues Weib und ihren nichtswürdigen Verführer aufopfert? Gegen das Mädchen, das in einer wonnevollen Stunde sich in den unaufhaltsamen Freuden der Liebe verliert? Unsere Gesetze selbst, diese kaltblütigen Pedanten, lassen sich rühren und halten ihre Strafe zurück."

„Das ist ganz was anders[117]", versetzte Albert, „weil ein Mensch, den seine Leidenschaften hinreißen, alle Besinnungskraft verliert und als ein Trunkener, als ein Wahnsinniger angesehen wird."

„Ach ihr vernünftigen Leute!" rief ich lächelnd aus. „Leidenschaft! Trunkenheit! Wahnsinn! Ihr steht so ge-

with a vehement gesture I pressed the mouth of the pistol to my forehead above my right eye. "Shame!" Albert said, pulling the pistol away from me. "What's the meaning of this?" "But it isn't loaded," I said.—"Even so, what is the meaning of it?" he replied impatiently. "I can't imagine anyone being stupid enough to shoot himself. The mere thought of it repels me."

"Why do you people," I exclaimed, "when you talk about something, have to say right off: this is foolish, this is wise, this is good, this is bad? And what is the meaning of it all? Have you investigated the hidden circumstances behind an action? Can you set forth with certainty the reasons why it happened, why it had to happen? If you could, you would not be so hasty with your judgments."

"You will admit," said Albert, "that certain actions remain vicious, no matter what the motive for them may be."

I shrugged my shoulders and admitted it. "However, my friend," I continued, "there are some exceptions here, too. It is true that theft is a crime. But does the man who commits a robbery to save himself and his family from imminent starvation deserve sympathy or punishment? Who will lift the first stone against the husband who, in righteous anger, sacrifices his unfaithful wife and her unworthy seducer? Against the girl who, in an hour of bliss, succumbs to the irresistible joys of love? Even our laws, these cold-blooded pedants, can be sympathetic and withhold their punishment."

"That's quite different," Albert replied, "because a person who is carried away by his passions loses all power of judgment and is regarded as intoxicated or mad."

"Oh you sensible people!" I exclaimed with a smile. "Passion! Drunkenness! Madness! You stand there so

111

lassen, so ohne Teilnehmung da, ihr sittlichen Menschen! Scheltet den Trinker, verabscheut den Unsinnigen, geht vorbei wie der Priester[118] und dankt Gott wie der Pharisäer, daß er euch nicht gemacht hat wie einen von diesen. Ich bin mehr als einmal trunken gewesen, meine Leidenschaften waren nie weit vom Wahnsinn, und beides reut mich nicht; denn ich habe in meinem Maße begreifen lernen, wie man alle außerordentlichen Menschen, die etwas Großes, etwas Unmöglichscheinendes wirkten, von jeher für Trunkene und Wahnsinnige ausschreien mußte.

„Aber auch im gemeinen Leben ist's unerträglich, fast einem jeden bei halbweg einer freien, edlen, unerwarteten Tat nachrufen zu hören: der Mensch ist trunken, der ist närrisch! Schämt euch, ihr Nüchternen! Schämt euch, ihr Weisen!"

„Das sind nun wieder von deinen Grillen", sagte Albert, „du überspannst alles und hast wenigstens hier gewiß unrecht, daß du den Selbstmord, wovon jetzt die Rede ist, mit großen Handlungen vergleichst: da man es doch für nichts anders als eine Schwäche halten kann. Denn freilich ist es leichter zu sterben, als ein qualvolles Leben standhaft zu ertragen."

Ich war im Begriff abzubrechen; denn kein Argument bringt mich so aus der Fassung, also wenn einer mit einem unbedeutenden Gemeinspruche[119] angezogen kommt, wenn ich aus ganzem Herzen rede. Doch faßte ich mich, weil ich's schon oft gehört und mich öfter darüber geärgert hatte, und versetzte ihm mit einiger Lebhaftigkeit: „Du nennst das Schwäche? Ich bitte dich, laß dich vom Anscheine nicht verführen. Ein Volk, das unter dem unerträglichen Joch eines Tyrannen seufzt, darfst du das schwach heißen, wenn es endlich aufgärt und seine Ketten zerreißt? Ein Mensch, der über dem Schrecken, daß Feuer sein Haus ergriffen hat, alle Kräfte gespannt fühlt und mit Leichtigkeit Lasten wegträgt, die er bei ruhigem Sinne kaum bewegen kann; einer, der in der Wut der Beleidigung es mit sechsen[120] aufnimmt und sie überwältigt, sind die schwach zu nennen? Und, mein Guter, wenn Anstrengung Stärke ist, warum soll die Überspannung das Gegenteil sein?" — Albert sah mich an und sagte: „Nimm mir's nicht

112

calm, so unsympathetic, you moral men. You condemn the drunkard, abhor the insane man, pass by like the priest and thank God like the Pharisee that He did not make you as one of these. I have been drunk more than once, my passions have never been far from insanity, and I regret neither; for on my own scale I have come to appreciate how it is that all extraordinary people who have achieved something great, something apparently impossible, have been decried as drunkards or madmen.

"But even in everyday life, whenever someone does something that is halfway free, noble, unexpected, it is intolerable to hear the cry: the man is drunk, he's insane! Shame on you, you sober people! Shame on you, wise men!"

"These are more of your whimsical notions," Albert said. "You exaggerate everything, and in this instance at least you are certainly wrong in comparing suicide—which is the subject under discussion—with great deeds, since it cannot be regarded as anything but weakness. For to be sure it is easier to die than steadfastly to endure a tormented life."

I was on the point of breaking off, for no argument so disconcerts me as when someone drags in some insignificant platitude when I am talking from the depths of my heart. However, I controlled myself, because I had heard the argument often before and had been frequently aggravated by it; I replied with some spirit: "You call that weakness? I beg you, don't be misled by appearances. When a nation has long sighed under the intolerable yoke of a tyrant, you dare call it weakness if it finally rises up and breaks its chains? A man who feels all his energies strained by the terror of seeing his house engulfed in flames, and easily carries away burdens which he can scarcely move when his mind is calm; someone who, in the fury of an insult, takes on six people and overpowers them —can he be called weak? And, my friend, if effort is strength, why should excessive effort be the opposite?"— Albert looked at me and said: "Excuse me for saying so, but the examples you have given don't seem to fit here at

113

übel, die Beispiele, die du da gibst, scheinen hieher gar nicht zu gehören." — „Es mag sein", sagte ich, „man hat mir schon öfters vorgeworfen, daß meine Kombinationsart manchmal an Radotage grenze. Laßt uns denn sehen, ob wir uns auf eine andere Weise vorstellen können, wie dem Menschen zumute sein mag, der sich entschließt, die sonst angenehme Bürde des Lebens abzuwerfen. Denn nur insofern wir mitempfinden, haben wir Ehre[121], von einer Sache zu reden.

„Die menschliche Natur", fuhr ich fort, „hat ihre Grenzen: sie kann Freude, Leid, Schmerzen bis auf einen gewissen Grad ertragen und geht zugrunde, sobald der überstiegen ist. Hier ist also nicht die Frage, ob einer schwach oder stark ist? sondern ob er das Maß seines Leidens ausdauern kann? es mag nun moralisch[122] oder körperlich sein. Und ich finde es ebenso wunderbar zu sagen, der Mensch ist feige, der sich das Leben nimmt, als es ungehörig wäre, den einen Feigen zu nennen, der an einem bösartigen Fieber stirbt."

„Paradox! sehr paradox!" rief Albert aus. — „Nicht so sehr, als du denkst", versetzte ich. „Du gibst mir zu, wir nennen das eine Krankheit zum Tode[123], wodurch die Natur so angegriffen wird, daß teils ihre Kräfte verzehrt, teils so außer Wirkung gesetzt werden, daß sie sich nicht wieder aufzuhelfen, durch keine glückliche Revolution den gewöhnlichen Umlauf des Lebens wieder herzustellen fähig ist.

„Nun, mein Lieber, laß uns das auf den Geist anwenden. Sieh den Menschen an in seiner Eingeschränktheit, wie Eindrücke auf ihn wirken, Ideen sich bei ihm festsetzen, bis endlich eine wachsende Leidenschaft ihn aller ruhigen Sinneskraft beraubt und ihn zugrunde richtet.

„Vergebens, daß der gelassene, vernünftige Mensch den Zustand des Unglücklichen übersieht, vergebens, daß er ihm zuredet! Ebenso wie ein Gesunder, der am Bette des Kranken steht, ihm von seinen Kräften nicht das geringste einflößen kann."

Alberten war das zu allgemein gesprochen. Ich erinnerte ihn an ein Mädchen, das man vor weniger Zeit im Wasser tot gefunden, und wiederholte ihm ihre Geschichte. — „Ein

all."—"That may be," I said, "I have often heard the reproach that my logic sometimes borders on absurdity. So let us see if we can imagine in some way how a person may feel when he decides to throw off the normally pleasant burden of life. For only to the extent that we can put ourselves in another's position are we justified in talking about a matter.

"Human nature," I continued, "has its limits. It can endure joy, sorrow, and pain to a certain point and goes to pieces as soon as this point is passed. The question, therefore, is not whether a man is weak or strong, but whether he can bear the measure of his suffering, whether mental or physical. And I find it just as strange to say that the man who takes his own life is a coward, as it would be improper to call that man a coward who dies of a vicious fever."

"Paradoxical! Very paradoxical!" Albert exclaimed. "Not as much as you think," I replied. "You admit that we speak of a sickness unto death by which the system is so deeply affected that its energies are partly exhausted, partly put out of commission, and thus are not capable of recuperating, of being restored to the normal course of life even through some fortunate turn of events.

"Now, my dear friend, let us apply this to the mind. Look at man in his limitations, with impressions affecting him, ideas establishing themselves in him, until finally a growing passion robs him of all calm, reflective power and destroys him.

"It is useless to hope that a calm, rational person could grasp the condition of the unhappy man, useless to counsel him. Just as a healthy man at the bedside of a sick person cannot impart to him even the slightest quantity of his strength."

This talk was too general for Albert. I reminded him of a girl who had recently been found dead in the water and repeated her story to him. "A decent young creature who

gutes, junges Geschöpf, das in dem engen Kreise häuslicher Beschäftigungen, wöchentlicher bestimmter Arbeit herangewachsen war, das weiter keine Aussicht von[124] Vergnügen kannte, als etwa sonntags in einem nach und nach zusammengeschafften Putz mit ihresgleichen um die Stadt spazierenzugehen, vielleicht alle hohen Feste einmal zu tanzen und übrigens mit aller Lebhaftigkeit des herzlichsten Anteils manche Stunde über den Anlaß eines Gezänkes, einer üblen Nachrede mit einer Nachbarin zu verplaudern. — Deren feurige Natur fühlt nun endlich innigere Bedürfnisse, die durch die Schmeicheleien der Männer vermehrt werden; ihre vorigen Freuden werden ihr nach und nach unschmackhaft, bis sie endlich einen Menschen antrifft, zu dem ein unbekanntes Gefühl sie unwiderstehlich hinreißt, auf den sie nun alle ihre Hoffnungen wirft, die Welt rings um sich vergißt, nichts hört, nichts sieht, nichts fühlt als ihn, den einzigen, sich nur sehnt nach ihm, dem einzigen. Durch die leeren Vergnügungen einer unbeständigen Eitelkeit nicht verdorben, zieht ihr Verlangen gerade nach dem Zweck, sie will die Seinige werden, sie will in ewiger Verbindung all das Glück antreffen, das ihr mangelt, die Vereinigung aller Freuden genießen, nach denen sie sich sehnte. Wiederholtes Versprechen, das ihr die Gewißheit aller Hoffnungen versiegelt, kühne Liebkosungen, die ihre Begierden vermehren, umfangen ganz ihre Seele; sie schwebt in einem dumpfen Bewußtsein, in einem Vorgefühl aller Freuden, sie ist bis auf den höchsten Grad gespannt. Sie streckt endlich ihre Arme aus, all ihre Wünsche zu umfassen — und ihr Geliebter verläßt sie. — Erstarrt, ohne Sinne steht sie vor dem Abgrunde; alles ist Finsternis um sie her, keine Aussicht, kein Trost, keine Ahnung[125]! denn der hat sie verlassen, in dem sie allein ihr Dasein fühlte. Sie sieht nicht die weite Welt, die vor ihr liegt, nicht die vielen, die ihr den Verlust ersetzen könnten, sie fühlt sich allein, verlassen von aller Welt — und blind, in die Enge gepreßt[126] von der entsetzlichen Not ihres Herzens, stürzt sie sich hinunter, um in einem rangs umfangenden Tode alle ihre Qualen zu ersticken. — Sieh, Albert, das ist die Geschichte so manches Menschen! und sag, ist das nicht der Fall der Krankheit? Die Natur findet keinen Ausweg

had grown up in the narrow sphere of domestic activity, of a weekly schedule of duties that included no prospects for fun except perhaps a stroll about town with her friends on Sunday, dressed in the finery she had gradually accumulated, perhaps to go to a dance on the principal holidays, and for the rest to spend the odd hour gossiping with a neighbor with complete emotional involvement, about the cause of a quarrel, or a bit of scandal. At last her warm nature feels deeper needs, which are nourished by the flattery of men; her former sources of gratification lose their savor for her bit by bit, until she finally meets a man to whom she is irresistibly drawn by a hitherto unknown feeling, on whom she now throws all her hopes, forgetting the world about her, hearing nothing, seeing nothing, feeling nothing but him, the only one; she yearns only for him, for him alone. Uncorrupted by the empty pleasures of fickle vanity, her desire moves straight toward its goal; she wants to become his; she wants to find in an eternal union all the happiness she lacks, to enjoy the sum of all the joys for which she yearned. Repeated promises which put the seal of certainty on all her hopes, bold caresses which increase her desire, encompass her whole being; she floats in a state of vague consciousness, in an anticipation of complete bliss, and she has reached a state of the highest tension; at last she stretches out her arms to embrace all her wishes—and her lover abandons her.—Frozen, her senses numbed, she stands before an abyss; everything about her is darkness, no prospects, no consolation, no light! He for whom alone she existed has forsaken her. She does not see the great world that lies before her, or the many others who could compensate her for her loss; she feels alone, abandoned by the whole world—and blindly, driven into a corner by the dreadful anguish of her heart, she leaps down to stifle all her torments in an all-encompassing death.—See, Albert, that is the story of many, many people! And can you say that is not a case of sickness? Nature finds no way out of the labyrinth of confused and contradictory forces, and the person must die.

117

aus dem Labyrinthe der verworrenen und widersprechen-
den Kräfte, und der Mensch muß sterben.

„Wehe dem, der zusehen und sagen könnte: ,Die Törin!
Hätte sie gewartet, hätte sie die Zeit wirken lassen, die
Verzweiflung würde sich schon gelegt, es würde sich schon
ein anderer, sie zu trösten, vorgefunden haben.' — Das ist
eben, als wenn einer sagte: ,Der Tor, stirbt am Fieber!
Hätte er gewartet, bis seine Kräfte sich erholt, seine Säfte[127]
sich verbessert, der Tumult seines Blutes sich gelegt hätten:
alles wäre gut gegangen, und er lebte bis auf den heutigen
Tag!' "

Albert, dem die Vergleichung noch nicht anschaulich
war, wandte noch einiges ein und unter andern[128]: ich
hätte nur von einem einfältigen Mädchen gesprochen;
wie aber ein Mensch von Verstande, der nicht so eingeschränkt sei, der mehr Verhältnisse übersehe, zu entschuldigen sein möchte, könne er nicht begreifen. — „Mein
Freund", rief ich aus, „der Mensch ist Mensch, und das
bißchen Verstand, das einer haben mag, kommt wenig oder
nicht in Anschlag, wenn Leidenschaft wütet und die
Grenzen der Menschheit einen drängen. Vielmehr — Ein
andermal davon", sagte ich, und griff nach meinem Hute.
Oh, mir war das Herz so voll — Und wir gingen ausein-
ander, ohne einander verstanden zu haben. Wie denn auf
dieser Welt keiner leicht den andern versteht.

Am 15. August

Es ist doch gewiß, daß in der Welt den Menschen nichts
notwendig macht als die Liebe. Ich fühl's an Lotten, daß sie
mich ungern verlöre, und die Kinder haben keinen andern
Begriff, als daß ich immer morgen wieder kommen würde.
Heute war ich hinausgegangen, Lottens Klavier zu stimmen, ich konnte aber nicht dazu kommen, denn die Kleinen
verfolgten mich um ein Märchen, und Lotte sagte selbst,
ich sollte ihnen den Willen tun. Ich schnitt ihnen das
Abendbrot, das sie nun fast so gern von mir als von Lotten
annehmen, und erzählte ihnen das Hauptstückchen[129] von
der Prinzessin, die von Händen bedient wird. Ich lerne viel
dabei, das versichre ich Dich, und ich bin erstaunt, was es

"Woe to the man who could look on and say: 'The foolish girl! If she had waited, if she had allowed time to produce its effect, her despair would have faded, another man would have come forward to console her.'—That's just as if one were to say: 'What a fool, to die of a fever! If he had waited till his strength had restored itself, his humors improved, the tumult of his blood calmed down, everything would have gone well and he would be alive this very day!'"

Albert, to whom the analogy was not yet clear, made some other objections, including the one that my story had concerned a simple-minded girl, but how one could excuse an intelligent person not so limited, with a broader grasp of things, was beyond his comprehension.—"My friend," I exclaimed, "man is man and the little bit of intelligence that we may possess is of small account when passion rages and we are driven to the limits of our human condition. Rather—but let's talk of this some other time," I said, snatching up my hat. Oh, my heart was so full.—And we parted, without having understood each other. As indeed no one understands another easily in this world.

August 15

One thing is certain: nothing in the world makes a person indispensable except love. I feel that Lotte would be sorry to lose me, and the children simply assume that I'll come again tomorrow. I had gone out today to tune Lotte's piano, but I couldn't get to the job because the children hounded me to tell them a fairy tale, and Lotte herself said that I must grant them their wish. I cut the bread for their supper, a service they now accept almost as willingly from me as from Lotte, and told them the favorite story of the princess who is served by hands. I assure you that I learn a lot from this and I'm astonished at the deep impression my stories make on them. Sometimes I

auf sie für Eindrücke macht. Weil ich manchmal einen Inzidentpunkt[130] erfinden muß, den ich beim zweitenmal vergesse, sagen sie gleich, das vorigemal wär' es anders gewesen, so daß ich mich jetzt übe, sie unveränderlich in einem singenden Silbenfall an einem Schnürchen[131] weg zu rezitieren. Ich habe daraus gelernt, wie ein Autor durch eine zweite veränderte Ausgabe seiner Geschichte, und wenn sie poetisch noch so besser geworden wäre, notwendig seinem Buche schaden muß. Der erste Eindruck findet uns willig, und der Mensch ist gemacht, daß man ihn das Abenteuerlichste überreden kann; das haftet aber auch gleich so fest, und wehe dem, der es wieder auskratzen und austilgen will!

Am 18. August

Mußte denn das so sein, daß das, was des Menschen Glückseligkeit macht, wieder die Quelle seines Elendes würde?

Das volle warme Gefühl meines Herzens an der lebendigen Natur, das mich mit so vieler Wonne überströmte, das ringsumher die Welt mir zu einem Paradiese schuf, wird mir jetzt zu einem unerträglichen Peiniger, zu einem quälenden Geist, der mich auf allen Wegen verfolgt. Wenn ich sonst vom Felsen über den Fluß bis zu jenen Hügeln das fruchtbare Tal überschaute und alles um mich her keimen und quellen sah; wenn ich jene Berge, vom Fuße bis auf zum Gipfel, mit hohen dichten Bäumen bekleidet, jene Täler in ihren mannigfaltigen Krümmungen von den lieblichsten Wäldern beschattet sah, und der sanfte Fluß zwischen den lispelnden Rohren dahin gleitete[132] und die lieben Wolken abspiegelte, die der sanfte Abendwind am Himmel herüberwiegte; wenn ich dann die Vögel um mich den Wald beleben hörte und die Millionen Mückenschwärme im letzten roten Strahle der Sonne mutig[133] tanzten und ihr letzter zuckender Blick den summenden Käfer aus seinem Grase befreite und das Schwirren und Weben um mich her mich auf den Boden aufmerksam machte und das Moos, das meinem harten Felsen seine Nahrung abzwingt, und das Geniste, das den dürren Sand-

must invent a minor incident which I forget when I repeat the story; at once they tell me that it was different the last time, so that I now practice reciting the story in a singsong tone, like clockwork. I've learned from this that an author must inevitably hurt his book by issuing a second, revised edition of his story, no matter how great the literary improvement in it. The first impression finds us receptive and man is so constituted that he can be persuaded of the strangest things; but these impressions at once cling firmly to his memory, and woe to him who tries to erase and destroy them.

August 18

Did it have to be so, that what constitutes man's happiness should also become the source of his misery?

The full, warm feeling in my heart for living nature which poured so much joy over me, which made the world about me into a paradise, is now becoming a source of unbearable torment for me, a torturing spirit which pursues me everywhere. When I used to survey the fertile valley from this rock and gazed across the river to the hills, I saw everything around me budding and swelling; when I saw the mountains, clad from foot to summit in tall, dense trees, the meandering valleys shaded by the loveliest forests, with the gentle stream gliding along among the whispering reeds, mirroring the charming clouds the gentle evening breeze wafted across the sky; when I then heard the birds about me animate the woods and the millions of insects dancing gaily in the last red radiance of the setting sun whose last quivering glance freed the humming beetle from the grass; and when the buzzing and stirring about me made me conscious of the ground, and the moss which draws its nourishment by force from my hard rock, and the shrubbery which grows down the bleak sand hill, opened up to me the inner, glowing, sacred life of nature—how I caught all this up into my warm heart, felt myself like a

hügel hinunter wächst, mir das innere, glühende, heilige
Leben der Natur eröffnete: wie faßte ich das alles in mein
warmes Herz, fühlte mich in der überfließenden Fülle wie
vergöttert[134], und die herrlichen Gestalten der unendlichen
Welt bewegten sich allbelebend in meiner Seele. Unge-
heure Berge umgaben mich, Abgründe lagen vor mir, und
Wetterbäche stürzten herunter, die Flüsse strömten unter
mir, und Wald und Gebirg erklang; und ich sah sie
wirken[135] und schaffen ineinander in den Tiefen der Erde,
alle die unergründlichen Kräfte; und nun über der Erde
und unter dem Himmel wimmeln die Geschlechter der
mannigfaltigen Geschöpfe. Alles, alles bevölkert mit tau-
sendfachen Gestalten und die Menschen dann sich in
Häuslein zusammen sichern[136] und sich annisten und herr-
schen in ihrem Sinne über die weite Welt! Armer Tor! der
du alles so gering achtest, weil du so klein bist. — Vom
unzugänglichen Gebirge über die Einöde, die kein Fuß
betrat, bis ans Ende des unbekannten Ozeans weht der
Geist des Ewigschaffenden, und freut sich jedes Staubes,
der ihn vernimmt und lebt. — Ach, damals, wie oft habe
ich mich mit Fittichen eines Kranichs, der über mich hin-
flog, zu dem Ufer des ungemessenen Meeres gesehnt, aus
dem schäumenden Becher des Unendlichen jene schwel-
lende Lebenswonne zu trinken und nur einen Augenblick,
in der eingeschränkten Kraft meines Busens, einen Tropfen
der Seligkeit des Wesens zu fühlen, das alles in sich und
durch sich hervorbringt.

Bruder, nur die Erinnerung jener Stunden macht mir
wohl. Selbst diese Anstrengung, jene unsäglichen Gefühle
zurückzurufen, wieder auszusprechen, hebt meine Seele
über sich selbst, und läßt mich dann das Bange des Zustandes doppelt empfinden, der mich jetzt umgibt.

Es hat sich vor meiner Seele wie ein Vorhang wegge-
zogen, und der Schauplatz des unendlichen Lebens verwandelt sich vor mir in den Abgrund des ewig offnen
Grabs. Kannst du sagen: Das ist! da alles vorüber geht?
da alles mit der Wetterschnelle vorüberrollt, so selten die
ganze Kraft seines Daseins ausdauert, ach in den Strom
fortgerissen, untergetaucht und an Felsen zerschmettert
wird? Da ist kein Augenblick, der nicht dich verzehrte und

god in my overflowing abundance, and the glorious forms of the infinite world stirred in my soul, giving life to everything. Enormous mountains surrounded me, abysses lay before me, and cataracts rushed down; the rivers flowed by below me, and the forests and mountains resounded; and I saw them creatively at work on each other in the depths of the earth, all those unfathomable forces; and now above the earth and beneath the heavens the races of the manifold creatures swarm. Everything, everything populated by myriad forms, and the humans then seek security close together in little houses, making their nests, believing that they control the great world! Poor fool, in whose opinion everything is so insignificant because you are so small!—From the inacessible mountain range to the wasteland which no foot has ever trod, and on to the end of the unexplored ocean, the spirit of the Eternal Creator blows, rejoicing in every speck of dust which perceives Him and lives.—Oh, how often did I then yearn to take the wings of a crane which flew overhead, and make for the shore of the boundless sea, to drink from the foaming cup of infinity that effervescent rapture of life, and to feel for only one moment, in the restricted power of my mind, a drop of the bliss of the Being who creates all things in Himself and through Himself.

My brother, the mere recollection of those hours does me good. Even the effort to recall those inexpressible feelings, to speak about them again, lifts my soul above itself, but also makes me feel doubly the wretchedness of the condition that surrounds me now.

A curtain has lifted from my soul, as it were, and the stage of infinite life is being transformed before me into the abyss of an ever-open grave. Can you say 'this is' when everything is transitory, when everything rolls by with the speed of a storm, seldom outlasts the whole force of its existence, is swept along, engulfed by the current and, alas, dashed on the rocks? There is no moment that does not consume you and those close to you, no moment when

123

die Deinigen um dich her, kein Augenblick, da du nicht ein Zerstörer bist, sein mußt; der harmloseste Spaziergang kostet tausend armen Würmchen das Leben, es zerrüttet ein Fußtritt die mühseligen Gebäude der Ameisen und stampft eine kleine Welt in ein schmähliches Grab. Ha! nicht die große, seltne Not der Welt, diese Fluten, die eure Dörfer wegspülen, diese Erdbeben, die eure Städte verschlingen, rühren mich; mir untergräbt das Herz die verzehrende Kraft, die in dem All der Natur verborgen liegt, die nichts gebildet hat, das nicht seinen Nachbar, nicht sich selbst zerstörte. Und so taumle ich beängstigt. Himmel und Erde und ihre webenden Kräfte um mich her; ich sehe nichts als ein ewig verschlingendes, ewig wiederkäuendes Ungeheuer.

Am 21. August

Umsonst strecke ich meine Arme nach ihr aus, morgens, wenn ich von schweren Träumen aufdämmere, vergebens suche ich sie nachts in meinem Bette, wenn mich ein glücklicher unschuldiger Traum getäuscht hat, als säß' ich neben ihr auf der Wiese und hielt' ihre Hand und deckte sie mit tausend Küssen. Ach, wenn ich dann noch halb im Taumel des Schlafes nach ihr tappe und drüber mich ermuntere — ein Strom von Tränen bricht aus meinem gepreßten Herzen, und ich weine trostlos einer finstern Zukunft entgegen.

Am 22. August

Es ist ein Unglück, Wilhelm, meine tätigen Kräfte sind zu einer unruhigen Lässigkeit verstimmt, ich kann nicht müßig sein und kann doch auch nichts tun. Ich habe keine Vorstellungskraft, kein Gefühl an der Natur, und die Bücher ekeln mich an. Wenn wir uns selbst fehlen, fehlt uns doch alles. Ich schwöre Dir, manchmal wünschte ich, ein Tagelöhner zu sein, um nur des Morgens beim Erwachen eine Aussicht auf den künftigen Tag, einen Drang, eine Hoffnung zu haben. Oft beneide ich Alberten, den ich über die Ohren in Akten begraben sehe, und bilde mir ein,

you are not a destroyer, and necessarily so; the most innocent stroll costs the lives of a thousand poor little worms; one step destroys the laborious structures of the ants and tramples a small world into a shameful grave. Ah! It is not the rare, great misfortunes in the world, these floods that wash away your villages, these earthquakes that engulf your cities, that move me; my heart is undermined by the destructive power that lies hidden in the universe of nature, which has created nothing that has not destroyed its neighbor, even itself. And so I stagger about in anguish, with heaven and earth and all the active forces all around me! I see nothing except a monster that perpetually devours, forever ruminates.

August 21

In vain I stretch out my arms toward her in the morning when I wake out of heavy dreams, in vain I seek her at night in my bed when a happy, innocent dream has deceived me into thinking that I was sitting beside her on the meadow, holding her hand and covering it with a thousand kisses. Ah, when I then grope for her, still half drunk with sleep, and then become fully awake—a stream of tears breaks from my anguished heart, and I weep at the hopelessness of my dark future.

August 22

It's a catastrophe, Wilhelm, my active powers have atrophied into a restless idleness; I can't be idle and yet can do nothing. I have no imagination, no feeling for nature, and books disgust me. When we feel inadequate ourselves, everything seems inadequate to us. I swear to you, sometimes I wish I were a day laborer, if only to have, on awakening in the morning, a prospect for the coming day, an urge, a hope. I often envy Albert, whom I see up to his ears in documents, and I imagine I would feel happy if I were in his place. Several times already the idea suddenly

125

mir wäre wohl, wenn ich an seiner Stelle wäre! Schon etlichemal[137] ist mir's so aufgefahren, ich wollte Dir schreiben und dem Minister, um die Stelle bei der Gesandtschaft anzuhalten, die, wie Du versicherst, mir nicht versagt werden würde. Ich glaube es selbst. Der Minister liebt mich seit langer Zeit, hatte lange mir angelegen, ich sollte mich irgendeinem Geschäfte widmen; und eine Stunde ist mir's auch wohl drum zu tun. Hernach, wenn ich wieder dran denke und mir die Fabel[138] vom Pferde einfällt, das, seiner Freiheit ungeduldig, sich Sattel und Zeug auflegen läßt, und zu Schanden geritten wird — ich weiß nicht, was ich soll — Und, mein Lieber! ist nicht vielleicht das Sehnen in mir nach Veränderung des Zustandes eine innere unbehagliche Ungeduld, die mich überall hin verfolgen wird?

Am 28. August[139]

Es ist wahr, wenn meine Krankheit zu heilen wäre, so würden diese Menschen es tun. Heute ist mein Geburtstag, und in aller Frühe empfange ich ein Päckchen von Alberten. Mir fällt beim Eröffnen sogleich eine der blaßroten Schleifen in die Augen, die Lotte vor hatte[140], als ich sie kennenlernte, und um die ich seither etlichemal gebeten hatte. Es waren zwei Büchelchen in Duodez[141] dabei, der kleine Wetsteinische Homer, eine Ausgabe, nach der ich so oft verlangt, um mich auf dem Spaziergange mit dem Ernestinischen nicht zu schleppen. Sieh! so kommen sie meinen Wünschen zuvor, so suchen sie alle die kleinen Gefälligkeiten der Freundschaft auf, die tausendmal werter sind als jene blendenden Geschenke, wodurch uns die Eitelkeit des Gebers erniedrigt. Ich küsse diese Schleife tausendmal, und mit jedem Atemzuge schlürfe ich die Erinnerung jener Seligkeiten ein, mit denen mich jene wenigen, glücklichen, unwiederbringlichen Tage überfüllten. Wilhelm, es ist so, und ich murre nicht, die Blüten des Lebens sind nur Erscheinungen[142]! Wie viele gehn vorüber, ohne eine Spur hinter sich zu lassen, wie wenige setzen Frucht an, und wie wenige dieser Früchte werden reif! Und doch sind deren noch genug da; und doch — oh mein Bruder! —

came to me to write you and the minister, to apply for the post at the embassy which you assure me would not be refused me. I think you are right. The minister has liked me a long time and has long urged me to devote myself to some occupation; and for an hour I take it seriously. Then, when I think of it again, and I recall the fable of the horse that, impatient to have its freedom, allowed itself to be saddled and bridled and was ridden to death—I don't know what I should do.—And, my dear friend, is my longing for a change of condition perhaps only an irritating inner impatience which will pursue me everywhere?

August 28

It is true, if my illness could be cured, these people would cure it. Today is my birthday, and early in the morning I received a little package from Albert. Upon opening it, I at once noticed one of the pink ribbons that Lotte was wearing when I was introduced to her and for which I had asked her several times since. There were two little volumes in *duodecimo,* the little Wetstein Homer, an edition I have long craved so that I would not have to drag the Ernesti edition with me on my walks. You see how they anticipate my wishes, they hunt out all the little favors of friendship which are worth a thousand times more than those splendid gifts which humiliate us through the vanity of the giver. I kiss this ribbon a thousand times, and with every breath I drink in the memory of those raptures which filled me during those few, happy, irretrievable days. Wilhelm, it is so, and I am not complaining; the flowers of life are mere phantoms. How many fade without leaving a trace behind them, how few of them produce fruit, and how few of those fruits ripen! And yet there are enough left; and yet —oh, my friend, can we allow ripened fruits to be neglected, despised, and to rot without being tasted?

127

können wir gereifte Früchte vernachlässigen, verachten, ungenossen verfaulen lassen?

Lebe wohl! Es ist ein herrlicher Sommer; ich sitze oft auf den Obstbäumen in Lottens Baumstück mit dem Obstbrecher, der langen Stange, und hole die Birnen aus dem Gipfel[143]. Sie steht unten und nimmt sie ab, wenn ich sie ihr herunterlasse.

Am 30. August

Unglücklicher! Bist du nicht ein Tor? Betrügst du dich nicht selbst? Was soll diese tobende endlose Leidenschaft? Ich habe kein Gebet mehr als an sie; meiner Einbildungskraft erscheint keine andere Gestalt als die ihrige, und alles in der Welt um mich her sehe ich nur im Verhältnisse mit ihr. Und das macht mir denn so manche glückliche Stunde — bis ich mich wieder von ihr losreißen muß! Ach Wilhelm! wozu mich mein Herz oft drängt! — Wenn ich bei ihr gesessen bin, zwei, drei Stunden, und mich an ihrer Gestalt, an ihrem Betragen, an dem himmlischen Ausdruck ihrer Worte geweidet habe und nun nach und nach alle meine Sinne aufgespannt werden, mir es düster vor den Augen wird, ich kaum noch höre und es mich an die Gurgel faßt wie ein Meuchelmörder, dann mein Herz in wilden Schlägen den bedrängten Sinnen Luft zu machen sucht und ihre Verwirrung nur vermehrt — Wilhelm, ich weiß oft nicht, ob ich auf der Welt bin! Und — wenn nicht manchmal die Wehmut das Übergewicht nimmt und Lotte mir den elenden Trost erlaubt, auf ihrer Hand meine Beklemmung auszuweinen — so muß ich fort, muß hinaus! und schweife dann weit im Feld umher; einen jähen Berg zu klettern ist dann meine Freude, durch einen unwegsamen Wald einen Pfad durchzuarbeiten, durch die Hecken, die mich verletzen, durch die Dornen, die mich zerreißen! Da wird mir's etwas besser! Etwas! Und wenn ich vor Müdigkeit und Durst manchmal unterwegs liegenbleibe, manchmal in der tiefen Nacht, wenn der hohe Vollmond über mir steht, im einsamen Walde auf einen krummgewachsenen Baum mich setze, um meinen verwundeten Sohlen nur einige Linderung zu verschaffen, und dann in einer

Farewell! It is a glorious summer; I often sit in the fruit trees in Lotte's orchard with the fruit picker, a long pole, plucking pears from the top of the tree. She stands below and takes them from me as I hand them to her.

August 30

Unhappy man! Aren't you a fool? Aren't you deceiving yourself? What sense is there in this raging, endless passion? I no longer have prayers except to her; no other form appears to my imagination except hers, and I see everything in the world about me only in relation to her. And this brings me many a happy hour—until I must tear myself away from her again. Oh Wilhelm! The things my heart often urges me to do!—When I have been sitting with her for two or three hours and have feasted on her form, her manner, the heavenly expression of her thoughts, and then my senses gradually become tense, a darkness appears before my eyes, I can scarcely hear anything, my throat is constricted as though by the hand of a murderer, and my heart beats wildly trying to relieve my oppressed senses, but only increasing their confusion—Wilhelm, I often don't know whether I really exist. And at times—when melancholy does not get the upper hand and Lotte permits me the wretched comfort of shedding the tears of my oppression on her hand—I must leave, I must get outside and roam far through the fields; to climb a steep mountain is then my joy, to cut a path through an untrodden forest, through hedges which tear me, through thorns which rend me. Then I feel a little better. A little. And sometimes I lie down on the way, overcome by weariness and thirst; sometimes in the depth of night, when the full moon stands high above me in the lonely forest, I sit down on a gnarled, crooked tree, to give my aching soles some relief, and then doze off in the twilight in an exhausted sleep. Oh, Wilhelm! The solitary dwelling of a cell, the hair shirt and belt of thorns are comforts for which my soul pines. Good-by; I

ermattenden Ruhe in dem Dämmerschein hinschlummre!
O Wilhelm! die einsame Wohnung einer Zelle, das härene
Gewand und der Stachelgürtel wären[144] Labsale, nach denen
meine Seele schmachtet. Adieu! Ich seh' dieses Elendes
kein Ende als das Grab.

Am 3. September

Ich muß fort! Ich danke Dir, Wilhelm, daß Du meinen
wankenden Entschluß bestimmt hast. Schon vierzehn Tage
gehe ich mit dem Gedanken um, sie zu verlassen. Ich muß
fort. Sie ist wieder in der Stadt bei einer Freundin. Und
Albert — und — ich muß fort!

Am 10. September

Das war eine Nacht! Wilhelm! Nun überstehe ich alles.
Ich werde sie nicht wiedersehn! Oh, daß ich nicht an
Deinen Hals fliegen, Dir mit tausend Tränen und Entzückungen ausdrücken kann, mein Bester, die Empfindungen, die mein Herz bestürmen. Hier sitze ich und
schnappe nach Luft, suche mich zu beruhigen, erwarte den
Morgen, und mit Sonnenaufgang sind die Pferde bestellt.

Ach, sie schläft ruhig und denkt nicht, daß sie mich nie
wieder sehen wird. Ich habe mich losgerissen, bin stark
genug gewesen, in einem Gespräch von zwei Stunden mein
Vorhaben nicht zu verraten. Und Gott, welch ein Gespräch!

Albert hatte mir versprochen, gleich nach dem Nacht-
essen mit Lotten im Garten[145] zu sein. Ich stand auf der
Terrasse unter den hohen Kastanienbäumen und sah der
Sonne nach, die mir[146] nun zum letztenmal über dem lieblichen Tale, über dem sanften Fluß unterging. So oft hatte
ich hier gestanden mit ihr und eben dem herrlichen Schau-
spiele zugesehen, und nun — Ich ging in der Allee auf und
ab, die mir so lieb war; ein geheimer sympathetischer Zug
hatte mich hier so oft gehalten, ehe ich noch Lotten kannte,
und wie freuten wir uns, als wir im Anfang unserer Bekanntschaft die wechselseitige Neigung zu diesem Plätzchen

see no end to this misery but the grave.

I must go! I thank you, Wilhelm, for strengthening my wavering resolution. For two weeks now I've been nursing the thought of leaving her. I must go. She's in town again visiting a friend. And Albert—and—I must go!

What a night that was, Wilhelm! Now I can endure anything. I shall not see her again. Oh why can't I fly to you, embrace you and express to you, my dear friend, with a thousand tears and raptures, the emotions that overwhelm my heart. Here I sit gasping for air, trying to calm myself, waiting for morning to come. The horses have been ordered for sunrise.

Ah, she is sleeping peacefully and does not suspect that she will never see me again. I've torn myself away, and I was strong enough not to betray my intention in a conversation that lasted two hours. And Heaven, what a conversation!

Albert had promised me to be in the garden with Lotte right after dinner. I was standing on the terrace under the tall chestnut trees, looking at the sun which was now setting for me for the last time over the lovely valley and the gentle stream. I had stood here with her so often and watched this same glorious spectacle, and now—I went up and down the walk that was so precious to me; a secret sympathy had so often held me here, even before I knew Lotte, and how happy we were to discover, at the beginning of our acquaintance, our mutual affection for this spot, which is truly one of the most romantic that I have seen

entdeckten, das wahrhaftig eins von den romantischsten ist, die ich von der Kunst[147] hervorgebracht gesehen habe.

Erst hast Du zwischen den Kastanienbäumen die weite Aussicht — Ach, ich erinnere mich, ich habe Dir, denk' ich, schon viel davon geschrieben, wie hohe Buchenwände einen endlich einschließen und durch ein daran stoßendes Boskett die Allee immer düsterer wird, bis zuletzt alles sich in ein geschlossenes Plätzchen endigt, das alle Schauer der Einsamkeit umschweben. Ich fühle es noch, wie heimlich mir's ward, als ich zum ersten Male an einem hohen Mittage hineintrat; ich ahnte ganz leise, was für ein Schauplatz das noch werden sollte von Seligkeit und Schmerz.

Ich hatte mich etwa eine halbe Stunde in den schmachtenden, süßen Gedanken des Abscheidens, des Wiedersehens geweidet, als ich sie die Terrasse heraufsteigen hörte. Ich lief ihnen entgegen, mit einem Schauer faßte ich ihre Hand und küßte sie. Wir waren eben heraufgetreten, als der Mond hinter dem buschigen Hügel aufging; wir redeten mancherlei und kamen unvermerkt dem düstern Kabinette[148] näher. Lotte trat hinein und setzte sich, Albert neben sie, ich auch; doch meine Unruhe ließ mich nicht lange sitzen; ich stand auf, trat vor sie, ging auf und ab, setzte mich wieder: es war ein ängstlicher Zustand. Sie machte uns aufmerksam auf die schöne Wirkung des Mondenlichtes, das am Ende der Buchenwände die ganze Terrasse vor uns erleuchtete: ein herrlicher Anblick, der um so viel frappanter war, weil uns rings eine tiefe Dämmerung einschloß. Wir waren still, und sie fing nach einer Weile an: „Niemals gehe ich im Mondenlichte spazieren, niemals, daß mir nicht der Gedanke an meine Verstorbenen begegnete, daß nicht das Gefühl von Tod, von Zukunft über mich käme. Wir werden sein[149]!" fuhr sie mit der Stimme des herrlichsten Gefühls fort; „aber, Werther, sollen wir uns wiederfinden? wieder erkennen? was ahnen Sie? was sagen Sie?"

„Lotte", sagte ich, indem ich ihr die Hand reichte und mir die Augen voll Tränen wurden, „wir werden uns wieder sehn! Hier und dort wieder sehn!" — Ich konnte nicht weiterreden — Wilhelm, mußte sie mich das fragen, da ich diesen ängstlichen Abschied im Herzen hatte!

produced by art.

First you have the distant view between the chestnut trees.—Oh, I remember, I think I've already written you much about it, how one is finally enclosed by high walls of beech, and how the walk becomes darker and darker because of an adjacent copse, until finally you reach a little enclosure which is permeated by all the thrills of solitude. I can still feel how mysterious it seemed when I stepped into it for the first time at high noon; I had a very faint premonition that this would some day become the setting for bliss and pain.

For about half an hour I had indulged myself in the sweet, languishing thoughts of departure and return, when I heard them coming up the terrace. I ran toward them; with a thrill I took her hand and kissed it. We had just reached the top when the moon rose behind the wooded hill; we talked about all sorts of things and, without noticing it, approached the secluded spot. Lotte went in and sat down, Albert beside her; I, too, but my restlessness would not let me sit long; I stood in front of her, walked back and forth, sat down again; my state was an unhappy one. She called our attention to the beautiful effect of the moonlight which illuminated the whole terrace lying before us at the end of the wall of beech trees; it was a magnificent sight, which was all the more striking because we were surrounded by a deep twilight. We were silent and after a while she began: "I never go walking in the moonlight without thinking of my deceased ones; the feeling of death, of life after death, comes over me. We shall exist!" she continued in a voice full of the most glorious feeling. "But, Werther, shall we ever find each other again, and know each other? What do you think? What do you say?"

"Lotte," I said, giving her my hand, my eyes filling with tears, "we shall see each other again, both here and here-after!"—I could not go on—Wilhelm, did she have to ask me that, when I had this unhappy departure on my mind?

„Und ob die lieben Abgeschiedenen von uns wissen", fuhr sie fort, „ob sie fühlen, wann's uns wohl geht, daß wir mit warmer Liebe uns ihrer erinnern? Oh! die Gestalt meiner Mutter schwebt immer um mich, wenn ich am stillen Abend unter ihren Kindern, unter meinen Kindern sitze und sie um mich versammelt sind, wie sie um sie versammelt waren. Wenn ich dann mit einer sehnenden Träne gen Himmel sehe und wünsche, daß sie hereinschauen könnte einen Augenblick, wie ich mein Wort halte, das ich ihr in der Stunde des Todes gab: die Mutter ihrer Kinder zu sein. Mit welcher Empfindung rufe ich aus: ,Verzeihe mir's, Teuerste, wenn ich ihnen nicht bin, was du ihnen warst. Ach! tue ich doch alles, was ich kann; sind sie doch gekleidet, genährt, ach, und was mehr ist als das alles, gepflegt und geliebt. Könntest du unsere Eintracht sehen, liebe Heilige! du würdest mit dem heißesten Danke den Gott verherrlichen, den du mit den letzten, bittersten Tränen um die Wohlfahrt deiner Kinder batest.' " —

Sie sagte das! Oh Wilhelm, wer kann wiederholen, was sie sagte! Wie kann der kalte, tote Buchstabe diese himmlische Blüte des Geistes darstellen! Albert fiel ihr sanft in die Rede: „Es greift Sie zu stark an, liebe Lotte! Ich weiß, Ihre Seele hängt sehr nach diesen Ideen, aber ich bitte Sie" — „Oh Albert", sagte sie, „ich weiß, du vergissest nicht die Abende, da wir zusammen saßen an dem kleinen, runden Tischchen, wenn der Papa verreist war und wir die Kleinen schlafen geschickt hatten. Du hattest oft ein gutes Buch und kamst so selten dazu, etwas zu lesen — War der Umgang dieser herrlichen Seele nicht mehr als alles? Die schöne, sanfte, muntere und immer tätige Frau! Gott kennt meine Tränen, mit denen ich mich oft in meinem Bette vor ihn hinwarf: er möchte mich ihr gleich machen."

„Lotte!" rief ich aus, indem ich mich vor sie hinwarf, ihre Hand nahm und mit tausend Tränen netzte, „Lotte! der Segen Gottes ruht über dir und der Geist deiner Mutter!" — „Wenn Sie sie gekannt hätten", sagte sie, indem sie mir die Hand drückte —, „sie war wert, von Ihnen gekannt zu sein!" — Ich glaubte zu vergehen. Nie war ein größeres, stolzeres Wort über mich ausgesprochen worden — und sie fuhr fort: „Und diese Frau mußte in

"And I wonder whether the dear departed ones know about us," she continued, "whether they feel, when we are happy, that we remember them with warm love? Oh! the form of my mother always hovers about me when I sit on a quiet evening among her children, among my children, and they are gathered about me as they used to gather about her. Then I look up to heaven with a tear of yearning and wish that she might look in for a moment and see how I am keeping the promise which I gave her in the hour of her death: to be the mother of her children. With what emotion I cry out: 'Forgive me, dearest one, if I am not to them what you were. Oh, I am really doing everything I can; they are dressed, fed, and what is more than all that, cared for and loved. If you could see our harmony, dear sainted one! you would glorify with the warmest gratitude the God to Whom you prayed for the welfare of your children with your last, most bitter tears.' "

She said this! Oh Wilhelm, who can repeat all that she said? How can the cold, dead letter convey this heavenly flowering of the spirit? Albert interrupted her gently: "You are too deeply affected, dear Lotte! I know your mind is strongly attached to these ideas, but I beg you——" "Oh, Albert," she said, "I know you haven't forgotten the evenings when we sat together at the little round table when Papa was away and we had sent the children to bed. You often had a good book, and so rarely got the chance to read anything.——Wasn't the association with that glorious soul worth more than anything else? That beautiful, gentle, bright and ever active woman! God knows the tears with which I often threw myself before Him in my bed, praying that He might make me like her."

"Lotte!" I exclaimed, throwing myself at her feet, taking her hand and wetting it with a thousand tears, "Lotte, God's blessing and the spirit of your mother are upon you!" "If only you had known her," she said, pressing my hand. "She was worthy of being known by you." I thought I would faint. Never had a greater, prouder word been spoken about me—and she continued: "And this woman had to pass away in the flower of her years, when her

135

der Blüte ihrer Jahre dahin, da ihr jüngster Sohn nicht sechs Monate alt war! Ihre Krankheit dauerte nicht lange; sie war ruhig, hingegeben[150], nur ihre Kinder taten ihr weh, besonders das kleine. Wie es gegen das Ende ging und sie zu mir sagte: ‚Bringe mir sie herauf', und wie ich sie hereinführte, die kleinen, die nicht, wußten, und die ältesten, die ohne Sinne waren, wie sie ums Bette standen, und wie sie die Hände aufhob und über sie betete und sie küßte nacheinander und sie wegschickte und zu mir sagte: ‚Sei ihre Mutter!' — Ich gab ihr die Hand drauf! — ‚Du versprichst viel, meine Tochter', sagte sie, ‚das Herz einer Mutter und das Aug' einer Mutter. Ich habe oft an deinen dankbaren Tränen gesehen, daß du fühlst, was das sei. Habe es für deine Geschwister und für deinen Vater die Treue und den Gehorsam einer Frau. Du wirst ihn trösten.' — Sie fragte nach ihm, er war ausgegangen, um uns den unerträglichen Kummer zu verbergen, den er fühlte; der Mann war ganz zerrissen.

„Albert, du warst im Zimmer. Sie hörte jemand gehn und fragte und forderte dich zu sich, und wie sie dich ansah und mich, mit dem getrösteten ruhigen Blicke, daß wir glücklich sein, zusammen glücklich sein würden." — Albert fiel ihr um den Hals und küßte sie und rief: „Wir sind es! Wir werden es sein!" — Der ruhige Albert war ganz aus seiner Fassung, und ich wußte nichts von mir selber.

„Werther", fing sie an, „und diese Frau sollte dahin sein! Gott! wenn ich manchmal denke, wie man das Liebste seines Lebens wegtragen läßt und niemand als die Kinder das so scharf fühlt, die sich noch lange beklagten, die schwarzen Männer hätten die Mama weggetragen!"

Sie stand auf, und ich ward erweckt[151] und erschüttert, blieb sitzen und hielt ihre Hand. — „Wir wollen fort", sagte sie, „es wird Zeit." — Sie wollte ihre Hand zurückziehen, und ich hielt sie fester. — „Wir werden uns wieder sehen", rief ich, „wir werden uns finden, unter allen Gestalten[152] werden wir uns erkennen. Ich gehe", fuhr ich fort, „ich gehe willig, und doch, wenn ich sagen sollte auf ewig, ich würde es nicht aushalten. Leb wohl, Lotte! Leb wohl, Albert! Wir sehn uns wieder." — „Morgen, denke

youngest son was not six months old. Her illness did not last long, she was calm, resigned; only the thought of her children, especially the youngest, alone caused her pain. When her end was approaching, she said to me: 'Bring them up to me,' and I led them in. The little ones did not know what was happening and the oldest were in despair as they stood about the bed; and she raised her hands and prayed over them, and kissed them one after the other and sent them away, and said to me: 'Be a mother to them!'—I gave her my hand on it.—'You are promising much, my daughter,' she said, 'the heart of a mother and the eyes of a mother. I have often seen from your tears of gratitude that you feel what that means. Have them for your brothers and sisters, and for your father have the loyalty and obedience of a wife. You will console him.'— She asked for him. He had gone out to hide from us the unbearable grief he felt; the man was completely broken.

"Albert, you were in the room. She heard someone moving about, asked who it was, and called you to her; and when she looked at you and at me, with that calm look of relief that we would be happy, happy together—." Albert threw his arms about her and kissed her and cried: "We are happy, and we shall be!"—The sedate Albert was completely beside himself and I was beyond all reason.

"Werther," she began again, "and this woman had to leave us! Lord! When I think sometimes how we let the dearest thing in life be carried away, and no one felt it as keenly as the children, who complained long afterwards that the black men had carried off their mama."

She stood up and I was brought back to myself, shaken; I sat there holding her hand. "Let's go," she said, "it's time to leave."—She wanted to withdraw her hand but I held onto it more tightly.—"We'll see each other again," I cried, "we shall find each other, we shall recognize each other among all the forms. I'm going," I continued, "I go willingly, and yet if I were to say 'forever' I couldn't bear it. Farewell, Lotte! Farewell, Albert! We shall meet again."—"Tomorrow, I suppose," she replied in a jesting tone.—

ich", versetzte sie scherzend. — Ich fühlte das Morgen! Ach, sie wußte nicht, als sie ihre Hand aus der meinen zog — Sie gingen die Allee hinaus, ich stand, sah ihnen nach im Mondscheine und warf mich an die Erde und weinte mich aus und sprang auf und lief auf die Terrasse hervor und sah noch dort unten im Schatten der hohen Lindenbäume ihr weißes Kleid nach der Gartentür schimmern; ich streckte meine Arme aus, und es verschwand.

I felt this "tomorrow." Ah, she did not know as she withdrew her hand from mine—they went away along the walk; I stood there looking after them in the moonlight, then flung myself on the ground and wept till I could weep no more, jumped up, and ran out on the terrace from where I could still see her white dress gleaming as it moved toward the garden gate, down there in the shadow of the tall linden trees. I stretched out my arms and it vanished.

Am 20. Oktober 1771

Gestern sind wir hier angelangt. Der Gesandte ist unpaß und wird sich also einige Tage einhalten. Wenn er nur nicht so unhold wäre, wär' alles gut. Ich merke, ich merke, das Schicksal hat mir harte Prüfungen zugedacht. Doch gutes Muts! Ein leichter Sinn trägt alles! Ein leichter Sinn? Das macht mich zu lachen, wie das Wort in meine Feder kommt. Oh, ein bißchen leichteres Blut würde mich zum Glücklichsten unter der Sonne machen. Was! da wo andere mit ihrem bißchen Kraft und Talent vor mir in behaglicher Selbstgefälligkeit herumschwadronieren, verzweifle ich an meiner Kraft, an meinen Gaben? Guter Gott, der du mir das alles schenktest, warum hieltest du nicht die Hälfte zurück und gabst mir Selbstvertrauen und Genügsamkeit!

Geduld! Geduld! Es wird besser werden. Denn ich sage Dir, Lieber, Du hast recht. Seit ich unter dem Volke alle Tage herumgetrieben werde und sehe, was sie tun, und wie sie's treiben, stehe ich viel besser mit mir selbst. Gewiß, weil wir doch einmal so gemacht sind, daß wir alles mit uns und uns mit allem vergleichen, so liegt Glück oder Elend in den Gegenständen, womit wir uns zusammenhalten, und da ist nichts gefährlicher als die Einsamkeit. Unsere Einbildungskraft, durch ihre Natur gedrungen, sich zu erheben, durch die phantastischen Bilder der Dichtkunst genährt, bildet sich eine Reihe Wesen hinauf, wo wir das unterste sind, und alles außer uns herrlicher erscheint, jeder andere vollkommner ist. Und das geht ganz natürlich zu. Wir fühlen so oft, daß uns manches mangelt, und eben was uns fehlt scheint uns oft ein anderer zu besitzen, dem wir denn auch alles dazu geben, was w i r haben, und noch eine gewisse idealische[1] Behaglichkeit dazu. Und so ist der Glückliche vollkommen fertig, das Geschöpf unserer selbst.

BOOK TWO

October 20, 1771

We arrived here yesterday. The ambassador is indisposed and will therefore be in retirement for a few days. If only he weren't so unpleasant, all would be well. I can see, I can see, destiny has planned harsh trials for me. But courage! A light heart endures anything. A light heart? It makes me laugh to see these words come from my pen. Oh, a little more lightheartedness would make me the happiest man under the sun. What if others with their little bit of energy and talent swagger about before me in comfortable self-complacency, am I to despair of my powers, my gifts? Good Lord, Who hast given me all this, why didst Thou not withhold half of it and give me self-confidence and contentment?

Patience, patience, things will improve. For I tell you, my dear friend, you are right. Since I have been drifting about among these people every day, seeing how they live and act, I'm much more pleased with myself. Of course, since we are so constituted that we compare everything with ourselves and ourselves with everything, happiness or misery lies in the objects with which we compare ourselves, and so nothing is more dangerous than solitude. Our imagination, compelled by its nature to elevate itself, nourished by the fantastic images of literature, creates a series of beings of whom we are the lowest, and everything outside ourselves seems more splendid to us, everyone else more perfect than we are. The process is quite natural. We feel so often that we lack many things and the very things we lack someone else often seems to possess, and we also attribute to him all that we have ourselves, and a certain ideal contentment into the bargain. And so the happy man stands there in perfection, our

141

Dagegen, wenn wir mit all unserer Schwachheit und Mühseligkeit nur gerade fortarbeiten, so finden wir gar oft, daß wir mit unserem Schlendern und Lavieren es weiter bringen als andere mit ihrem Segeln und Rudern — und — das ist doch ein wahres Gefühl seiner selbst, wenn man andern gleich oder gar vorläuft.

Am 26. November

Ich fange an, mich insofern ganz leidlich hier zu befinden. Das Beste ist, daß es zu tun genug gibt; und dann die vielerlei Menschen, die allerlei neuen Gestalten machen mir ein buntes Schauspiel vor meiner Seele. Ich habe den Grafen C . . . kennenlernen, einen Mann, den ich jeden Tag mehr verehren muß, einen weiten großen Kopf, und der deswegen nicht kalt ist, weil er viel übersieht[2]; aus dessen Umgange so viel Empfindung für Freundschaft und Liebe hervorleuchtet. Er nahm teil an mir, als ich einen Geschäftsauftrag an ihn ausrichtete und er bei den ersten Worten merkte, daß wir uns verstanden, daß er mit mir reden konnte wie nicht mit jedem. Auch kann ich sein offnes Betragen gegen mich nicht genug rühmen. So eine wahre, warme Freude ist nicht in der Welt, als eine große Seele zu sehen, die sich gegen einen öffnet.

Am 24. Dezember

Der Gesandte macht mir viel Verdruß, ich habe es vorausgesehn. Er ist der pünktlichste Narr, den es nur geben kann; Schritt vor Schritt und umständlich wie eine Base[3]; ein Mensch, der nie mit sich selbst zufrieden ist, und dem es daher niemand zu Danke machen kann. Ich arbeite gern leicht weg[4], und wie es steht, so steht es; da ist er imstande, mir einen Aufsatz zurückzugeben und zu sagen: „Er ist gut, aber sehen Sie ihn durch, man findet immer ein besseres Wort, eine reinere Partikel[5]. — Da möchte ich des Teufels werden[6]. Kein Und, kein Bindewörtchen darf außenbleiben[7], und von allen Inversionen, die mir

own creation.

On the other hand, if we but continue to work, laboriously, and weak as we are, we very often find that, in spite of our straggling and tacking, we get farther than others with their sailing and rowing—and—there is a true feeling of satisfaction in keeping up with or even outdistancing others.

November 26, 1771

I am beginning to find life here quite tolerable, everything considered. The best thing about it is that there is enough to do; and then the many kinds of people, a variety of new types, present a gay spectacle before my mind's eye. I have become acquainted with Count C——, a man whom I am compelled to respect more every day, a man of broad and great understanding who is not cold because he is able to see so much, whose company shows clearly his great capacity for friendship and love. He showed an interest in me when I went to him on a matter of business, and he noticed after our first words that we understood each other, that he could talk to me better than to most people. Moreover I cannot praise his frank behavior toward me highly enough. There is no other joy as true or as warm in this world as that of finding a great mind in sympathy with one's own.

December 24, 1771

The ambassador is causing me much annoyance. I foresaw it. He is the most punctilious fool in existence. He does things step by step and is as fussy as an old woman, a man who is never satisfied with himself and whom, therefore, no one can please. I like to work casually and to leave things as they come out; but he's capable of handing a document back to me and saying, "It's good, but look through it again, you can always finds a better word, a more accurate particle."—I could go mad! No "and," no conjunction may be left out, and he's a mortal enemy to every inversion that may occasionally escape me; if you don't

manchmal entfahren, ist er ein Todfeind; wenn man seinen Perioden[8] nicht nach der hergebrachten Melodie herab-orgelt, so versteht er gar nichts drin. Das ist ein Leiden, mit so einem Menschen zu tun zu haben.

Das Vertrauen des Grafen von C . . . ist noch das einzige, was mich schadlos hält. Er sagte mir letzthin ganz aufrichtig, wie unzufrieden er mit der Langsamkeit und Bedenklichkeit meines Gesandten sei. „Die Leute er-schweren es sich und andern; doch", sagte er, „man muß sich darein resignieren, wie ein Reisender, der über einen Berg muß; freilich, wäre der Berg nicht da, so wäre der Weg viel bequemer und kürzer; er ist nun aber da, und man soll hinüber!" —

Mein Alter spürt auch wohl den Vorzug, den mir der Graf vor ihm gibt, und das ärgert ihn, und er ergreift jede Gelegenheit, Übles gegen mich vom Grafen zu reden: ich halte, wie natürlich, Widerpart, und dadurch wird die Sache nur schlimmer. Gestern gar brachte er mich auf, denn ich war mitgemeint: zu so Weltgeschäften sei der Graf ganz gut, er habe viele Leichtigkeit zu arbeiten und führe eine gute Feder; doch an gründlicher Gelehrsamkeit mangle es ihm wie allen Belletristen. Dazu machte er eine Miene, als ob er sagen wollte: Fühlst du den Stich? Aber es tat bei mir nicht die Wirkung, ich verachtete den Menschen, der so denken und sich so betragen konnte. Ich hielt ihm stand und focht mit ziemlicher Heftigkeit. Ich sagte, der Graf sei ein Mann, vor dem man Achtung haben müsse wegen seines Charakters sowohl als wegen seiner Kennt-nisse. „Ich habe", sagte ich, „niemand gekannt, dem es so geglückt wäre, seinen Geist zu erweitern, ihn über un-zählige Gegenstände zu verbreiten und doch diese Tätig-keit fürs gemeine Leben zu behalten." — Das waren dem Gehirne spanische Dörfer, und ich empfahl mich, um nicht über ein weiteres Deraisonnement noch mehr Galle zu schlucken.

Und daran seid ihr alle schuld, die ihr mich in das Joch geschwatzt und mir so viel von Aktivität vorgesungen habt. Aktivität! Wenn nicht der mehr tut, der Kartoffeln legt und in die Stadt reitet, sein Korn zu verkaufen, als ich,

pound out your periods according to the traditional melody, he's completely bewildered. It's martyrdom to deal with such a person.

The confidence shown me by Count C— is the only thing that offers me some compensation. He recently told me quite frankly how dissatisfied he was with the slowness and pedantry of my ambassador. "Such people make things hard for themselves and for others. However," he added, "you must resign yourself to it like a traveler who has to go over a mountain. Of course, if the mountain weren't there, the road would be much more convenient and shorter; but it simply is there, and you have to get over it!"—

The old man no doubt senses the Count's liking for me; this annoys him, and he seizes every opportunity to tell me bad things about the Count. I naturally contradict him and that merely makes matters worse. Yesterday he really aroused me, for he included me in his censure: the Count was quite well-suited for the affairs of the world, he works easily and writes a good style, but, like all men of letters, he lacks thorough scholarship. And in saying this he made a face as if to say: "Do you feel the jab?" But it missed its effect on me; I despised a man who could think and act in this way. I stood my ground and fought back quite vigorously. I said the Count was a man whom one had to respect both for his character and his knowledge. "I've never known anyone," I said, "who has been so successful in broadening his mind, extending it over such a vast field and who yet continues to be active in everyday life."—This was all Greek to his mind, and I took my leave, so that I would not have to swallow even more anger over his twaddle.

And you are all to blame for this, who talked me into putting on this yoke and sang me such a song about an active life. An active life! If the man who plants potatoes and rides to town to sell his wheat doesn't do more than

145

so will ich zehn Jahre noch mich auf der Galeere abar-
beiten, auf der ich nun angeschmiedet bin.

Und das glänzende Elend, die Langeweile unter dem
garstigen Volke, das sich hier nebeneinander sieht! Die
Rangsucht unter ihnen, wie sie nur wachen und aufpassen,
einander ein Schrittchen abzugewinnen; die elendesten,
erbärmlichsten Leidenschaften, ganz ohne Röckchen. Da
ist ein Weib, zum Exempel, die jedermann von ihrem Adel
und ihrem Lande unterhält, so daß jeder Fremde denken
muß: das ist eine Närrin, die sich auf das bißchen Adel
und auf den Ruf ihres Landes Wunderstreiche einbildet. —
Aber es ist noch viel ärger: eben das Weib ist hier aus der
Nachbarschaft, eines Amtschreibers Tochter. — Sieh, ich
kann das Menschengeschlecht nicht begreifen, das so wenig
Sinn hat, um sich so platt zu prostituieren.

Zwar ich merke täglich mehr, mein Lieber, wie töricht
man ist, andere nach sich zu berechnen. Und weil ich so
viel mit mir selbst zu tun habe und dieses Herz so
stürmisch ist — ach, ich lasse gern die andern ihres Pfades
gehen, wenn sie mich nur auch könnten gehen lassen.

Was mich am meisten neckt, sind die fatalen bürgerlichen
Verhältnisse. Zwar weiß ich so gut als einer, wie nötig der
Unterschied der Stände ist, wie viel Vorteile er mir selbst
verschafft; nur soll er mir nicht eben gerade im Wege
stehen, wo ich noch ein wenig Freude, einen Schimmer von
Glück auf dieser Erde genießen könnte. Ich lernte neulich
auf dem Spaziergange ein Fräulein von B . . . kennen,
ein liebenswürdiges Geschöpf, das sehr viele Natur mitten
in dem steifen Leben erhalten hat. Wir gefielen uns in unserem Gespräche, und da wir schieden, bat ich sie um
Erlaubnis, sie bei sich sehen zu dürfen. Sie gestattete mir
das mit so vieler Freimütigkeit, daß ich den schicklichen
Augenblick kaum erwarten konnte, zu ihr zu gehen. Sie ist
nicht von hier und wohnt bei einer Tante im Hause. Die
Physiognomie der Alten gefiel mir nicht. Ich bezeigte ihr
viel Aufmerksamkeit, mein Gespräch war meist an sie
gewandt, und in minder als einer halben Stunde hatte ich
so ziemlich weg, was mir das Fräulein nachher selbst
gestand: daß die liebe Tante in ihrem Alter Mangel von[9]
allem, kein anständiges Vermögen, keinen Geist und keine

I, I will spend ten more years slaving on the galley to which I am now chained.

And the splendid misery, the boredom among these horrid people who come together here, their snobbery which keeps them awake and alert to get one tiny step ahead of the others: the most wretched, most pitiable passions, in all their nakedness. There is a woman, for instance, who never stops talking about her nobility and her country, so that a stranger must think: that's a fool who has absurd illusions about her bit of nobility and the renown of her country.—But it is even much worse than that: this same woman is the daughter of a magistrate's clerk from near-by.—Really, I can't understand our human race, to behave with such low stupidity.

Though I must say, my friend, that I notice more and more every day how foolish it is to judge others by one-self. And because I am so preoccupied with myself and my heart is so tempestuous—oh, I'll gladly let the others go their own way if only they would let me go mine.

What annoys me most of all is the disagreeable social conditions. Of course I know as well as the next man how necessary it is to have class differences, and what advantages I myself derive from them; but they shall not stand in my way in my experiencing a little joy, a gleam of happiness on this earth. Recently, while taking a walk, I became acquainted with a Fräulein von B—, a charming creature, who has remained quite natural in the midst of an artificial existence. We enjoyed our conversation, and when we parted I asked permission to call on her. She gave me leave to do so with such frankness that I could hardly wait for the proper moment to go to her home. She is not from around here, and lives with an aunt. I did not like the old lady's face. I was very attentive to her, my conversation was mostly directed to her, and in less than half an hour I was fairly certain of what the young lady later admitted to me: that her dear aunt, at her age, lacked everything: a respectable fortune, intelligence, and any support except her pedigree, any protection except her rank, behind which she entrenches herself, and any pleasure

Stütze hat als die Reihe ihrer Vorfahren, keinen Schirm als den Stand, in den sie sich verpalisadiert, und kein Ergötzen, als von ihrem Stockwerk herab über die bürgerlichen Häupter wegzusehen. In ihrer Jugend soll sie schön gewesen sein und ihr Leben weggegaukelt, erst mit ihrem Eigensinne[10] manchen armen Jungen gequält und in den reiferen Jahren sich unter den Gehorsam eines alten Offiziers geduckt haben, der gegen diesen Preis und einen leidlichen Unterhalt das eherne Jahrhundert[11] mit ihr zubrachte und starb. Nun sieht sie im eisernen sich allein und würde nicht angesehn, wär' ihre Nichte nicht so liebenswürdig.

Den 8. Januar 1772

Was das für Menschen sind, deren ganze Seele auf dem Zeremoniell ruht, deren Dichten[12] und Trachten jahrelang dahin geht, wie sie um einen Stuhl weiter hinauf bei Tische sich einschieben wollen! Und nicht, daß sie sonst keine Angelegenheit hätten; nein, vielmehr häufen sich die Arbeiten, eben weil man über den kleinen Verdrießlichkeiten von Beförderung der wichtigen Sachen abgehalten wird. Vorige Woche gab es bei der Schlittenfahrt Händel, und der ganze Spaß wurde verdorben.

Die Toren, die nicht sehen, daß es eigentlich auf den Platz gar nicht ankommt, und daß der, der den ersten hat, so selten die erste Rolle spielt! Wie mancher König wird durch seinen Minister, wie mancher Minister durch seinen Sekretär regiert! Und wer ist dann der Erste? Der, dünkt mich, der die andern übersieht und so viel Gewalt oder List hat, ihre Kräfte und Leidenschaften zu Ausführung seiner Pläne anzuspannen.

Am 20. Januar

Ich muß Ihnen schreiben, liebe Lotte, hier in der Stube einer geringen Bauernherberge, in die ich mich vor einem schweren Wetter geflüchtet habe. So lange ich in dem traurigen Neste D . . ., unter dem fremden, meinem Herzen ganz fremden Volke herumziehe, habe ich keinen

except to look down from her upstairs apartment on the common heads below. She is said to have been beautiful in her youth, and to have frittered away her life, torturing many a poor young man with her caprices, while in her more mature years she submitted obediently to an old officer who, in return for this obedience and a tolerable style of life, spent his bronze age with her and then died. Now she sees herself alone in her iron age, and would not be noticed if her niece were not so charming.

January 8, 1772

What sort of people are they, whose whole mental life is based on ceremony, who for years direct all their thoughts and efforts toward the goal of pushing their way one chair up at the dinner table! Not that they have nothing better to do; no, on the contrary, the work piles up simply because these petty annoyances keep them from attending to important matters. Last week a quarrel broke out during a sleigh ride and all the fun was spoiled.

Can't the fools see that the place doesn't matter at all, and that the man who has first place so rarely plays the first role? How many kings are ruled by their ministers, and how many ministers by their secretaries! And who is first then? The man, it seems to me, who completely understands others, and possesses enough power or cunning to harness their energies and passions for the realization of his own plans.

January 20

I must write to you, dear Lotte, here in the parlor of a humble country inn, in which I have taken refuge from a severe storm. As long as I moved about in the sad hole of D—, among people who were totally alien to my mind, there was not a moment, not a single one, in which my

149

Augenblick gehabt, keinen, an dem mein Herz mich geheißen hätte, Ihnen zu schreiben; und jetzt in dieser Hütte, in dieser Einsamkeit, in dieser Einschränkung, da Schnee und Schloßen wider mein Fensterchen wüten, hier waren Sie mein erster Gedanke. Wie ich hereintrat, überfiel mich Ihre Gestalt, Ihr Andenken, o Lotte! so heilig, so warm! Guter Gott! Der erste glückliche Augenblick wieder.

Wenn Sie mich sähen, meine Beste, in dem Schwall von Zerstreuung! wie ausgetrocknet meine Sinne werden; nicht einen Augenblick der Fülle des Herzens, nicht eine selige Stunde! nichts! nichts! Ich stehe wie vor einem Raritätenkasten[13] und sehe die Männchen und Gäulchen vor mir herumrücken und frage mich oft, ob es nicht optischer Betrug ist. Ich spiele mit, vielmehr, ich werde gespielt wie eine Marionette und fasse manchmal meinen Nachbar an der hölzernen Hand und schaudere zurück. Des Abends nehme ich mir vor, den Sonnenaufgang zu genießen, und komme nicht aus dem Bette; am Tage hoffe ich, mich des Mondscheins zu erfreuen, und bleibe in meiner Stube. Ich weiß nicht recht, warum ich aufstehe, warum ich schlafen gehe.

Der Sauerteig, der mein Leben in Bewegung setzte, fehlt; der Reiz, der mich in tiefen Nächten munter erhielt, ist hin, der mich des Morgens aus dem Schlafe weckte, ist weg.

Ein einzig weibliches Geschöpf habe ich hier gefunden, eine[14] Fräulein von B . . ., sie gleicht Ihnen, liebe Lotte, wenn man Ihnen gleichen kann. „Ei!" werden Sie sagen, „der Mensch legt sich auf niedliche Komplimente!" Ganz unwahr ist es nicht. Seit einiger Zeit bin ich sehr artig, weil ich doch nicht anders sein kann, habe viel Witz, und die Frauenzimmer sagen, es wüßte niemand so fein zu loben als ich (und zu lügen, setzen Sie hinzu, denn ohne das geht es nicht ab, verstehen Sie?). Ich wollte von Fräulein B . . . reden. Sie hat viel Seele, die voll aus ihren blauen Augen hervorblickt. Ihr Stand ist ihr zur Last, der keinen der Wünsche ihres Herzens befriedigt. Sie sehnt sich aus dem Getümmel, und wir verphantasieren manche Stunde in ländlichen Szenen von ungemischter Glückseligkeit; ach! und von Ihnen! Wie oft muß sie Ihnen huldigen, muß nicht, tut es freiwillig, hört so gern von Ihnen, liebt Sie. —

heart urged me to write to you; but now, in this cabin, in this solitude, in this confinement, when snow and sleet batter my little window, here you were my first thought. As I entered the place, your form, oh Lotte, the memory of you filled me, so sacred, so warm! Kind God, the first happy moment again!

If you could see me, my dear, in this orgy of distraction! How desiccated my senses become; not one moment of emotional richness, not one hour of happiness! Nothing, nothing! I stand as before a peep show and see the tiny men and horses racing around before my eyes, and keep asking myself whether it isn't an optical illusion. I, too, play the game, or rather I am played like a puppet, and sometimes seize my neighbor's wooden hand and start back in horror. In the evening I resolve to enjoy the sunrise, but I don't get out of bed; by day I hope to enjoy the moonlight, but I stay in my room. I don't really know why I get up or why I go to bed.

The leaven that used to set my life in motion is lacking; the stimulus which kept me alert in the deep nights and which awakened me from my sleep in the morning is gone.

I have met one sole female creature here, a Fräulein von B——; she resembles you, dear Lotte, if anyone can resemble you. "My," you will say, "the man is indulging in pretty compliments." That's not altogether untrue. For some time I've been very gallant, because I can't be anything else; I have much wit, and the ladies say that no one can give such elegant praise as I (or lie, you will add, for it can't be done without lying, don't you know?). I was going to talk of Fräulein B——. She has much soulfulness, which shines out fully from her blue eyes. Her social position is a burden to her, satisfying none of her heart's desires. She yearns to be out of this turmoil, and we dream away many an hour in rustic scenes of unalloyed bliss; ah, and of you! How often she must pay homage to you; she doesn't have to—she does it willingly; she takes such pleasure in hearing about you, and loves you.—

151

O säß’ ich zu Ihren Füßen in dem lieben, vertraulichen Zimmerchen, und unsere kleinen Lieben wälzten sich miteinander um mich herum, und wenn sie Ihnen zu laut würden, wollte ich sie mit einem schauerlichen Märchen um mich zur Ruhe versammeln.

Die Sonne geht herrlich unter über der schneeglänzenden Gegend, der Sturm ist hinübergezogen, und ich — muß mich wieder in meinen Käfig sperren. — Adieu! Ist Albert bei Ihnen? Und wie —? Gott verzeihe mir diese Frage!

Den 8. Februar

Wir haben seit acht Tagen das abscheulichste Wetter, und mir ist es wohltätig. Denn solang ich hier bin, ist mir noch kein schöner Tag am Himmel erschienen, den mir nicht jemand verdorben oder verleidet hätte. Wenn’s nun recht regnet und stöbert und fröstelt und taut — ha! denk’ ich, kann’s doch zu Hause nicht schlimmer werden, als es draußen ist, oder umgekehrt, und so ist’s gut. Geht die Sonne des Morgens auf und verspricht einen feinen Tag, erwehr’ ich mir[15] niemals auszurufen: Da haben sie doch wieder ein himmliches Gut, worum sie einander bringen können. Es ist nichts, worum sie einander nicht bringen. Gesundheit, guter Name, Freudigkeit, Erholung! Und meist aus Albernheit, Unbegriff und Enge, und wenn man sie anhört, mit der besten Meinung. Manchmal möcht’ ich sie auf den Knien bitten, nicht so rasend in ihre eigenen Eingeweide[16] zu wüten.

Am 17. Februar

Ich fürchte, mein Gesandter und ich halten es zusammen nicht lange mehr aus. Der Mann ist ganz und gar unerträglich. Seine Art zu arbeiten und Geschäfte zu treiben ist so lächerlich, daß ich mich nicht enthalten kann, ihm zu widersprechen und oft eine Sache nach meinem Kopf und meiner Art zu machen, das ihm denn, wie natürlich, niemals recht ist. Darüber hat er mich neulich bei Hofe verklagt, und der Minister gab mir einen zwar sanften Verweis, aber es war doch ein Verweis, und ich stand im

Oh, I wish I were sitting at your feet in that dear, familiar little room, with the dear little children all tumbling about me. And if they became too noisy for you, I would gather them about me and calm them with a gruesome fairy tale.

The sun is setting gloriously over the snow-covered region, the storm has passed, and I—must lock myself in my cage once more.—Adieu! Is Albert with you? And how —? Heaven forgive me this question!

February 8

For a week we have been having the most horrible weather, but it's beneficial for me. For as long as I've been here there hasn't been a single beautiful day which someone has not spoiled or marred for me. Now when it rains hard and the wind blows and it freezes and thaws—ha! I think, it can't get worse in the house than it is outside or vice versa, and so it's all right. If the sun goes up in the morning and promises a fine day, I never fail to exclaim: there they have another gift from Heaven of which they can deprive each other. There is nothing of which they don't rob each other. Health, reputation, joy, rest! And mostly out of silliness, stupidity, and narrowness, and if you are to believe them, with the best of intentions. Sometimes I feel like begging them on my knees not to ravage their own intestines so brutally.

February 17

I fear my ambassador and I will not endure each other much longer. The man is utterly unbearable. His way of working and doing business is so ridiculous that I cannot refrain from contradicting him and often doing something in my own way, according to my own idea; and this, of course, he never approves of. On this score he recently complained about me at the Court, and the minister rebuked me—gently to be sure, still it was a rebuke. I was on the point of submitting my resignation when I received

Begriffe, meinen Abschied zu begehren, als ich einen Privatbrief* von ihm erhielt, einen Brief, vor dem ich niedergekniet und den hohen, edlen, weisen Sinn angebetet habe. Wie er meine allzugroße Empfindlichkeit zurechtweiset, wie er meine überspannten Ideen von Wirksamkeit, von Einfluß auf andere, von Durchdringen in Geschäften als jugendlichen guten Mut zwar ehrt, sie nicht auszurotten, nur zu mildern und dahin zu leiten sucht, wo sie ihr wahres Spiel haben, ihre kräftige Wirkung tun können. Auch bin ich auf acht Tage gestärkt und in mir selbst einig geworden. Die Ruhe der Seele ist ein herrliches Ding und die Freude an sich selbst. Lieber Freund, wenn nur das Kleinod nicht ebenso zerbrechlich wäre, als es schön und kostbar ist.

Am 20. Februar

Gott segne Euch, meine Lieben, gebe Euch alle die guten Tage, die er mir abzieht!

Ich danke Dir, Albert, daß Du mich betrogen hast: ich wartete auf Nachricht, wann Euer Hochzeitstag sein würde, und hatte mir vorgenommen, feierlichst an demselben Lottens Schattenriß von der Wand zu nehmen und ihn unter andere Papiere zu begraben. Nun seid Ihr ein Paar, und ihr Bild ist noch hier! Nun, so soll es bleiben! Und warum nicht? Ich weiß, ich bin ja auch bei Euch, bin, Dir unbeschadet, in Lottens Herzen, habe, ja ich habe den zweiten Platz darin und will und muß ihn behalten. Oh, ich würde rasend werden, wenn sie vergessen könnte — Albert, in dem Gedanken liegt eine Hölle. Albert, leb wohl! Leb wohl, Engel des Himmels! Leb wohl, Lotte!

Den 15. März

Ich habe einen Verdruß gehabt, der mich von hier wegtreiben wird. Ich knirsche mit den Zähnen! Teufel! Er ist nicht zu ersetzen, und Ihr seid doch allein schuld daran, die Ihr mich sporntet und triebt und quältet, mich in einen

---

* Man hat aus Ehrfurcht für diesen trefflichen Herrn gedachten Brief und einen andern, dessen weiter hinten erwähnt wird, dieser Sammlung entzogen, weil man nicht glaubte, eine solche Kühnheit durch den wärmsten Dank des Publikums entschuldigen zu können.

a private letter from him,* a letter which made me kneel down and worship his lofty, noble, wise spirit. How he reprimands my excessive sensitivity, how he respects my exaggerated ideas of efficiency, of influence on others, of getting things done, as the fruit of my youthful ardor, and does not seek to eradicate them, only to soften them and direct them into channels where they can really come into play and produce a strong effect. I have thus been strengthened for another week and have become at one with myself. Peace of mind is a glorious thing and so is delight with oneself. My dear friend, if only this jewel were not as fragile as it is beautiful and precious.

February 20

God bless you, my dear ones, may He give you all the good days He withholds from me.

Thanks, Albert, for having deceived me; I was waiting to hear when the wedding-day would be, and had resolved ceremoniously to take down Lotte's silhouette from the wall on that day and bury it among other papers. Now you are married and her picture is still here. Well, it shall remain so. And why not? I know that I am with you, too, and in Lotte's heart, without injury to you; I have, yes, I have second place in it, and I will and must retain it. Oh, I would go mad if she could forget—Albert, there is hell in that thought. Albert, farewell! Farewell, angel of Heaven— farewell, Lotte!

March 15

I have experienced an annoyance which will drive me from here. I am gnashing my teeth. The devil! It can't be undone and you alone are to blame, you who spurred and drove and tormented me to take a positon that didn't

* The letter in question, and another mentioned below, have been withdrawn from this collection out of respect for this excellent gentleman, because we did not believe that such an impropriety could be excused even by the warmest gratitude of the public.

Posten zu begeben, der nicht nach meinem Sinne war. Nun habe ich's! Nun habt Ihr's! Und daß Du nicht wieder sagst, meine überspannten Ideen verdürben alles, so hast Du hier, lieber Herr, eine Erzählung, plan und nett, wie ein Chronikenschreiber das aufzeichnen würde.

Der Graf von C . . . liebt mich, distinguiert mich, das ist bekannt, das habe ich Dir schon hundertmal gesagt. Nun war ich gestern bei ihm zu Tafel, eben an dem Tage, da abends die noble Gesellschaft von Herrn und Frauen bei ihm zusammenkommt, an die ich nie gedacht habe, auch mir nie aufgefallen ist, daß wir Subalternen[17] nicht hineingehören. Gut. Ich speise bei dem Grafen, und nach Tische gehn wir in dem großen Saal auf und ab, ich rede mit ihm, mit dem Obristen[18] B . . ., der dazu kommt, und so rückt die Stunde der Gesellschaft heran. Ich denke, Gott weiß, an nichts. Da tritt herein die übergnädige Dame von S . . . mit ihrem Herrn Gemahle und wohl ausgebrüteten Gänslein Tochter, mit der flachen Brust und niedlichem Schnürleibe, machen en passant[19] ihre hergebrachten hochadeligen Augen und Naslöcher, und wie mir die Nation von Herzen zuwider ist, wollte ich mich eben empfehlen und wartete nur, bis der Graf vom garstigen Gewäsche frei wäre, als meine Fräulein B . . . hereintrat. Da mir das Herz immer ein bißchen aufgeht, wenn ich sie sehe, blieb ich eben, stellte mich hinter ihren Stuhl und bemerkte erst nach einiger Zeit, daß sie mit weniger Offenheit als sonst, mit einiger Verlegenheit mit mir redete. Das fiel mir auf. Ist sie auch wie alle das Volk, dachte ich und war angestochen und wollte gehen, und doch blieb ich, weil ich sie gerne entschuldigt hätte und es nicht glaubte und noch ein gut Wort von ihr hoffte und — was Du willst. Unterdessen füllt sich die Gesellschaft. Der Baron F . . . mit der ganzen Garderobe von den Krönungszeiten Franz des Ersten[20] her, der Hofrat R . . ., hier aber in qualitate[21] Herr von R . . . genannt, mit seiner tauben Frau usw., den übel fournierten J . . . nicht zu vergessen, der die Lücken seiner altfränkischen Garderobe mit neumodischen Lappen ausflickt, das kommt zu Hauf, und ich rede mit einigen meiner Bekanntschaft, die alle sehr lakonisch sind. Ich dachte — und gab nur auf meine B . . . acht.

appeal to me. Serves me right—and you too! And so that you won't say again that my extravagant ideas have ruined everything, here is the tale, my dear sir, simple and clear, the way a chronicler would write it down.

Count von C— loves me, distinguishes me, you know that—I've told it to you a hundred times. Well, I was at his house for dinner yesterday, the very day on which the aristocratic ladies and gentlemen gather at his place in the evening. I hadn't remembered it and it never occurred to me that we subalterns don't belong there. Well, I had dinner at the Count's, and after dinner we were walking up and down in the great hall; I was talking to him, and to Colonel B—, who joined us, and so the hour of the soiree approached. Heaven knows, I was suspecting nothing when in came the supergracious Lady von S— with Her Consort and Her well-hatched little goose of a daughter with the flat chest and the dainty, laced bodice. *En passant* they turn up their highly aristocratic eyes and noses in the usual manner. I heartily detest the whole breed and was just on the point of taking my leave, only waiting till the Count was free from the dreadful chatter, when my Fräulein B— came in. As I always feel cheered when I see her, I simply stayed on, stood behind her chair and noticed only after a while that she was talking to me with less than her usual frankness, and with some embarrassment. I was perplexed at this. Is she, too, like all the others? I thought. I was nettled and wanted to go, but stayed nevertheless, because I wanted to find excuses for her, and didn't believe it, and still hoped for a kind word from her and—anything you please. Meanwhile the rest of the company arrived. There was Baron F— dressed entirely in clothes dating from the coronation of Emperor Francis I, Court Councillor R— (here called Herr von R— *in qualitate*) with his deaf wife, etc., not to forget the shabbily dressed J—, who repairs the holes in his old-fashioned wardrobe with modern patches. They came in droves. I talked with some people of my acquaintance, all of whom were very laconic. I thought about—and paid attention only to my Fräulein B—. I did not notice that

Ich merkte nicht, daß die Weiber am Ende des Saales sich in die Ohren flüsterten, daß es auf die Männer zirkulierte, daß Frau von S . . . mit dem Grafen redete (das alles hat mir Fräulein B . . . nachher erzählt[22]), bis endlich der Graf auf mich losging und mich in ein Fenster nahm. — „Sie wissen", sagte er, „ unsere wunderbaren Verhältnisse; die Gesellschaft ist unzufrieden, merke ich, Sie hier zu sehn. Ich wollte nicht um alles" — „Ihro Exzellenz", fiel ich ein, „ich bitte tausendmal um Verzeihung; ich hätte eher dran denken sollen, und ich weiß, Sie vergeben mir diese Inkonsequenz; ich wollte schon vorhin mich empfehlen, ein böser Genius hat mich zurückgehalten", setzte ich lächelnd hinzu, indem ich mich neigte. — Der Graf drückte meine Hände mit einer Empfindung, die alles sagte. Ich strich mich sacht aus der vornehmen Gesellschaft, ging, setzte mich in ein Kabriolett, und fuhr nach M . . ., dort vom Hügel die Sonne untergehen zu sehen und dabei in meinem Homer den herrlichen Gesang zu lesen, wie Ulyß[23] von dem trefflichen Schweinehirten bewirtet wird. Das war alles gut.

Des Abends komme ich zurück zu Tische, es waren noch wenige in der Gaststube; die würfelten auf einer Ecke, hatten das Tischtuch zurückgeschlagen. Da kommt der ehrliche Adelin hinein, legt seinen Hut nieder, indem er mich ansieht, tritt zu mir und sagt leise: „Du hast Verdruß gehabt?" — „Ich?" sagte ich. — „Der Graf hat dich aus der Gesellschaft gewiesen." — „Hole sie der Teufel!" sagt' ich, „mir war's lieb, daß ich in die freie Luft kam." — „Gut", sagte er, „daß Du es auf die leichte Achsel nimmst[24]. Nur verdrießt mich's, es ist schon überall herum." — Da fing mich das Ding erst an zu wurmen. Alle, die zu Tische kamen und mich ansahen, dachte ich, die sehen dich darum an! Das gab böses Blut.

Und da man nun heute gar, wo ich hintrete, mich bedauert, da ich höre, daß meine Neider nun triumphieren und sagen: da sähe man's, wo es mit den Übermütigen hinausginge, die sich ihres bißchen Kopfs überhöben und glaubten, sich darum über alle Verhältnisse hinaussetzen zu dürfen, und was des Hundegeschwätzes[25] mehr ist — da möchte man sich ein Messer ins Herz bohren; denn man

the women were whispering to each other at the end of the hall, that the whispering reached the men, that Frau von S— was talking to the Count (all this I learned later from Fräul 'n B—) until finally the Count came up to me and took me over to a window. "You know about our strange ways," he said, "the company, I notice, is not happy about seeing you here. I would not wish, for anything in the world . . ." "I beg your pardon a thousand times, Your Excellency," I interrupted, "I should have thought of it sooner, and I know you will forgive me my stupidity. I meant to leave some time ago, but an evil genius kept me here," I added with a smile, and bowed to him.—The Count pressed my hands with a depth of feeling which spoke eloquently. I quietly slipped away from the noble company, took my seat in a cabriolet and drove to M— to watch the sun set there from the hilltop, and to read that glorious canto in Homer in which Odysseus is the guest of the excellent swineherd. So far, so good.

I returned for dinner in the evening and there were only a few people left in the dining room of the inn; they had turned back the table cloth and were playing dice on a corner of the table. Then good Adelin came in, put down his hat, looked at me, came over and said quietly: "You've had an unpleasant experience?" "I?" I said. "The Count asked you to leave the company." "The devil take them!" I said, "I was glad to get out into the fresh air."—"Good," he said, "that you take the matter lightly; but I'm annoyed, the story has already got round everywhere."—It was only then that the thing began to gnaw at me. Anyone who came to dinner and looked at me made me think: he's looking at you because of that. That poisoned my blood.

And today, wherever I appear, people pity me. I hear my enemies are triumphant now and say: you see where the arrogant end up, those who feel superior because of their bit of intelligence and think it entitles them to disregard all rules of etiquette—and all the rest of this rotten gossip. You feel like plunging a knife into your heart; for you may say what you like about independence, I'd like

159

rede von Selbständigkeit, was man will, den will ich sehen, der dulden kann, daß Schurken über ihn reden, wenn sie einen Vorteil über ihn haben; wenn ihr Geschwätze leer ist, ach, da kann man sie leicht lassen.

Am 16. März

Es hetzt mich alles. Heute treffe ich die Fräulein B . . . in der Allee, ich konnte mich nicht enthalten, sie anzureden und ihr, sobald wir etwas entfernt von der Gesellschaft waren, meine Empfindlichkeit über ihr neuliches Betragen zu zeigen. — „O Werther", sagte sie mit einem innigen Tone, „konnten Sie meine Verwirrung so auslegen, da Sie mein Herz kennen? Was ich gelitten habe um Ihretwillen, von dem Augenblicke an, da ich in den Saal trat! Ich sah alles voraus, hundertmal saß mir's auf der Zunge, es Ihnen zu sagen. Ich wußte, daß die von S . . . und T . . . mit ihren Männern eher aufbrechen würden, als in Ihrer Gesellschaft zu bleiben; ich wußte, daß der Graf es mit ihnen nicht verderben darf — und jetzt der Lärm!" — „Wie, Fräulein?" sagte ich, und verbarg meinen Schrecken; denn alles, was Adelin mir ehegestern[26] gesagt hatte, lief mir wie siedend Wasser durch die Adern in diesem Augenblicke. — „Was hat mich es schon gekostet!" sagte das süße Geschöpf, indem ihr die Tränen in den Augen standen. — Ich war nicht Herr mehr von mir selbst, war im Begriffe, mich ihr zu Füßen zu werfen. — „Erklären Sie sich", rief ich. — Die Tränen liefen ihr die Wangen herunter. Ich war außer mir. Sie trocknete sie ab, ohne sie verbergen zu wollen. — „Meine Tante kennen Sie", fing sie an; „sie war gegenwärtig und hat, oh, mit was für Augen hat sie das angesehen! Werther, ich habe gestern nacht[27] ausgestanden und heute früh eine Predgt über meinen Umgang mit Ihnen, und ich habe müssen zuhören Sie herabsetzen, erniedrigen, und konnte und durfte Sie nur halb verteidigen."

Jedes Wort, das sie sprach, ging mir wie ein Schwert durchs Herz. Sie fühlte nicht, welche Barmherzigkeit es gewesen wäre, mir das alles zu verschweigen; und nun fügte sie noch dazu, was weiter würde geträtscht[28] werden,

to see the man who can bear to have rogues talk about him when they have an advantage over him; if their prattle is empty, well, then you can easily disregard them.

Everything is against me. Today I met Fräulein B— on the avenue. I could not resist talking to her and, as soon as we were a little distance from her companions, showing her my vexation with her recent behavior.—"Oh Werther," she said in a passionate tone, "could you interpret my confusion this way, when you know my heart? What I suffered for your sake, from the moment I stepped into the hall! I saw it all in advance, a hundred times it was on the tip of my tongue to tell you. I knew that the von S— woman and T— with their husbands would sooner leave than remain in your company. I knew that the Count must not break with them—and now all this row!"— "What row, dear lady?" I said, concealing my alarm; for everything Adelin had told me the day before yesterday rushed through my veins at this moment like boiling water.—"What grief it has already caused me," the sweet creature said, with tears in her eyes.—I was not in control of my emotions; I was on the point of throwing myself at her feet.—"Explain yourself," I cried.—The tears ran down her cheeks. I was beside myself. She dried them, without trying to conceal them.—"You know my aunt," she began. "She was there and saw it—oh, with what eyes! Werther, what I endured last night, and this morning a sermon about my association with you, and I had to hear you disparaged and degraded, and I could and dared only half defend you."

Every word she uttered pierced my heart like a sword. She did not feel what an act of mercy it would have been to keep all this from me, and she even added what further gossip would be spread and what kind of people would

was eine Art Menschen darüber triumphieren würde. Wie man sich nunmehr über die Strafe meines Übermuts und meiner Geringschätzung anderer, die sie mir schon lange vorwerfen, kitzeln und freuen würde. Das alles, Wilhelm, von ihr zu hören, mit der Stimme der wahrsten Teilnehmung — ich war zerstört und bin noch wütend in mir. Ich wollte, daß sich einer unterstünde, mir es vorzuwerfen, daß ich ihm den Degen durch den Leib stoßen könnte; wenn ich Blut sähe, würde mir es besser werden. Ach, ich habe hundertmal ein Messer ergriffen, um diesem gedrängten Herzen Luft zu machen. Man erzählt von einer edlen Art Pferde, die, wenn sie schrecklich erhitzt und aufgejagt sind, sich selbst aus Instinkt eine Ader aufbeißen, um sich zum Atem zu helfen. So ist mir's oft, ich möchte mir eine Ader öffnen, die mir die ewige Freiheit schaffte.

Am 24. März

Ich habe meine Entlassung vom Hofe verlangt und werde sie, hoffe ich, erhalten, und Ihr werdet mir verzeihen, daß ich nicht erst Erlaubnis dazu bei Euch geholt habe. Ich mußte nun einmal[29] fort, und was Ihr zu sagen hattet, um mir das Bleiben einzureden, weiß ich alles, und also — Bringe das meiner Mutter in einem Säftchen[30] bei, ich kann mir selbst nicht helfen, und sie mag sich gefallen lassen, wenn ich ihr auch nicht helfen kann. Freilich muß es ihr wehe tun. Den schönen Lauf, den ihr Sohn gerade zum Geheimenrat[31] und Gesandten ansetzte, so auf einmal Halte[32] zu sehen und rückwärts mit dem Tierchen in den Stall! Macht nun daraus was Ihr wollt, und kombiniert die möglichen Fälle, unter denen ich hätte bleiben können und sollen; genug, ich gehe, und damit Ihr wißt, wo ich hinkomme, so ist hier der Fürst * *, der vielen Geschmack an meiner Gesellschaft findet; der hat mich gebeten, da er von meiner Absicht hörte, mit ihm auf seine Güter zu gehen und den schönen Frühling da zuzubringen. Ich soll ganz mir selbst gelassen sein, hat er mir versprochen, und da wir uns zusammen bis auf einen gewissen Punkt verstehn, so will ich es denn auf gut Glück[33] wagen und mit ihm gehen.

feel triumphant about it. How they would now gloat and delight in the punishment of my arrogance and my contempt for others, for which I have long been reproached. To hear all this from her, Wilhelm, in a tone of genuine compassion—I was devastated and I am still in an inner rage. I wish someone would dare to reproach me, so that I could run my sword through his body; at the sight of blood I would feel better. Oh, I've seized a knife a hundred times, to ease this oppressed heart of mine. I have heard of a noble race of horses that, when they are terribly overheated and excited, instinctively bite into a vein to breathe more freely. So it is often with me, I'd like to open a vein to give myself eternal freedom.

March 24

I have asked for my release from the Court and will, I hope, receive it, and you will both pardon me for not first obtaining permission from you. I simply had to get away; I know everything you had to say by way of encouraging me to stay and so—Break it gently to mother. I can't help myself and she will have to make the best of the fact that I can't help her either. Of course it's bound to hurt her. To see the beautiful beginning her son had just made toward becoming a privy councillor and ambassador suddenly halted, and back to the stable with the beast! Make of it what you will and calculate the possible situations in which I could and should have stayed on; enough, I'm going, and so that you may know where I'll be, let me tell you that Prince — is here, who finds much pleasure in my company; when he heard of my intention, he asked me to accompany him to his estates and spend the lovely spring there. He promised that I would be left to myself, and since we understand each other up to a certain point, I'll take a chance on it and go with him.

Zur Nachricht

Danke für Deine beiden Briefe. Ich antwortete nicht, weil ich dieses Blatt liegen ließ, bis mein Abschied vom Hofe da wäre; ich fürchtete, meine Mutter möchte sich an den Minister wenden und mir mein Vorhaben erschweren. Nun aber ist es geschehen, mein Abschied ist da. Ich mag Euch nicht sagen, wie ungern man mir ihn gegeben hat, und was mir der Minister schreibt: Ihr würdet in neue Lamentationen ausbrechen. Der Erbprinz hat mir zum Abschiede fünfundzwanzig Dukaten geschickt, mit einem Wort, das mich bis zu Tränen gerührt hat; also brauche ich von der Mutter das Geld nicht, um das ich neulich schrieb.

Am 5. Mai

Morgen gehe ich von hier ab, und weil mein Geburtsort nur sechs Meilen vom Wege liegt, so will ich den auch wieder sehen, will mich der alten, glücklich verträumten Tage erinnern. Zu eben dem Tore will ich hineingehn, aus dem meine Mutter mit mir herausfuhr, als sie nach dem Tode meines Vaters den lieben, vertraulichen Ort verließ, um sich in ihre unerträgliche Stadt einzusperren. Adieu, Wilhelm, Du sollst von meinem Zuge hören.

Am 9. Mai

Ich habe die Wallfahrt nach meiner Heimat mit aller Andacht eines Pilgrims[34] vollendet, und manche unerwarteten Gefühle haben mich ergriffen. An der großen Linde, die eine Viertelstunde vor der Stadt nach S . . . zu steht, ließ ich halten, stieg aus und hieß den Postillon fortfahren, um zu Fuße jede Erinnerung ganz neu, lebhaft, nach meinem Herzen zu kosten. Da stand ich nun unter der Linde, die ehedem, als Knabe, das Ziel und die Grenze meiner Spaziergänge gewesen. Wie anders! Damals sehnte ich mich in glücklicher Unwissenheit hinaus in die unbe-

April 19

Thanks for your two letters. I did not reply because I left this sheet blank until my release from the Court was here; I feared my mother might write the minister and make my plan more difficult to realize. But now it's happened, my release is here. I don't like to tell you how reluctantly they gave it to me and what the minister writes me—you would break out into new lamentations. The Prince sent me twenty-five ducats as a parting gift, with a note that moved me to tears; so I don't need the money from mother about which I recently wrote.

May 5

I am leaving here tomorrow, and because my birthplace is only six miles off the direct road, I want to see it again, and recall the old, happy, dreamy days. I will enter it at the very gate by which my mother drove out with me when she left the dear, intimate spot after the death of my father, to imprison herself in her unbearable city. Adieu, Wilhelm, you shall hear about my journey.

May 9

I have completed the pilgrimage to my native town with all the devotion of a pilgrim, and many unexpected emotions possessed me. I had the coach stop at the big linden tree which stands about a quarter of an hour's distance from the town in the direction of S—, got out and told the postilion to go on so that I might savor on foot every memory as something quite new, vivid, to my heart's content. There I now stood under the linden, which once, when I was a boy, had been the goal and limit of my walks. How different! Then, in the bliss of ignorance, I yearned

kannte Welt, wo ich für mein Herz so viele Nahrung, so vielen Genuß hoffte, meinen strebenden, sehnenden Busen auszufüllen und zu befriedigen. Jetzt komme ich zurück aus der weiten Welt — o mein Freund, mit wie viel fehlgeschlagenen Hoffnungen, mit wie viel zerstörten Plänen! — Ich sah das Gebirge vor mir liegen, das so tausendmal der Gegenstand meiner Wünsche gewesen war. Stundenlang konnt' ich hier sitzen und mich hinübersehnen, mit inniger Seele mich in den Wäldern, den Tälern verlieren, die sich meinen Augen so freundlich-dämmernd darstellten; und wenn ich dann um die bestimmte Zeit wieder zurück mußte, mit welchem Widerwillen verließ ich nicht den lieben Platz! — Ich kam der Stadt näher, alle die alten, bekannten Gartenhäuschen wurden von mir gegrüßt, die neuen waren mir zuwider, so auch alle Veränderungen, die man sonst vorgenommen hatte. Ich trat zum Tor hinein, und fand mich doch gleich und ganz wieder. Lieber, ich mag nicht ins Detail gehn; so reizend, als es mir war, so einförmig würde es in der Erzählung werden. Ich hatte beschlossen, auf dem Markte zu wohnen, gleich neben unserem alten Hause. Im Hingehen bemerkte ich, daß die Schulstube, wo ein ehrliches altes Weib unsere Kindheit zusammengepfercht hatte, in einen Kramladen verwandelt war. Ich erinnerte mich der Unruhe, der Tränen, der Dumpfheit des Sinnes, der Herzensangst, die ich in dem Loche ausgestanden hatte. — Ich tat keinen Schritt, der nicht merkwürdig war. Ein Pilger im heiligen Lande trifft nicht so viel Stätten religiöser Erinnerungen an, und seine Seele ist schwerlich so voll heiliger Bewegung. — Noch eins für tausend. Ich ging den Fluß hinab, bis an einen gewissen Hof; das war sonst auch mein Weg, und die Plätzchen, wo wir Knaben uns übten, die meisten Sprünge der flachen Steine im Wasser hervorzubringen. Ich erinnerte mich so lebhaft, wenn ich manchmal stand und dem Wasser nachsah, mit wie wunderbaren Ahnungen ich es vorfolgte, wie abenteuerlich ich mir die Gegenden vorstellte, wo es nun hinflösse, und wie ich da so bald Grenzen meiner Vorstellungskraft fand; und doch mußte das weitergehen, immer weiter, bis ich mich ganz in dem Anschauen einer unsichtbaren Ferne verlor. — Sieh, mein Lieber, so be-

to get out into the unfamiliar world where I hoped to find so much nourishment, so much enjoyment, for my heart to fulfill my aspirations and to satisfy my yearning. Now I am returning from the big world—oh my friend, with how many frustrated hopes, with how many ruined plans!—Stretched out before me I saw the mountains which had been the object of my wishes a thousand times. I could sit here for hours, yearning to be beyond them, to lose myself with all my soul in the forests and valleys that stood before my eyes in such a friendly half light; and when I had to return at the appointed time, how unwillingly I left the beloved spot!—I approached the city and greeted all the old, familiar summerhouses; the new ones displeased me, as did all the other changes that had taken place. I entered the gate and at once felt at home again. Dear friend, I don't want to go into details; it would become as boring in the narration as it was charming to me in reality. I had resolved to live on the market place, right next to our old house. On my way there I noticed that the schoolhouse in which a good old woman had cooped up our childhood had been converted into a grocery store. I remembered the restlessness, the tears, the dullness of mind, the anguish of heart which I had endured in that hole. I could not take a single step that was not remarkable for me. A pilgrim in the Holy Land does not encounter so many scenes of religious memories, and his soul is scarcely so full of sacred emotion.—One more memory to stand for a thousand. I followed the stream to a certain farm; I used to walk this road, and I found the places where we boys used to practice skipping flat stones on the water. I recalled so vividly how I sometimes stood watching the flowing water, with what wonderful hopes I followed it with my eyes, how exciting I pictured the regions to which it was now flowing; and how I soon came to the limits of my imaginative powers; and yet the water must go on, on and on, and I lost myself completely in the contemplation of an invisible distance.—See, my dear friend, the glorious patriarchs were just so limited, and happy; so childlike was their feeling and their poetry! When Odysseus speaks of the boundless sea and the infinite earth, it is so true, so human, so sincere,

167

schränkt und so glücklich waren die herrlichen Altväter, so kindlich ihr Gefühl, ihre Dichtung! Wenn Ulyß von dem ungemess'nen Meer und von der unendlichen Erde spricht, das ist so wahr, menschlich, innig, eng und geheimnisvoll. Was hilft mir's, daß ich jetzt mit jedem Schulknaben nachsagen kann, daß sie rund sei? Der Mensch braucht nur wenige Erdschollen, um drauf zu genießen, weniger, um drunter zu ruhen.

Nun bin ich hier, auf dem fürstlichen Jagdschloß. Es läßt sich[35] noch ganz wohl mit dem Herrn leben, er ist wahr und einfach. Wunderliche Menschen sind um ihn herum, die ich gar nicht begreife. Sie scheinen keine Schelme und haben doch auch nicht das Ansehen von ehrlichen Leuten. Manchmal kommen sie mir ehrlich vor, und ich kann ihnen doch nicht trauen. Was mir noch leid tut, ist, daß er oft von Sachen redet, die er nur gehört und gelesen hat, und zwar aus eben dem Gesichtspunkte, wie sie ihm der andere vorstellen mochte.

Auch schätzt er meinen Verstand und meine Talente mehr als dies Herz, das doch mein einziger Stolz ist, das ganz allein die Quelle von allem ist, aller Kraft, aller Seligkeit und alles Elendes. Ach, was ich weiß, kann jeder wissen — mein Herz habe ich allein.

Am 25. Mai

Ich hatte etwas im Kopfe, davon[36] ich Euch nichts sagen wollte, bis es ausgeführt wäre: jetzt, da nichts draus wird, ist es ebensogut. Ich wollte in den Krieg; das hat mir lange am Herzen gelegen. Vornehmlich darum bin ich dem Fürsten hierher gefolgt, der General in * * *schen Diensten ist. Auf einem Spaziergang entdeckte ich ihm mein Vorhaben; er widerriet mir es, und es müßte bei mir mehr Leidenschaft als Grille gewesen sein, wenn ich seinen Gründen nicht hätte Gehör geben wollen.

Am 11. Junius

Sage, was Du willst, ich kann nicht länger bleiben. Was soll ich hier? Die Zeit wird mir lang. Der Fürst hält[37]

so naïve, and so mysterious. What good is it to me that I can repeat with every schoolboy that it is round? Man needs only a few clods of earth to enjoy life on, and fewer still to rest beneath.

Now I am here in the Prince's hunting lodge. It is quite easy to live with the gentleman; he is genuine and simple. Strange people surround him, people I do not understand at all. They don't appear to be rogues and yet they haven't the look of honest men. Sometimes they appear to me to be honest and yet I can't trust them. One thing I regret is that he often speaks of things which he has only heard or read, and moreover from the point of view from which the other chose to present them.

Besides, he values my intelligence and talents more than my heart, which is really my sole source of pride, and which alone is the source of everything, of all my strength, all my bliss, and all my misery. Ah, what I know, everyone can know—my heart is mine alone.

May 25

I had something in mind that I did not want to mention until it was executed; now that it has come to nothing, it's just as well. I wanted to enter the army; I have long cherished the idea. This is the principal reason for my following the Prince to this place, for he is a general in the service of —. On one of our walks I revealed my plan to him; he advised me against it, and if I had not heeded his reasoning it would have indicated passion for the idea rather than the whim it was.

June 11

Say what you will, I can't stay any longer. What am I to do here? Time is hanging heavy on my hands. The Prince

mich, so gut man nur kann, und doch bin ich nicht in meiner Lage[38]. Wir haben im Grunde nichts gemein miteinander. Er ist ein Mann von Verstande, aber von ganz gemeinem Verstande; sein Umgang unterhält mich nicht mehr, als wenn ich ein wohlgeschriebenes Buch lese. Noch acht Tage bleibe ich, und dann ziehe ich wieder in der Irre herum. Das Beste, was ich hier getan habe, ist mein Zeichnen. Der Fürst fühlt in der Kunst und würde noch stärker fühlen, wenn er nicht durch das garstige wissenschaftliche Wesen[39] und durch die gewöhnliche Terminologie eingeschränkt wäre. Manchmal knirsche ich mit den Zähnen, wenn ich ihn mit warmer Imagination an Natur und Kunst herumführe und er es auf einmal recht gut zu machen denkt, wenn er mit einem gestempelten[40] Kunstworte dreinstolpert.

Am 16. Junius

Ja, wohl bin ich nur ein Wandrer, ein Waller auf der Erde! Seid Ihr denn mehr?

Am 18. Junius

Wo ich hin will? Das laß Dir im Vertrauen eröffnen. Vierzehn Tage muß ich doch noch hier bleiben, und dann habe ich mir weis gemacht[41], daß ich die Bergwerke im * * *schen besuchen wollte; ist aber im Grunde nichts dran, ich will nur Lotte wieder näher, das ist alles. Und ich lache über mein eignes Herz — und tu' ihm seinen Willen.

Am 29. Julius

Nein, es ist gut! Es ist alles gut! — Ich — ihr Mann! O Gott, der du mich machtest, wenn du mir diese Seligkeit bereitet hättest, mein ganzes Leben sollte ein anhaltendes Gebet sein. Ich will nicht rechten, und verzeihe mir diese Tränen, verzeihe mir meine vergeblichen Wünsche! — Sie meine Frau! Wenn ich das liebste Geschöpf unter der Sonne in meine Arme geschlossen hätte — Es geht mir ein

is treating me as well as anyone could, and yet I am not comfortable. Basically we have nothing in common. He is a man of intelligence, but of very common intelligence; my association with him is no more entertaining than if I were to read a well-written book. I will stay another week and then I'll set out on my wanderings again. The best thing I've done here is my sketching. The Prince has a feeling for art and would be even more sensitive if he were not limited by a horrid scientific concern and traditional terminology. Sometimes I gnash my teeth when I lead him about in nature and art with my warm imagination and he suddenly thinks he's helping matters by stumbling in with some hackneyed technical term.

June 16

I am indeed but a wanderer, a pilgrim on earth. But are you anything more?

June 18

Where do I want to go? Let me tell you in confidence. I must stay here another fortnight, and then I've persuaded myself that I want to visit the mines at —. But there's really no truth in it, I only want to be closer to Lotte, that's all. I laugh at my own heart—and do what it wants.

July 29

No, it's all right, everything is well. I—her husband! O God, Who has made me, if Thou hadst prepared this happiness for me, my whole life would be a perpetual prayer. I will not quarrel with you, and forgive me these tears, forgive me my vain desires. She—my wife! If I had held her, the dearest creature under the sun, in my arms—A shudder goes through my whole body, Wilhelm, when

171

Schauder durch den ganzen Körper, Wilhelm, wenn Albert sie um den schlanken Leib faßt.

Und, darf ich es sagen? Warum nicht, Wilhelm? Sie wäre mit mir glücklicher geworden als mit ihm! Oh, er ist nicht der Mensch, die Wünsche dieses Herzens alle zu füllen. Ein gewisser Mangel an Fühlbarkeit, ein Mangel — nimm es, wie Du willst, daß sein Herz nicht sympathetisch schlägt bei — oh! — bei der Stelle eines lieben Buches, wo mein Herz und Lottens in Einem zusammentreffen; in hundert andern Vorfällen, wenn es kommt, daß unsere Empfindungen über eine Handlung eines Dritten laut werden. Lieber Wilhelm! — Zwar er liebt sie von ganzer Seele, und so eine Liebe, was verdient die nicht! —

Ein unerträglicher Mensch hat mich unterbrochen. Meine Tränen sind getrocknet. Ich bin zerstreut. Adieu, Lieber!

Am 4. August

Es geht mir nicht allein so. Alle Menschen werden in ihren Hoffnungen getäuscht, in ihren Erwartungen betrogen. Ich besuchte mein gutes Weib unter der Linde. Der älteste Junge lief mir entgegen, sein Freudengeschrei führte die Mutter herbei, die sehr niedergeschlagen aussah. Ihr erstes Wort war: „Guter Herr, ach mein Hans ist mir gestorben!" — Es war der jüngste ihrer Knaben. Ich war stille. — „Und mein Mann", sagte sie, „ist aus der Schweiz zurück und hat nichts mitgebracht, und ohne gute Leute hätte er sich herausbetteln müssen, er hatte das Fieber unterwegs gekriegt." — Ich konnte ihr nichts sagen und schenkte dem Kleinen was, sie bat mich, einige Äpfel anzunehmen, das[42] ich tat und den Ort des traurigen Andenkens verließ.

Am 21. August

Wie man eine Hand umwendet, ist es anders mit mir. Manchmal will wohl ein freudiger Blick des Lebens wieder aufdämmern, ach! nur für einen Augenblick! — Wenn ich mich so in Träumen verliere, kann ich mich des Gedankens

Albert puts his arms about her slender body.

And dare I say it? Why not, Wilhelm? She would have been happier with me than with him. Oh, he's not the man to fulfill all the wishes of that heart. A certain lack of sensibility, a lack—take it as you wish; that his heart does not beat in sympathy over—oh!—over a passage in a favorite book, when my heart and Lotte's are in harmony; in a hundred other instances when it happens that our emotions about the behavior of a third person are revealed. Dear Wilhelm!—Of course he loves her with all his heart, and such a love deserves everything.—

An unbearable person has interrupted me. My tears are dry. I am distracted. Adieu, dear friend.

August 4

I am not the only one. All people are disappointed in their hopes, deceived in their expectations. I visited my good woman under the linden tree. Her oldest boy ran out to meet me; his cry of joy brought his mother out; she looked very dejected. Her first words were: "My dear sir, alas, my Hans has died." He was the youngest of her boys. I was silent. "And my husband," she said, "returned from Switzerland, and brought nothing back with him, and if it weren't for some good people he would have had to beg his way home. He had contracted a fever on the way."—I could say nothing to her and gave the little boy something; she asked me to accept a few apples, which I did, and I left that place of sad memory.

August 21

With a turn of the hand, things have changed for me. Sometimes a joyful spark of life is about to shine for me again, but alas! only for a moment. When I lose myself in dreams, I cannot keep out the thought: suppose Albert

nicht erwehren: wie, wenn Albert stürbe? Du würdest! Ja, sie würde — und dann laufe ich dem Hirngespinste nach, bis es mich an Abgründe führt, vor denen ich zurückbebe.

Wenn ich zum Tor hinausgehe, den Weg, den ich zum erstenmal fuhr, Lotten zum Tanze zu holen, wie war das so ganz anders! Alles, alles ist vorübergegangen! Kein Wink der vorigen Welt, kein Pulsschlag meines damaligen Gefühles. Mir ist es, wie es einem Geiste sein müßte, der in das ausgebrannte zerstörte Schloß zurückkehrte, das er als blühender Fürst einst gebaut und, mit allen Gaben der Herrlichkeit ausgestattet, sterbend seinem geliebten Sohne hoffnungsvoll hinterlassen hätte.

Am 3. September

Ich begreife manchmal nicht, wie sie ein anderer lieb haben kann, lieb haben darf, da ich sie so ganz allein, so innig, so voll liebe, nichts anders kenne, noch weiß, noch habe als sie!

Am 4. September

Ja, es ist so. Wie die Natur sich zum Herbste neigt, wird es Herbst in mir und um mich her. Meine Blätter werden gelb, und schon sind die Blätter der benachbarten Bäume abgefallen. Hab' ich Dir nicht einmal von einem Bauerburschen geschrieben, gleich da ich herkam? Jetzt erkundigte ich mich wieder nach ihm in Wahlheim; es hieß, er sei aus dem Dienste gejagt worden, und niemand wollte was weiter von ihm wissen. Gestern traf ich ihn von ungefähr auf dem Wege nach einem andern Dorfe, ich redete ihn an, und er erzählte mir seine Geschichte, die mich doppelt und dreifach gerührt hat, wie Du leicht begreifen wirst, wenn ich Dir sie wieder erzähle. Doch wozu das alles? Warum behalt' ich nicht für mich, was mich ängstigt und kränkt[43]? Warum betrüb' ich noch Dich? Warum geb' ich Dir immer Gelegenheit, mich zu bedauern und mich zu schelten? Sei's denn, auch das mag zu meinem Schicksal gehören!

Mit einer stillen Traurigkeit, in der ich ein wenig scheues Wesen zu bemerken schien, antwortete der Mensch

were to die? You would, yes, she would—and then I chase this chimera until it leads me to abysses from which I shrink back.

When I walk out of the gate, on the road on which I traveled the first time to fetch Lotte for the dance; how different it all was then. Everything, everything has passed. No trace of that former world, not a throb of the feelings I had then. I feel as a ghost would have to feel if he returned to the burnt-out, ruined castle he had once built as a flourishing prince, equipped with all the gifts of splendor, leaving it hopefully, at his death, to his beloved son.

September 3

Sometimes I cannot understand how another man can love her, dare love her, since I love her so wholly, so fervently, so fully, and recognize nothing and know nothing, and have nothing but her!

September 4

Yes, it is so. As nature declines into autumn, so autumn begins within me and about me. My leaves are turning yellow and the leaves of neighboring trees have already fallen. Didn't I write you once about a peasant boy soon after I got here? I've made inquiries about him again at Wahlheim; they told me he had been chased from his job and no one wanted to have anything to do with him. Yesterday I met him by chance on the road to another village; I spoke to him and he told me his story, which has moved me doubly and triply, as you will easily understand when I tell it to you. But why all this? Why don't I keep to myself what causes me anxiety and grief? Why do I sadden you as well? And why do I always give you opportunities for pitying and blaming me? Let us say, this too is perhaps part of my fate.

At first the lad answered my questions with a quiet sadness, in which I seemed to notice a bit of shyness; but

mir erst auf meine Fragen; aber gar bald offner, als wenn er sich und mich auf einmal wieder erkennte, gestand er mir seine Fehler, klagte er mir sein Unglück. Könnt' ich Dir, mein Freund, jedes seiner Worte vor Gericht stellen! Er bekannte, ja er erzählte mit einer Art von Genuß und Glück der Wiedererinnerung, daß die Leidenschaft zu seiner Hausfrau sich in ihm tagtäglich vermehrt, daß er zuletzt nicht gewußt habe was er tue, nicht, wie er sich ausdrückte, wo er mit dem Kopfe hingesollt. Er habe weder essen noch trinken noch schlafen können, es habe ihm an der Kehle gestockt, er habe getan, was er nicht tun sollen, was ihm aufgetragen worden, hab' er vergessen; er sei als wie von einem bösen Geist verfolgt gewesen, bis er eines Tags, als er sie in einer obern Kammer gewußt, ihr nachgegangen, ja vielmehr ihr nachgezogen worden sei; da sie seinen Bitten kein Gehör gegeben, hab' er sich ihrer mit Gewalt bemächtigen wollen, er wisse nicht, wie ihm geschehen sei, und nehme Gott zum Zeugen, daß seine Absichten gegen sie immer redlich gewesen, und daß er nichts sehnlicher gewünscht, als daß sie ihn heiraten, daß sie mit ihm ihr Leben zubringen möchte. Da er eine Zeitlang geredet hatte, fing er an zu stocken wie einer, der noch etwas zu sagen hat und sich es nicht herauszusagen getraut; endlich gestand er mir auch mit Schüchternheit, was sie ihm für kleine Vertraulichkeiten erlaubt, und welche Nähe sie ihm vergönnet. Er brach zwei-, dreimal ab und wiederholte die lebhaftesten Protestationen, daß er das nicht sage, um sie schlecht zu machen, wie er sich ausdrückte, daß er sie liebe und schätze wie vorher, daß so etwas nicht über seinen Mund gekommen sei, und daß er es mir nur sage, um mich zu überzeugen, daß er kein ganz verkehrter und unsinniger Mensch sei. — Und hier, mein Bester, fang' ich mein altes Lied wieder an, das ich ewig anstimmen werde: könnt' ich Dir den Menschen vorstellen, wie er vor mir stand, wie er noch vor mir steht! Könnt' ich Dir alles recht sagen, damit Du fühltest, wie ich an seinem Schicksale teilnehme, teilnehmen muß! Doch genug, da Du auch mein Schicksal kennst, auch mich kennst, so weißt Du nur zu wohl, was mich zu allen Unglücklichen, was mich besonders zu diesem Unglücklichen hinzieht.

very soon he spoke more frankly, as if he suddenly recognized himself and me again; he admitted his mistakes to me, and lamented his misfortune. If only I could, my friend, put every one of his words to your judgment! He confessed, indeed he told me with a sort of delight and happiness in remembering, that a passion for his employer had grown in him daily, until at last he didn't know what he was doing, nor, as he expressed it, where to turn his head. He had not been able to eat, drink, or sleep; he had had a lump in his throat, had done what he should not have done, had forgotten the orders that were given him; it was as if he had been pursued by an evil spirit, until one day, when he knew that she was in an upstairs room, he had followed her, or rather been drawn after her. When she refused to grant his wishes, he tried to take her by force. He did not know what had come over him, and took God to witness that his intentions toward her had always been honorable, and that he had wished for nothing more fervently than that she should marry him and spend her life with him. After he had talked a while he began to hesitate, like someone who has something more to say but does not dare utter it. Finally he confessed to me shyly the little intimacies she had permitted him and how much familiarity she had granted him. He broke off two or three times and repeated the most vehement protestations that he was not saying this to put her in a bad light, as he put it, that he loved and esteemed her as before, that he would not have dared to say such things, but was telling it to me only to convince me that he was not totally depraved and senseless.—And at this point, my dear friend, I must begin the old song again, which I shall always sing. If I could only put the man before you as he stood before me, as he still stands before me. If I could express everything precisely, so that you might feel how much I sympathize, must sympathize, with his fate. But enough, since you know my fate too, and know me too, you know only too well what it is that draws me to all unhappy people, and especially to this unhappy man.

Da ich das Blatt wieder durchlese, seh' ich, daß ich das Ende der Geschichte zu erzählen vergessen habe, das sich aber leicht hinzudenken läßt. Sie erwehrte sich sein[44]; ihr Bruder kam dazu, der ihn schon lange gehaßt, der ihn schon lange aus dem Hause gewünscht hatte, weil er fürchtet, durch eine neue Heirat der Schwester werde seinen Kindern die Erbschaft entgehn, die ihnen jetzt, da sie kinderlos ist, schöne Hoffnungen gibt; dieser habe ihn gleich zum Hause hinausgestoßen und einen solchen Lärm von der Sache gemacht, daß die Frau, auch selbst wenn sie gewollt, ihn nicht wieder hätte aufnehmen können. Jetzt habe sie wieder einen andern Knecht genommen; auch über den, sage man, sei sie mit dem Bruder zerfallen, und man behaupte für gewiß, sie werde ihn heiraten; aber er sei fest entschlossen, das nicht zu erleben.

Was ich Dir erzähle, ist nicht übertrieben, nichts verzärtelt, ja ich darf wohl sagen, schwach, schwach hab' ich's erzählt, und vergröbert hab' ich's, indem ich's mit unsern hergebrachten sittlichen Worten vorgetragen habe.

Diese Liebe, diese Treue, diese Leidenschaft ist also keine dichterische Erfindung. Sie lebt, sie ist in ihrer größten Reinheit unter der Klasse von Menschen, die wir ungebildet, die wir roh nennen. Wir Gebildeten — zu nichts Verbildeten[45]! Lies die Geschichte mit Andacht, ich bitte Dich. Ich bin heute still, indem ich das hinschreibe; Du siehst an meiner Hand, daß ich nicht so strudele und sudele wie sonst. Lies, mein Geliebter, und denke dabei, daß es auch die Geschichte Deines Freundes ist. Ja, so ist mir's gegangen, so wird mir's gehn, und ich bin nicht halb so brav, nicht halb so entschlossen als der arme Unglückliche, mit dem ich mich zu vergleichen mich fast nicht getraue.

Am 5. September

Sie hatte ein Zettelchen an ihren Mann aufs Land geschrieben, wo er sich Geschäfte wegen aufhielt. Es fing an: „Bester, Liebster, komme, sobald Du kannst, ich erwarte Dich mit tausend Freuden." — Ein Freund, der hereinkam, brachte Nachricht, daß er wegen gewisser Umstände so

As I read this page through again, I see that I forgot to tell the end of the story; but you can easily imagine it. She resisted him; her brother came along, who had long hated him, and had wanted him out of the house for a long time because he feared that if his sister married again his own children would lose the inheritance which raises fine prospects for them, as she is childless. The brother had driven him out of the house at once and made such a fuss about the matter that the woman could not have taken him back even if she had wanted to. Now she had hired another man; it is said that she has quarreled with her brother about this one too, and it is said that she is certain to marry him; but he is firmly resolved not to live to see that day.

What I am telling you is not exaggerated, not sentimentalized at all; indeed, I may say that I have told it feebly, very feebly, and I have coarsened it by putting it in our traditional moral terms.

This love, this faithfulness, this passion is, then, not an invention of poets. It exists, and it is purest in that class of people whom we call uncultivated, rude—we who are formed by culture and deformed into nobodies! Please read this story with reverence. I am calm today as I write this down; you see from my handwriting that I am not boiling and bubbling as usual. Read it, my dear friend, and think as you read that it is also the story of your friend. Yes, this has happened to me, this will happen to me; and I am not half so worthy nor half so resolute as that poor, unhappy man, with whom I hardly dare compare myself.

September 5

She had written a note to her husband in the country, where he was on business. It began: "My dearest and best, come as soon as you can; I await you with a thousand joys." A friend who came in brought the news that Albert would not come back so soon because of certain circum-

bald noch nicht zurückkehren würde. Das Billett blieb liegen und fiel mir abends in die Hände. Ich las es und lächelte; sie fragte worüber? — „Was die Einbildungskraft für ein göttliches Geschenk ist", rief ich aus, „ich konnte mir einen Augenblick vorspiegeln, als wäre es an mich geschrieben." — Sie brach ab, es schien ihr zu mißfallen, und ich schwieg.

Am 6. September

Es hat schwer gehalten[46], bis ich mich entschloß, meinen blauen einfachen Frack, in dem ich mit Lotten zum erstenmal tanzte, abzulegen, er ward aber zuletzt gar unscheinbar. Auch habe ich mir einen machen lassen ganz wie den vorigen, Kragen und Aufschlag und auch wieder so gelbe Weste und Beinkleider dazu.

Ganz will es doch die Wirkung nicht tun. Ich weiß nicht — Ich denke, mit der Zeit soll mir der auch lieber werden.

Am 12. September

Sie war einige Tage verreist, Alberten abzuholen. Heute trat ich in ihre Stube, sie kam mir entgegen, und ich küßte ihre Hand mit tausend Freuden.

Ein Kanarienvogel flog von dem Spiegel ihr auf die Schulter. — „Einen neuen Freund", sagte sie und lockte ihn auf ihre Hand, „er ist meinen Kleinen zugedacht. Er tut[47] gar zu lieb! Sehen Sie ihn! Wenn ich ihm Brot gebe, flattert er mit den Flügeln und pickt so artig. Er küßt mich auch, sehen Sie!"

Als sie dem Tierchen den Mund hinhielt, drückte es sich so lieblich in die süßen Lippen, als wenn es die Seligkeit hätte fühlen können, die es genoß.

„Er soll Sie auch küssen", sagte sie und reichte den Vogel herüber. — Das Schnäbelchen machte den Weg von ihrem Munde zu dem meinigen, und die pickende Berührung war wie ein Hauch, eine Ahnung liebevollen Genusses.

„Sein Kuß", sagte ich, „ist nicht ganz ohne Begierde, er sucht Nahrung und kehrt unbefriedigt von der leeren Liebkosung zurück."

180

stances. The note was not sent and fell into my hands that evening. I read it and smiled; she asked me why. "What a divine gift is imagination," I exclaimed, "for a moment I could imagine it was written to me." She dropped the subject; it seemed to displease her and I kept quiet.

September 6

It was a difficult decision for me to abandon my simple blue dress coat in which I first danced with Lotte; but it was becoming quite threadbare. Besides, I had had one made exactly like the other, even to the collar and facings, and another yellow vest and trousers to go with it.

But it does not produce quite the same effect. I don't know—I think in time I'll get to like this one better.

September 12

She has been away for a few days to fetch Albert. Today I entered her room; she came toward me and I kissed her hand with a thousand joys.

A canary flew from the mirror to her shoulder. "A new friend," she said, coaxing it on to her hand. "I got him for the children. Isn't he adorable? Look at him! When I give him bread he flutters his wings and pecks so nicely. He kisses me too, you see?"

When she held out her lips to the little creature, it pressed against her sweet lips as charmingly as if it could feel the bliss it was enjoying.

"He shall kiss you too," she said and handed me the bird.—The little bill made its way from her lips to mine and the peck was like a wafting, faint suggestion of the delights of love.

"His kiss," I said, "is not entirely free from greed; he is seeking nourishment and returns unsatisfied from the empty caress."

181

„Er ißt mir auch aus dem Munde", sagte sie. — Sie reichte ihm einige Brosamen mit ihren Lippen, aus denen die Freuden unschuldig teilnehmender Liebe in aller Wonne lächelten.

Ich kehrte das Gesicht weg. Sie sollte es nicht tun! Sollte nicht meine Einbildungskraft mit diesen Bildern himmlischer Unschuld und Seligkeit reizen und mein Herz aus dem Schlafe, in den es manchmal die Gleichgültigkeit des Lebens wiegt, nicht wecken! — Und warum nicht? — Sie traut mir so! Sie weiß, wie ich sie liebe!

Am 15. September

Man möchte resend werden, Wilhelm, daß es Menschen geben soll ohne Sinn und Gefühl an dem wenigen, was auf Erden noch einen Wert hat. Du kennst die Nußbäume, unter denen ich bei dem ehrlichen Pfarrer zu St . . . mit Lotten gesessen, die herrlichen Nußbäume! die mich, Gott weiß, immer mit dem größten Seelenvergnügen füllten! Wie vertraulich sie den Pfarrhof machten, wie kühl! und wie herrlich die Äste waren! Und die Erinnerung bis zu den ehrlichen Geistlichen, die sie vor so vielen Jahren pflanzten. Der Schulmeister hat uns den einen Namen oft genannt, den er von seinem Großvater gehört hatte; und so ein braver Mann soll er gewesen sein, und sein Andenken war mir immer heilig unter den Bäumen. Ich sage Dir, dem Schulmeister standen die Tränen in den Augen, da wir gestern davon redeten, daß sie abgehauen worden — Abgehauen! Ich möchte toll werden, ich könnte den Hund ermorden, der den ersten Hieb dran tat. Ich, der ich mich vertrauern könnte, wenn so ein paar Bäume in meinem Hofe stünden, und einer davon stürbe vor Alter ab, ich muß zusehen. Lieber Schatz, eins ist doch dabei[48]! Was Menschengefühl ist! Das ganze Dorf murrt, und ich hoffe, die Frau Pfarrerin soll es an Butter und Eiern und übrigem Zutrauen[49] spüren, was für eine Wunde sie ihrem Orte gegeben hat. Denn sie ist es, die Frau des neuen Pfarrers (unser alter ist auch gestorben), ein hageres kränkliches Geschöpf, das sehr Ursache hat, an der Welt keinen Anteil zu nehmen; denn niemand nimmt Anteil an ihr. Eine

"He also takes food from my mouth," she said.—She gave him a few crumbs with her lips, on which the joys of an innocently shared love smiled delightfully.

I averted my face. She shouldn't do this! She should not stir my imagination with these pictures of heavenly innocence and bliss, nor wake my heart out of the sleep to which the indifference of life sometimes rocks it.—And why not?—She trusts me so! She knows how much I love her.

September 15

It makes you raging mad, Wilhelm, that there are people without understanding or feeling for the few things on earth that still have value. You know the nut trees under which I sat with Lotte at the home of the honest parson of St. —, those glorious nut trees which, Heaven knows, always filled me with the greatest happiness! How cozy they made the parsonage, how cool, and how glorious their branches were! And the memory they carried back to the good clergymen who planted them so many years ago. The schoolmaster often mentioned the name of one of them, which he had heard from his grandfather; and he's said to have been such a fine man, and his memory was always sacred to me under the trees. I tell you the tears stood in the schoolmaster's eyes when we spoke about it yesterday, and he told us that they had been cut down.— Cut down! I could go mad, I could murder the dog who struck the first blow at them. I, who could die of grief if such a pair of trees stood in my yard and one of them died of old age, I must stand by and watch. But, my dear fellow, there's at least one thing about it. The power of human feeling! The whole village is grumbling, and I hope the pastor's wife will be made to feel what a wound she has dealt the place, in the butter and eggs and the other tokens of esteem she receives. For she's the one, the wife of the new pastor (the old one died), a skinny, sickly creature who has good reason for showing no interest in the world, for no one shows any interest in her. A foolish

Närrin, die sich abgibt, gelehrt zu sein, sich in die Untersuchung des Kanons[50] meliert, gar viel an der neumodischen moralisch-kritischen Reformation des Christentums arbeitet und über Lavaters Schwärmereien[51] die Achseln zuckt, eine ganz zerrüttete Gesundheit hat und deswegen auf Gottes Erdboden keine Freude. So einer Kreatur war es auch allein möglich, meine Nußbäume abzuhauen. Siehst Du, ich komme nicht zu mir[52]! Stelle Dir vor, die abfallenden Blätter machen ihr den Hof unrein und dumpfig, die Bäume nehmen ihr das Tageslicht, und wenn die Nüsse reif sind, so werfen die Knaben mit Steinen danach, und das fällt ihr auf die Nerven, das stört sie in ihren tiefen Überlegungen, wenn sie Kennikot[53], Semler und Michaelis gegeneinander abwiegt. Da ich die Leute im Dorfe, besonders die alten, so unzufrieden sah, sagte ich: „Warum habt ihr es gelitten?" — „Wenn der Schulze will, hierzulande", sagten sie, „was kann man machen?" — Aber eins ist recht geschehen. Der Schulze und der Pfarrer, der doch auch von seiner Frauen[54] Grillen, die ihm ohnedies die Suppen nicht fett machen[55], was haben wollte, dachten es miteinander zu teilen; da erfuhr es die Kammer und sagte: „hier herein!" Denn sie hatte noch alte Prätensionen an den Teil des Pfarrhofes, wo die Bäume standen, und verkaufte sie an den Meistbietenden. Sie liegen! Oh, wenn ich Fürst wäre! Ich wollte die Pfarrerin, den Schulzen und die Kammer — Fürst! — Ja, wenn ich Fürst wäre, was kümmerten mich die Bäume in meinem Lande!

Am 10. Oktober

Wenn ich nur ihre schwarzen Augen sehe, ist mir es schon wohl! Sieh, und was mich verdrießt, ist, daß Albert nicht so beglückt zu sein scheinet, als er — hoffte — als ich zu sein glaubte — wenn — Ich mache nicht gern Gedankenstriche, aber hier kann ich mich nicht anders ausdrücken — und mich dünkt deutlich genug.

Am 12. Oktober

Ossian[56] hat in meinem Herzen den Homer verdrängt.

woman, who affects to be learned and interferes in the questions of the canonical books, works hard on the new-fangled moral-critical reformation of Christianity, and shrugs her shoulders at Lavater's enthusiasms. Her health is badly shaken, and so she has no joy on God's earth. Only such a creature could possibly have cut down my nut trees. You see, I can't regain control of myself! Just imagine, the falling leaves make her yard messy and damp, the trees shut out the light, and when the nuts are ripe the boys throw stones at them and this gets on her nerves, disturbs her profound meditation when she is weighing the merits of Kennicott, Semler, and Michaelis against one another. When I saw that the people in the village were so dissatisfied, especially the old ones, I said, "Why did you allow it?" "In these parts," they replied, "if the mayor is willing, what can you do?"—But one good thing happened. The mayor and the pastor, who after all wanted to gain some advantage from his wife's notions—which certainly add no nourishment to his soup—thought of sharing the trees between them. But the treasury learned of it and said: "This way!" for it still had old claims on that part of the parsonage in which the trees had stood, and sold them to the highest bidder. They are down! Oh, if I were the Prince! I would have the pastor's wife, the mayor and the treasury—the Prince! Yes, if I were the Prince, what would I care about the trees in my domain?

October 10

I have only to look into her black eyes to feel happy. And what annoys me is that Albert does not seem to be as happy as he—hoped—as I—thought I would have been—if—I don't like to use dashes, but in this instance I can't express myself in any other way—and it seems to me they are clear enough.

October 12

Ossian has displaced Homer in my heart. What a world

Welch eine Welt, in die der Herrliche mich führt! Zu
wandern über die Heide, umsaust vom Sturmwinde, der in
dampfenden Nebeln die Geister der Väter im dämmernden Lichte des Mondes hinführt. Zu hören vom Gebirge
her im Gebrülle des Waldstroms halb verwehtes Ächzen
der Geister aus ihren Höhlen, und die Wehklagen des zu
Tode sich jammernden Mädchens, um die vier moosbe-
deckten grasbewachsenen Steine des Edelgefallnen, ihres
Geliebten. Wenn ich ihn dann finde, den wandelnden
grauen Barden, der auf der weiten Heide die Fußstapfen
seiner Väter sucht, und ach! ihre Grabsteine findet und
dann jammernd nach dem lieben Sterne des Abends hin-
blickt, der sich ins rollende Meer verbirgt, und die Zeiten
der Vergangenheit in des Helden Seele lebendig werden,
da noch der freundliche Strahl den Gefahren der Tapferen
leuchtete und der Mond ihr bekränztes, siegrückkehrendes
Schiff beschien. Wenn ich den tiefen Kummer auf seiner
Stirn lese, den letzten verlassenen Herrlichen in aller Ermattung dem Grabe zuwanken sehe, wie er immer neue,
schmerzlich glühende Freuden in der kraftlosen Gegenwart der Schatten seiner Abgeschiedenen einsaugt und
nach der kalten Erde, dem hohen wehenden Grase nieder-
sieht und ausruft: „Der Wanderer[57] wird kommen, kommen, der mich kannte in meiner Schönheit, und fragen:
‚Wo ist der Sänger, Fingals trefflicher Sohn?‘ Sein Fußtritt
geht über mein Grab hin, und er fragt vergebens nach mir
auf der Erde.“ — O Freund! ich möchte gleich einem edlen
Waffenträger das Schwert ziehen, meinen Fürsten von der
zuckenden Qual des langsam absterbenden Lebens auf
einmal befreien und dem befreiten Halbgott meine Seele
nachsenden.

Am 19. Oktober

Ach, diese Lücke! Diese entsetzliche Lücke, die ich hier
in meinem Busen fühle! — Ich denke oft, wenn du sie nur
Einmal, nur Einmal an dieses Herz drücken könntest, diese
ganze Lücke würde ausgefüllt sein.

into which the glorious man leads me! To wander over the heath, with the tempestuous winds roaring about you, carrying the spirits of your ancestors in steaming mists by the half light of the moon. To hear from the mountains, amid the roar of the brook in the forest, half lost in the wind, the groaning of the spirits from their caves, and the lamentations of the maiden, grieving her life away by the four moss-covered, grass-overgrown stones on the tomb of her lover, nobly killed in battle. When I then find him, the wandering gray-haired bard; who seeks the footsteps of his fathers on the spacious heath but finds, alas, only their tombstones; who then gazes in misery at the beloved evening star which hides in the rolling sea; the memory of past ages comes alive in the hero's soul, the time when its friendly light still shone on the dangers of the brave and the moon lit their garlanded ship returning victorious. When I read the deep sorrow on his brow, and see the last of the glorious men as he lonely and feebly totters to the grave, as he draws ever new and painfully burning delight from the impotent presence of the shadows of his departed ones, and looks down on the cold earth and the tall, waving grass and exclaims: "The wanderer will come who knew me in my beauty, and will ask, 'Where is the singer, Fingal's excellent son?' His footstep will pass over my grave, and he will ask in vain after me on earth."—Oh, my friend! I would like to draw my sword like a noble warrior, to liberate my prince with one stroke from the quivering torment of a slow, living death, and send my soul to follow the liberated demigod.

October 19

Oh, this void, this horrible void which I feel here in my bosom!—I often think: if you could only once, just once press her to this heart, this whole void would be filled.

Ja es wird mir gewiß, Lieber! gewiß und immer gewisser, daß an dem Dasein eines Geschöpfs wenig gelegen ist, ganz wenig. Es kam eine Freundin zu Lotten, und ich ging herein ins Nebenzimmer, ein Buch zu nehmen, und konnte nicht lesen, und dann nahm ich eine Feder, zu schreiben. Ich hörte sie leise reden; sie erzählten einander unbedeutende Sachen, Stadtneuigkeiten: Wie diese heiratet, wie jene krank, sehr krank ist. — „Sie hat einen trocknen Husten, die Knochen stehn ihr zum Gesichte heraus, und kriegt Ohnmachten; ich gebe keinen Kreuzer für ihr Leben", sagte die eine. — „Der N. N. ist auch so übel dran", sagte Lotte. — „Er ist geschwollen", sagte die andere. — Und meine lebhafte Einbildungskraft versetzte mich ans Bett dieser Armen; ich sah sie, mit welchem Widerwillen sie dem Leben den Rücken wandten, wie sie — Wilhelm! und meine Weibchen redeten davon, wie man eben davon redet — daß ein Fremder stirbt. — Und wenn ich mich umsehe, und sehe das Zimmer an und rings um mich Lottens Kleider und Alberts Skripturen und diese Möbeln, denen ich nun so befreundet bin, sogar diesem Tintenfasse, und denke: Siehe, was du nun diesem Hause bist! Alles in allem. Deine Freunde ehren dich! Du machst oft ihre Freude, und deinem Herzen scheint es, als wenn es ohne sie nicht sein könnte; und doch — wenn du nun gingst, wenn du aus diesem Kreise schiedest? Würden sie, wie lange würden sie die Lücke fühlen, die dein Verlust in ihr Schicksal reißt? Wie lange? — Oh, so vergänglich ist der Mensch, daß er auch da, wo er seines Daseins eigentliche Gewißheit hat, da, wo er den einzigen wahren Eindruck seiner Gegenwart macht, in dem Andenken, in der Seele seiner Lieben, daß er auch da verlöschen, verschwinden muß, und das so bald!

Am 27. Oktober

Ich möchte mir oft die Brust zerreißen und das Gehirn einstoßen, daß man einander so wenig sein kann. Ach die Liebe, Freude, Wärme und Wonne, die ich nicht hinzubringe, wird mir der andere nicht geben, und mit einem

Yes, it is becoming certain to me, dear friend, certain and ever more certain that little, very little, matters in the existence of a human creature. One of Lotte's friends came in to see her. I went into the next room to fetch a book, but I could not read and then I took a pen to write. I heard them talking softly; they were telling each other insignificant things, town gossip: how this one was getting married, that one was sick, very sick. "She has a dry cough, her cheekbones protrude and she has fainting spells; I wouldn't give a penny for her life," said the friend. "N. N. is in a bad state too," said Lotte. "He's all swollen up," said the other girl.—And my lively imagination transported me to the bedsides of these poor people; I saw them turn their backs on life with the utmost repugnance, saw them— and Wilhelm, my little ladies were talking about it, well, as one would talk—about the death of a stranger.—And when I look about me and examine the room, with Lotte's dresses and Albert's papers around me, and this furniture which is so familiar to me, even to this inkwell—and I think: see what you now mean to this family—all in all! Your friends respect you; you often cause them pleasure, and your heart feels as if it could not exist without them, and yet—if you went now, if you left this circle, would they feel, how long would they feel, the void which your loss has torn in their destiny? How long?—Oh, man is so transitory that he must vanish even where he has complete certainty of his existence, where his presence makes the only true impression, in the memory, in the soul of his loved ones, even there he must fade and vanish, and that so soon!

I often feel like tearing out my heart and bashing in my brain to think that we can mean so little to each other. Alas, the love, joy, warmth, and bliss which I do not con- tribute myself no one else will give me, and even with a

ganzen Herzen voll Seligkeit werde ich den andern nicht
beglücken, der kalt und kraftlos vor mir steht.

Am 27. Oktober abends

Ich habe so viel, und die Empfindung an ihr verschlingt
alles, ich habe so viel, und ohne sie wird mir alles zu nichts.

Am 30. Oktober

Wenn ich nicht schon hundertmal auf dem Punkte
gestanden bin, ihr um den Hals zu fallen! Weiß der große
Gott, wie einem das tut, so viel Liebenswürdigkeit vor
einem herumkreuzen zu sehen und nicht zugreifen zu
dürfen; und das Zugreifen ist doch der natürlichste Trieb
der Menschheit. Greifen die Kinder nicht nach allem, was
ihnen in den Sinn fällt? — Und ich?

Am 3. November

Weiß Gott! ich lege mich so oft zu Bette mit dem
Wunsche, ja manchmal mit der Hoffnung, nicht wieder zu
erwachen; und morgens schlage ich die Augen auf, sehe
die Sonne wieder und bin elend. Oh, daß ich launisch sein
könnte, könnte die Schuld aufs Wetter, auf einen Dritten,
auf eine fehlgeschlagene Unternehmung schieben, so
würde die unerträgliche Last des Unwillens doch nur halb
auf mir ruhen. Wehe mir! Ich fühle zu wahr, daß an mir
allein alle Schuld liegt — nicht Schuld! Genug, daß in mir
die Quelle allen Elendes verborgen ist wie ehemals die
Quelle aller Seligkeiten. Bin ich nicht noch eben derselbe,
der ehemals in aller Fülle der Empfindung herumschwebte,
dem auf jedem Tritte ein Paradies folgte, der ein Herz
hatte, eine ganze Welt liebevoll zu umfassen? Und dies
Herz ist jetzt tot, aus ihm fließen keine Entzückungen mehr,
meine Augen sind trocken, und meine Sinne[58], die nicht
mehr von erquickenden Tränen gelabt werden, ziehen
ängstlich meine Stirn zusammen. Ich leide viel; denn ich
habe verloren, was meines Lebens einzige Wonne war, die

heart full of happiness I will not make anyone happy who stands before me cold and indifferent.

October 27, in the evening

I have so much, and my feeling for her devours everything; I have so much, and without her it all turns into nothing.

October 30

A hundred times I have been on the point of throwing my arms about her. The good Lord knows how it feels to see so much charm cruising around before one and not dare to touch it; and yet to touch is man's most natural impulse. Don't children touch everything they see?— And I?

November 3

Heaven knows, so often I go to bed with the wish, sometimes even with the hope, that I shall not awaken again; and the next morning I open my eyes, look at the sun again and am miserable. Oh, I wish I could be capricious, blame the weather, or someone else, or some undertaking that has failed; then only half of the unbearable burden of my resentment would rest on me. Woe is me! I feel only too clearly that the guilt is all mine—not guilt! It is enough that the source of all my wretchedness is buried in myself, just as was formerly the source of all my happiness. For am I not still the same person who once floated about in the abundance of his emotions, whom paradise followed everywhere, who had a heart that could embrace a whole world with love? And this heart is now dead, no raptures flow from it any longer; my eyes are dry, and my senses, no longer invigorated by refreshng tears, cause my brow to wrinkle in anxiety. I suffer much, for I have lost what was the sole joy of my life: the sacred, animating force with which I created worlds about me; it is no more!—When I

heilige belebende Kraft, mit der ich Welten um mich schuf;
sie ist dahin! — Wenn ich zu meinem Fenster hinaus an
den fernen Hügel sehe, wie die Morgensonne über ihn her
den Nebel durchbricht und den stillen Wiesengrund bescheint und der sanfte Fluß zwischen seinen entblätterten
Weiden zu mir herschlängelt — oh! wenn da diese herrliche Natur so starr vor mir steht wie ein lackiertes Bild-
chen und alle die Wonne keinen Tropfen Seligkeit aus
meinem Herzen herauf in das Gehirn pumpen kann und
der ganze Kerl[59] vor Gottes Angesicht steht wie ein ver-
siegter Brunnen, wie ein verlechter[60] Eimer. Ich habe mich
oft auf den Boden geworfen und Gott um Tränen gebeten
wie ein Ackersmann um Regen, wenn der Himmel ehern
über ihm ist und um ihn die Erde verdürstet.

Aber ach! ich fühle es, Gott gibt Regen und Sonnen-
schein nicht unserm ungestümen Bitten, und jene Zeiten,
deren Andenken mich quält, warum waren sie so selig, als
weil ich mit Geduld seinen Geist erwartete und die Wonne,
die er über mich ausgoß, mit ganzem, innig dankbarem
Herzen aufnahm!

Am 8. November

Sie hat mir meine Exzesse vorgeworfen! Ach, mit so viel
Liebenswürdigkeit! Meine Exzesse, daß ich mich manchmal
von einem Glase Wein verleiten lasse, eine Bouteille zu
trinken. — „Tun Sie es nicht", sagte sie, „denken Sie an
Lotten!" — „Denken!" sagte ich, „brauchen Sie mir das zu
heißen? Ich denke! — ich denke nicht! Sie sind immer vor
meiner Seele. Heute saß ich an dem Flecke, wo Sie neulich
aus der Kutsche stiegen." — Sie redete was anders, um
mich nicht tiefer in den Text kommen zu lassen. Bester!
ich bin dahin! Sie kann mit mir machen, was sie will.

Am 15. November

Ich[61] danke Dir, Wilhelm, für Deinen herzlichen Anteil,
für Deinen wohlmeinenden Rat und bitte Dich, ruhig zu
sein. Laß mich ausdulden, ich habe bei aller meiner Müdseligkeit[62] noch Kraft genug durchzusetzen. Ich ehre die

look out from my window toward the distant hill, how the morning sun breaks through the mist above it and illuminates the quiet meadow in the valley, and the gentle river winds its way toward me between its leafless willows—oh! when this glorious scene stands before me as stiff as a lacquered little painting and all this joy cannot pump one drop of happiness from my heart into my brain, and the whole man stands before the countenance of God like a dried-out well, like a leaking pail. I have often thrown myself to the ground and begged God for tears, as a farmer begs for rain when the sky above him is brazen and the earth about him is parched.

But alas! I feel it, God does not grant rain and sunshine to our impetuous requests. Those bygone days, whose memories torment me so, why were they so happy? Because I waited for His spirit with patience, and received the joy which He poured out over me with an undivided, fervently grateful heart.

November 8

She has reproached me for my excesses, ah, with such charm! My excesses, because I sometimes allow myself to be tempted by a glass of wine to drink a whole bottle. "Don't do it," she said, "think of Lotte." "Think of you!" I said, "do you need to command me to do that? I think— I don't think. You are always in my mind. Today I was sitting on the spot where you recently got out of the carriage—" She changed the subject, to prevent me from getting deeper into this one. My dear friend, I am lost, she can do with me what she pleases.

November 15

I thank you, Wilhelm, for your warm sympathy, for your well-meant advice; and I beg you to be at ease. Let me suffer to the end; with all my weariness I still have enough strength to hold out. I respect religion, you know that; I

Religion, das weißt Du, ich fühle, daß sie manchem Ermatteten Stab, manchem Verschmachtenden[63] Erquickung ist. Nur — kann sie denn, muß sie denn das einem jeden sein? Wenn Du die große Welt ansiehst, so siehst Du Tausende, denen sie es nicht war, Tausende, denen sie es nicht sein wird, gepredigt oder ungepredigt, und muß sie mir es denn sein? Sagt[64] nicht selbst der Sohn Gottes: daß die um ihn sein würden, die ihm der Vater gegeben hat? Wenn ich ihm nun nicht gegeben bin? Wenn mich nun der Vater für sich behalten will, wie mir mein Herz sagt? — Ich bitte Dich, lege das nicht falsch aus; sieh nicht etwa Spott in diesen unschuldigen Worten; es ist meine ganze Seele, die ich Dir vorlege; sonst wollte ich lieber, ich hätte geschwiegen; wie ich denn über alles das, wovon jedermann so wenig weiß als ich, nicht gern ein Wort verliere. Was ist es anders als Menschenschicksal, sein Maß auszuleiden, seinen Becher auszutrinken? — Und ward der Kelch dem Gott vom Himmel auf seiner Menschenlippe zu bitter, warum soll ich groß tun und mich stellen, als schmeckte er mir süß? Und warum sollte ich mich schämen, in dem schrecklichen Augenblick, da mein ganzes Wesen zwischen Sein und Nichtsein zittert, da die Vergangenheit wie ein Blitz über dem finstern Abgrunde der Zukunft leuchtet und alles um mich her versinkt und mit mir die Welt untergeht? — Ist es da nicht die Stimme der ganz in sich gedrängten, sich selbst ermangelnden und unaufhaltsam hinabstürzenden Kreatur, in den innern Tiefen ihrer vergebens aufarbeitenden Kräfte zu knirschen: „Mein Gott! mein Gott! warum hast du mich verlassen?" Und sollt' ich mich des Ausdruckes schämen, sollte mir es vor dem Augenblicke bange sein[65], da ihm der nicht entging, der die Himmel zusammenrollt wie ein Tuch[66]?

Am 21. November

Sie sieht nicht, sie fühlt nicht, daß sie ein Gift bereitet, das mich und sie zugrunde richten wird; und ich mit voller Wollust schlürfe den Becher aus, den sie mir zu meinem Verderben reicht. Was soll der gütige Blick, mit dem sie mich oft — oft? — nein, nicht oft, aber doch manchmal

feel that it is a staff for many a weary man, a refreshment for many a parched throat. Only—can it, must it be that for everyone? If you look at the great world, you will see thousands for whom it is not, thousands for whom it will not be so, whether it is preached or not preached; and must it be so for me? Does not the Son of God Himself say that they shall be His whom the Father has given to Him? Well, suppose I have not been given to Him? Suppose the Father wants to keep me for Himself, as my heart tells me?—Please do not misinterpret this; do not, for instance, see mockery in these innocent words; it is my whole soul that I bare before you; otherwise I would wish I had been silent, as I do not like to waste words on matters about which people know as little as I do. What else is it but human destiny to suffer one's measure to the end, to drain one's cup?—And if the cup became too bitter on the human lips of God from Heaven, why should I brag and pretend that it tastes sweet to me? And why should I feel shame in the terrible moment when my whole soul trembles between being and non-being, when my past, like lightning, lights up the dark abyss of the future, and everything about me is swallowed up, and the world perishes with me?—Is it not the voice of the creature, thrown completely upon itself, failing and plunging inevitably to destruction, that groans from the innermost depth, laboring in vain to reach the surface: "My God, my God, why hast Thou forsaken me?" And should I feel ashamed to utter these words? Should I fear the moment, when even He Who rolls up the heavens like a garment did not escape it?

November 21

She does not see, she does not feel that she is preparing a poison that will destroy both me and her; and voluptuously I drain the cup which she hands me for my ruin. What good are the kind looks she often gives me— often?—no, not often, but at least sometimes; the favor

ansieht, die Gefälligkeit, womit sie einen unwillkürlichen Ausdruck meines Gefühles aufnimmt, das Mitleiden[67] mit meiner Duldung, das sich auf ihrer Stirne zeichnet?

Gestern, als ich wegging, reichte sie mir die Hand und sagte: „Adieu, lieber Werther!" — Lieber Werther! Es war das erstemal, daß sie mich Lieber hieß, und es ging mir durch Mark und Bein. Ich habe es mir hundertmal wiederholt und gestern nacht, da ich zu Bette gehen wollte und mit mir selbst allerlei schwatzte, sagte ich so auf einmal: „Gute Nacht, lieber Werther!" und mußte hernach selbst über mich lachen.

Am 22. November

Ich kann nicht beten: „Laß mir sie!" und doch kommt sie mir oft als die Meine vor. Ich kann nicht beten: „Gib mir sie!" denn sie ist eines andern. Ich witzle mich mit meinen Schmerzen herum; wenn ich mir's nachließe, es gäbe eine ganze Litanei von Antithesen.

Am 24. November

Sie fühlt was ich dulde. Heute ist mir ihr Blick tief durchs Herz gedrungen. Ich fand sie allein; ich sagte nichts und sie sah mich an. Und ich sah nicht mehr in ihr die liebliche Schönheit, nicht mehr das Leuchten des trefflichen Geistes, das war alles vor meinen Augen verschwunden. Ein weit herrlicherer Blick wirkte auf mich, voll Ausdruck des innigsten Anteils, des süßesten Mitleidens. Warum durfte ich mich nicht ihr zu Füßen werfen? Warum durfte ich nicht an ihrem Halse mit tausend Küssen antworten? Sie nahm ihre Zuflucht zum Klavier und hauchte mit süßer leiser Stimme harmonische Laute zu ihrem Spiele. Nie habe ich ihre Lippen so reizend gesehn; es war, als wenn sie sich lechzend öffneten, jene süßen Töne in sich zu schlürfen, die aus dem Instrument hervorquollen, und nur der heimliche Widerschall aus dem reinen Munde zurückklänge — Ja, wenn ich Dir das so sagen könnte! — Ich widerstand nicht länger, neigte mich und schwur[68]: nie will ich es wagen, einen Kuß euch aufzudrücken, Lippen! auf denen

with which she receives some involuntary expression of my feelings, the compassion for my suffering which shows on her face?

Yesterday when I went away she gave me her hand and said: "Adieu, dear Werther!" Dear Werther! It was the first time she called me "dear," and it went right through me. I have repeated it to myself a hundred times, and last night, as I was about to go to bed and was chattering away to myself, I suddenly said: "Good night, dear Werther," and then had to laugh at myself.

November 22

I cannot pray, "Let her be mine!" and yet she often seems to me to be mine. I cannot pray, "Give her to me!" for she belongs to another. I joke around with my suffering; if I let myself go, the result would be a whole litany of paradoxes.

November 24

She feels what I am enduring. Today she gave me a look that penetrated deep into my heart. I found her alone; I said nothing, and she looked at me. And I no longer saw in her face the lovely beauty, no longer the light of her excellent mind; all that had vanished before my eyes. A far more glorious sight affected me, full of the expression of the most tender sympathy, the sweetest compassion. Why could I not throw myself at her feet? Why could I not take her in my arms and answer her with a thousand kisses? She took refuge at the piano and in a sweet, low voice, accompanied her playing with harmonious sounds. Never have I seen her lips so charming; it was as if they opened to yearn, to drink in those sweet tones that flowed from the instrument, as if only a mysterious echo reverberated from her pure lips.—Oh, if only I could express this to you!—I could resist no longer, bent forward and swore: I will never dare to imprint a kiss upon you, you lips on which the spirits of heaven hover.—And yet—I will—Ha!

die Geister des Himmels schweben — Und doch — ich will
— Ha! siehst Du, das steht wie eine Scheidewand vor
meiner Seele — diese Seligkeit — und dann untergegangen[69], diese Sünde abzubüßen — Sünde?

Am 26. November

Manchmal sag' ich mir: Dein Schicksal ist einzig; preise
die übrigen glücklich — so ist noch keiner gequält worden.
Dann lese ich einen Dichter der Vorzeit, und es ist mir,
als säh' ich in mein eignes Herz. Ich habe so viel auszu-
stehen! Ach sind denn Menschen vor mir schon so elend
gewesen?

Am 30. November

Ich soll, ich soll nicht zu mir selbst kommen! Wo ich
hintrete, begegnet mir eine Erscheinung, die mich aus aller
Fassung bringt. Heute! Oh Schicksal! Oh Menschheit!

Ich gehe an dem Wasser hin in der Mittagsstunde, ich
hatte keine Lust zu essen. Alles war öde, ein naßkalter
Abendwind blies vom Berge, und die grauen Regenwolken
zogen das Tal hinein. Von fern seh' ich einen Menschen
in einem grünen schlechten Rocke, der zwischen den Felsen
herumkrabbelte und Kräuter zu suchen schien. Als ich
näher zu ihm kam und er sich auf das Geräusch, das ich
machte, herumdrehte, sah ich eine gar interessante Physiognomie, darin[70] eine stille Trauer den Hauptzug machte,
die aber sonst nichts als einen geraden guten Sinn ausdrückte; seine schwarzen Haare waren mit Nadeln[71] in
zwei Rollen gesteckt und die übrigen in einen starken Zopf
geflochten, der ihm den Rücken herunter hing. Da mir
seine Kleidung einen Menschen von geringem Stande zu
bezeichnen schien, glaubte ich, er würde es nicht übel
nehmen, wenn ich auf seine Beschäftigung aufmerksam
wäre, und daher fragte ich ihn, was er suchte? — „Ich
suche", antwortete er mit einem tiefen Seufzer, „Blumen
— und finde keine." — „Das ist auch die Jahreszeit nicht",
sagte ich lächelnd. — „Es gibt so viele Blumen", sagte er,
indem er zu mir herunterkam. „In meinem Garten sind

198

you see, this stands like a barrier before my soul—this bliss—and then destruction, in atonement for this sin—sin?

November 26

Sometimes I say to myself: Your fate is unique; consider other men lucky—no one has ever been tormented like this. Then I read some poet of ancient times and I feel as if I were looking into my own heart. I must endure so much! Oh, have people before me ever been so wretched?

November 30

I am not, I am not to recover. Wherever I go I meet an apparition that makes me lose all my composure. Today, oh Destiny! Oh Humanity!

I was walking by the river at noon and felt no desire to eat. Everything was desolate, a cold, moist evening wind was blowing from the mountain, and gray rain clouds were moving into the valley. From a distance I saw a man in a shabby green coat crawling about between the rocks, apparently looking for herbs. When I came closer to him and he turned around because of the noise I made, I saw a most interesting face, whose chief feature was a quiet sorrow, but which otherwise expressed nothing but straightforward common sense. His black hair was done in two rolls held by pins, the rest plaited in a thick pigtail which hung down his back. As his dress seemed to betoken a man of humble rank, I thought he would not resent it if I watched what he was doing, so I asked him what he was looking for. "I am looking for flowers," he replied with a deep sigh, "but find none."—"But it isn't the season for them," I said with a smile.—"There are so many flowers," he said, coming down to me. "In my garden there are roses and two species of honeysuckle; one was given to me by my father; they grow like weeds; I have been seeking them for two days now and can't find them. There are always

199

Rosen und Jelängerjelieber zweierlei Sorten, eine hat mir mein Vater gegeben, sie wachsen wie Unkraut; ich suche schon zwei Tage darnach und kann sie nicht finden. Da haußen[72] sind auch immer Blumen, gelbe und blaue und rote, und das Tausendgüldenkraut hat ein schönes Blümchen. Keines kann ich finden." — Ich merkte was Unheimliches, und drum fragte ich durch einen Umweg: „Was will Er[73] denn mit den Blumen?" — Ein wunderbares, zuckendes Lächeln verzog sein Gesicht. — „Wenn Er mich nicht verraten will", sagte er, indem er den Finger auf den Mund drückte, „ich habe meinem Schatz einen Strauß versprochen." — „Das ist brav", sagte ich. — „Oh", sagte er, „sie hat viel andere Sachen, sie ist reich." — „Und doch hat sie Seinen[74] Strauß lieb", versetzte ich. — „Oh!" fuhr er fort, „sie hat Juwelen und eine Krone." — „Wie heißt sie denn?" — „Wenn mich die Generalstaaten[75] bezahlen wollten", versetzte er, „ich wär' ein anderer Mensch! Ja, es war einmal eine Zeit, da mir es so wohl war! Jetzt ist es aus mit mir. Ich bin nun" — Ein nasser Blick zum Himmel drückte alles aus. — „Er war also glücklich?" fragte ich. — „Ach ich wollte, ich wäre wieder so!" sagte er. „Da war mir es so wohl, so lustig, so leicht wie einem Fisch im Wasser!" — „Heinrich!" rief eine alte Frau, die den Weg herkam, „Heinrich, wo steckst du? Wir haben dich überall gesucht, komm zum Essen!" — „Ist das Euer[76] Sohn?" fragt' ich, zu ihr tretend. — „Wohl, mein armer Sohn!" versetzte sie. „Gott hat mir ein schweres Kreuz aufgelegt." — „Wie lange ist er so?" fragte ich. — „So stille", sagte sie, „ist er nun ein halbes Jahr. Gott sei Dank, daß er nur so weit ist, vorher war er ein ganzes Jahr rasend, da hat er an Ketten im Tollhause gelegen. Jetzt tut er niemand nichts[77], nur hat er immer mit Königen und Kaisern zu schaffen. Es war ein so guter, stiller Mensch, der mich ernähren half, seine schöne Hand schrieb, und auf einmal wird er tiefsinnig, fällt in ein hitziges Fieber, daraus in Raserei, und nun ist er, wie Sie ihn sehen. Wenn ich Ihnen erzählen sollte, Herr" — Ich unterbrach den Strom ihrer Worte mit der Frage: „Was war denn das für eine Zeit, von der er rühmt, daß er so glücklich, so wohl darin gewesen sei?" — „Der törichte Mensch!" rief sie mit mitleidigem Lächeln, „da

flowers out here, yellow and blue and red, and the centaury has a lovely flower. But I can't find a single one of them." I noticed that there was something weird about him, so I asked in a roundabout way: "What do you want the flowers for?"—A strange, quivering smile distorted his face. "If you will not betray me," he said, pressing his finger to his lips, "I've promised my girl a bouquet." "That's nice," I said. "Oh," he said, "she has many other things; she's rich." "And yet she appreciates your bouquet," I added. "Oh," he continued, "she has jewels and a crown." "And what is her name?" "If the Estates General would pay me," he replied, "I'd be a different person. Yes, there was a time once when I was so happy! Now it's all over with me. Now I am. . . ." A tearful glance at the sky expressed everything.—"So you were happy?" I asked.—"Oh, I wish I were so again," he said. "At that time I was as happy, as merry, as light as a fish in water."—"Heinrich," cried an old woman who was walking along the road, "Heinrich, where are you? We've been looking for you everywhere; come and eat." "Is that your son?" I asked, going up to her. "My poor soon, indeed," she replied. "God has given me a heavy cross to bear." "How long has he been like this?" I asked. "He has been so gentle for half a year," she said. "Thank heaven he's come at last this far; earlier he was raving mad for a whole year; he lay in chains in the madhouse. Now he doesn't hurt anyone, but he always talks of consorting with kings and emperors. He was such a good, quiet person, who helped support me; he wrote such a beautiful hand; but suddenly he started brooding, fell into a violent fever, from that into raving madness, and now he is as you see him. If I were to tell you, sir—" I interrupted the stream of her words with the question: "What time was that he talks about so fondly, when he was so happy, so well off?" "The foolish boy," she exclaimed with a compassionate smile, "he means the time when he was out of his mind; he's always praising that; that's the time when he was in the madhouse, when he knew nothing about himself."—This struck me like a thunderclap; I pressed a coin into her hand and left her in haste.

201

meint er die Zeit, da er von sich[78] war, das rühmt er immer; das ist die Zeit, da er im Tollhause war, wo er nichts von sich wußte." — Das fiel mir auf[79] wie ein Donnerschlag, ich drückte ihr ein Stück Geld in die Hand und verließ sie eilend.

„Da du glücklich warst!" rief ich aus, schnell vor mich hin nach der Stadt zu gehend, „da dir es wohl war wie einem Fisch im Wasser!" — Gott im Himmel! hast du das zum Schicksale der Menschen gemacht, daß sie nicht glücklich sind, als ehe sie zu ihrem Verstande kommen und wenn sie ihn wieder verlieren! — Elender! Und auch wie beneide ich deinen Trübsinn, die Verwirrung deiner Sinne, in der du verschmachtest! Du gehst hoffnungsvoll aus, deiner Königin Blumen zu pflücken — im Winter — und trauerst, da du keine findest, und begreifst nicht, warum du keine finden kannst. Und ich — und ich gehe ohne Hoffnung, ohne Zweck heraus und kehre wieder heim, wie ich gekommen bin. — Du wähnst, welcher Mensch du sein würdest, wenn die Generalstaaten dich bezahlten. Seliges Geschöpf! das den Mangel seiner Glückseligkeit einer irdischen Hindernis[80] zuschreiben kann. Du fühlst nicht! Du fühlst nicht, daß in deinem zerstörten Herzen, in deinem zerrütteten Gehirne dein Elend liegt, wovon alle Könige der Erde dir nicht helfen können.

Müsse[81] der trostlos umkommen, der eines Kranken spottet, der nach der entferntesten Quelle reist, die seine Krankheit vermehren, sein Ausleben schmerzhafter machen wird! der sich über das bedrängte Herz erhebt, das, um seine Gewissensbisse los zu werden und die Leiden seiner Seele abzutun, eine Pilgrimschaft nach dem Heiligen Grabe[82] tut. Jeder Fußtritt, der seine Sohlen auf ungebahntem Wege durchschneidet, ist ein Linderungtropfen der geängsteten Seele, und mit jeder ausgedauerten Tagereise legt sich das Herz um viele Bedrängnisse leichter nieder. — Und dürft ihr das Wahn nennen, ihr Wortkrämer auf euren Polstern? — Wahn! — O Gott! du siehst meine Tränen! Mußtest du, der du den Menschen arm genug erschufst, ihm auch Brüder zugeben, die ihm das bißchen Armut, das bißchen Vertrauen noch raubten, das er auf dich hat, auf dich, du Allliebender! Denn das Vertrauen zu

"When you were happy!" I exclaimed, walking swiftly toward the city, "when you felt as happy as a fish in the water!"—Lord in Heaven! Hast Thou so decreed men's fate that they are happy only before they attain the state of reason and after they have lost it again?—Wretched man! And yet how I envy you your melancholy, the confusion of your senses in which you are pining away. You start out hopefully to pick flowers for your queen—in winter—and feel sad when you find none, and don't understand why you can find none. And I—and I go out without hope, without purpose, and return home in the same spirit.—You dream of what sort of person you would be if the Estates General paid you a salary. Happy creature, who can ascribe your unhappiness to an earthly obstacle! You don't feel that your misery, for which all the kings on earth can do nothing to help you, is rooted in your devastated heart, in your deranged brain.

Perish the man without consolation who scoffs at a sick man traveling to the remotest spring which will only increase his malady and make his death more painful; or who feels superior to the man whose oppressed heart makes him undertake a pilgrimage to the Holy Sepulchre to rid himself of his bad conscience and to be relieved of the anguish of his soul. Every step that cuts through his soles on an untrodden road is a drop of comfort for his anguished soul, and with every day's journey he endures, his heart is relieved of many tribulations.—And dare you call this delusion, you phrasemongers on your soft cushions?—Delusion!—Oh Lord: Thou seest my tears! Thou who didst create man poor enough, why didst Thou also give him brothers who rob him even of his bit of poverty and the little trust he has in Thee, in Thee, Thou all-loving One? For what is trust in the virtue of a healing root or in

einer heilenden Wurzel, zu den Tränen des Weinstockes[83], was ist es als Vertrauen zu dir, daß du in alles, was uns umgibt, Heil- und Linderungskraft gelegt hast, der wir so stündlich bedürfen? Vater! den ich nicht kenne! Vater! der sonst meine ganze Seele füllte und nun sein Angesicht von mir gewendet hat! rufe mich zu dir! schweige nicht länger! Dein Schweigen wird diese dürstende Seele nicht aufhalten — Und würde ein Mensch, ein Vater zürnen können, dem sein unvermutet rückkehrender Sohn um den Hals fiele und riefe: „Ich bin wieder da, mein Vater! Zürne nicht, daß ich die Wanderschaft abbreche, die ich nach deinem Willen länger aushalten sollte. Die Welt ist überall einerlei, auf Mühe und Arbeit Lohn und Freude; aber was soll mir das? Mir ist nur wohl, wo du bist, und vor deinem Angesichte will ich leiden und genießen." — Und du, lieber himmlischer Vater, solltest ihn von dir weisen?

Am 1. Dezember

Wilhelm! der Mensch, von dem ich Dir schrieb, der glückliche Unglückliche, war Schreiber bei Lottens Vater, und eine Leidenschaft zu ihr, die er nährte, verbarg, entdeckte und worüber er aus dem Dienst geschickt wurde, hat ihn rasend gemacht. Fühle bei diesen trocknen Worten, mit welchem Unsinne mich die Geschichte ergriffen hat, da mir sie Albert ebenso gelassen erzählte, als Du sie vielleicht liesest.

Am 4. Dezember

Ich bitte Dich — Siehst Du, mit mir ist's aus, ich trag' es nicht länger! Heute saß ich bei ihr — saß, sie spielte auf ihrem Klavier, mannigfaltige Melodien, und all den Ausdruck! all! — all! — Was willst Du? — Ihr Schwesterchen putzte ihre Puppe auf meinem Knie. Mir kamen die Tränen in die Augen. Ich neigte mich, und ihr Trauring fiel mir ins Gesicht — meine Tränen flossen — Und auf einmal fiel sie in die alte, himmelsüße Melodie[84] ein, so auf einmal, und mir durch die Seele gehn ein Trostgefühl und eine Erinnerung des Vergangenen, der Zeiten, da ich das

the tears of the vine but trust in Thee, that Thou hast placed in everything around us the power of healing and relieving that we need at every hour? Father Whom I do not know! Father, Who hast once filled my whole soul, and now turnest Thy countenance from me, call me to Thee; be silent no longer! Thy silence will not sustain this thirsting soul.—And could a man, a father, be angry if his son returned unexpectedly, threw his arms about his neck, and cried: "I am back, my father! Be not angry because I cut short my journey, which you expected me to endure longer. The world is the same everywhere, work and effort followed by reward and joy; but what meaning has that for me? I feel happy only where you are, and in your presence I want to suffer and enjoy."—And Thou, dear, heavenly Father, wouldst Thou turn him away?

December 1

Wilhelm! the man about whom I wrote you, the man so happy in his unhappiness was a clerk in the service of Lotte's father, and a passion for her which he nourished, cherished, concealed, and then revealed, causing him to be dismissed from his position, drove him mad. Feel, as you read these dry words, with what insane power this story gripped me when Albert told it to me as calmly as you may be reading it now!

December 4

I beg of you—you see, it's all up with me, I can't stand it any longer! Today I was sitting beside her—as I sat, she played the piano, various tunes, and with what expression, what expression! What do you expect?—Her little sister sat on my lap dressing her doll. Tears came to my eyes. I bent down, caught sight of her wedding ring—and my tears flowed—And suddenly she fell into that old, divinely sweet melody, as if by chance, and a feeling of comfort passed through my heart, and a memory of the past, of times when I had heard the song, of the gloomy intervals

205

Lied gehört, der düstern Zwischenräume, des Verdrusses, der fehlgeschlagenen Hoffnungen, und dann — Ich ging in der Stube auf und nieder, mein Herz erstickte unter dem Zudringen. — „Um Gottes willen", sagte ich, mit einem heftigen Ausbruch hin gegen sie fahrend, „um Gottes willen, hören Sie auf!" — Sie hielt und sah mich starr an. — „Werther", sagte sie mit einem Lächeln, das mir durch die Seele ging, „Werther, Sie sind sehr krank, Ihre Lieblingsgerichte[85] widerstehen Ihnen. Gehen Sie! Ich bitte Sie, beruhigen Sie sich." — Ich riß mich von ihr weg, und — Gott! du siehst mein Elend und wirst es enden.

Am 6. Dezember

Wie mich die Gestalt verfolgt! Wachend und träumend füllt sie meine ganze Seele! Hier, wenn ich die Augen schließe, hier in meiner Stirne, wo die innere Sehkraft sich vereinigt, stehen ihre schwarzen Augen. Hier! Ich kann Dir es nicht ausdrücken. Mache ich meine Augen zu, so sind sie da; wie ein Meer, wie ein Abgrund ruhen sie vor mir, in mir, füllen die Sinne meiner Stirn.

Was ist der Mensch, der gepriesene Halbgott! Ermangeln ihm nicht eben da die Kräfte, wo er sie am nötigsten braucht? Und wenn er in Freude sich aufschwingt oder im Leiden versinkt, wird er nicht in beiden eben da aufgehalten, eben da zu dem stumpfen kalten Bewußtsein wieder zurückgebracht, da er sich in der Fülle des Unendlichen zu verlieren sehnte?

Der Herausgeber an den Leser

Wie sehr wünscht' ich, daß uns von den letzten merkwürdigen Tagen unsers Freundes so viel eigenhändige Zeugnisse übrig geblieben wären, daß ich nicht nötig hätte, die Folge seiner hinterlassenen Briefe durch Erzählung zu unterbrechen.

Ich habe mir angelegen sein lassen, genaue Nachrichten aus dem Munde derer zu sammeln, die von seiner Geschichte wohl unterrichtet sein konnten; sie ist einfach, und

of vexation, of frustrated hopes; and then—I walked up and down the room, my heart suffocating under the pressure.—"For heaven's sake," I said, moving toward her with a vehement outburst, "for heaven's sake, stop!" She stopped and looked at me blankly. "Werther," she said with a smile that went right through me, "Werther, you are very ill; your favorite dishes disagree with you. Go. I beg you, calm yourself." I tore myself away from her and—God, Thou seest my misery and wilt put an end to it.

December 6

How her form pursues me! Whether I am awake or dreaming, she fills my mind wholly. When I close my eyes, here, in my brain, where my inner vision is concentrated, her black eyes are before me. Here, I can't express it to you in words. If I close my eyes, they are there; like an ocean, like an abyss they lie before me, in me, fill my inner senses.

What is man, that vaunted demigod? Do not his powers fail him precisely where he most needs them? And when he soars in joy or sinks in suffering, is he not arrested in both, brought back to empty, cold consciousness just at the moment when he yearned to lose himself in the fullness of the infinite?

The Editor to the Reader

How I wish that enough testimony about our friend's last remarkable days remained from his own hand so that I should not find it necessary to interrupt the sequence of his posthumous letters by a narrative.

I have made an effort to gather precise information from the lips of those who were in a position to know his story well. It is a simple story, and all accounts of it agree except

es kommen alle Erzählungen davon, bis auf wenige Kleinigkeiten, miteinander überein; nur über die Sinnesarten der handelnden Personen sind die Meinungen verschieden und die Urteile geteilt.

Was bleibt uns übrig, als dasjenige, was wir mit wiederholter Mühe erfahren können, gewissenhaft zu erzählen, die von dem Abscheidenden[86] hinterlassenen Briefe einzuschalten und das kleinste aufgefundene Blättchen nicht gering zu achten; zumal da es so schwer ist, die eigensten wahren Triebfedern auch nur einer einzelnen Handlung zu entdecken, wenn sie unter Menschen vorgeht, die nicht gemeiner Art sind.

Unmut und Unlust hatten in Werthers Seele immer tiefer Wurzel geschlagen, sich fester untereinander verschlungen und sein ganzes Wesen nach und nach eingenommen. Die Harmonie seines Geistes war völlig zerstört, eine innerliche Hitze und Heftigkeit, die alle Kräfte seiner Natur durcheinander arbeitete, brachte die widrigsten Wirkungen hervor und ließ ihm zuletzt nur eine Ermattung übrig, aus der er noch ängstlicher emporstrebte, als er mit allen Übeln bisher gekämpft hatte. Die Beängstigung seines Herzens zehrte die übrigen Kräfte seines Geistes, seine Lebhaftigkeit, seinen Scharfsinn auf, er ward ein trauriger Gesellschafter, immer unglücklicher und immer ungerechter, je unglücklicher er ward. Wenigstens sagen dies Alberts Freunde; sie behaupten, daß Werther einen reinen, ruhigen Mann, der nun eines lang gewünschten Glücks teilhaftig geworden, und sein Betragen, sich dieses Glück auch auf die Zukunft zu erhalten, nicht habe beurteilen können, er, der gleichsam mit jedem Tage sein ganzes Vermögen verzehrte, um an dem Abend zu leiden und zu darben. Albert, sagen sie, hatte sich in so kurzer Zeit nicht verändert, er war noch immer derselbige, den Werther so vom Anfang her kannte, so sehr schätzte und ehrte. Er liebte Lotten über alles, er war stolz auf sie und wünschte sie auch von jedermann als das herrlichste Geschöpf anerkannt zu wissen. War es ihm daher zu verdenken, wenn er auch jeden Schein des Verdachtes abzuwenden wünschte, wenn er in dem Augenblicke mit niemand diesen köstlichen Besitz auch auf die unschuldigste Weise zu teilen Lust hatte? Sie

for a few slight details. Opinions differ and judgments are divided only on the states of mind of the principal actors involved.

What is left for us but to narrate conscientiously what we have learned after repeated efforts, to insert the letters left by the departed one, and not to disregard even the most trivial slip of paper that has turned up, especially since it is so difficult to discover the true and authentic motives for even a single act performed among people who are not of the common stamp?

Discouragement and apathy had struck ever deeper root in Werther's mind, had become more firmly intertwined, and had gradually taken possession of his whole being. The harmony of his mind was completely destroyed; an inner heat and violence which churned up all his natural powers produced the most contradictory effects, and finally left him with only a weariness against which he struggled even more anxiously than he had until now fought against all his misfortunes. The growing anxiety in his heart consumed the other forces of his mind, his vivacity, his alertness; he became a sad social companion, more and more unhappy and more and more unjust the unhappier he became. At least this is what Albert's friends say; they assert that Werther was unable to appreciate the pure, quiet man who had achieved a degree of happiness for which he had long yearned and who strove to maintain this happiness for the future too; whereas he, as it were, consumed his whole substance every day, to end up in the evening in suffering and starvation. Albert, they say, had not changed in this short span of time; he was still the same person whom Werther had known in the beginning, whom he esteemed and honored so highly. He loved Lotte above everything else; he was proud of her and wished her to be recognized by everyone as the most glorious creature. Could he, then, be blamed for wishing to avert even the shadow of a suspicion, or for his unwillingness to share at this moment this precious possession with anyone, even in the most innocent way? They admit that Albert

gestehen ein, daß Albert oft das Zimmer seiner Frau verlassen, wenn Werther bei ihr war, aber nicht aus Haß noch Abneigung gegen seinen Freund, sondern nur, weil er gefühlt habe, daß dieser von seiner Gegenwart gedrückt sei.

Lottens Vater war von einem Übel befallen worden, das ihn in der Stube hielt, er schickte ihr seinen Wagen, und sie fuhr hinaus. Es war ein schöner Wintertag, der erste Schnee war stark gefallen und deckte die ganze Gegend.

Werther ging ihr den andern Morgen nach, um, wenn Albert sie nicht abzuholen käme, sie herein zu begleiten.

Das klare Wetter konnte wenig auf sein trübes Gemüt wirken, ein dumpfer Druck lag auf seiner Seele, die traurigen Bilder hatten sich bei ihm festgesetzt, und sein Gemüt kannte keine Bewegung als von einem schmerzlichen Gedanken zum andern.

Wie er mit sich in ewigem Unfrieden lebte, schien ihm auch der Zustand andrer nur bedenklicher und verworrner, er glaubte, das schöne Verhältnis zwischen Albert und seiner Gattin gestört zu haben, er machte sich Vorwürfe darüber, in die sich ein heimlicher Unwille gegen den Gatten mischte.

Seine Gedanken fielen auch unterwegs auf diesen Gegenstand. Ja, ja, sagte er zu sich selbst, mit heimlichem Zähneknirschen: das ist der vertraute, freundliche, zärtliche, an allem teilnehmende Umgang, die ruhige dauernde Treue! Sattigkeit ist's und Gleichgültigkeit! Zieht ihn nicht jedes elende Geschäft mehr an als die teure köstliche Frau? Weiß er sein Glück zu schätzen? Weiß er sie zu achten, wie sie es verdient? Er hat sie, nun gut, er hat sie — Ich weiß das, wie ich was anders auch weiß; ich glaube an den Gedanken gewöhnt zu sein, er wird mich noch rasend machen, er wird mich noch umbringen — Und hat denn die Freundschaft zu mir Stich gehalten? Sieht er nicht in meiner Anhänglichkeit an Lotten schon einen Eingriff in seine Rechte, in meiner Aufmerksamkeit für sie einen stillen Vorwurf? Ich weiß es wohl, ich fühl' es, er sieht mich ungern, er wünscht meine Entfernung, meine Gegenwart ist ihm beschwerlich.

Oft hielt er seinen raschen Schritt an, oft stand er stille und schien umkehren zu wollen; allein er richtete seinen

often left his wife's room when Werther was with her, although not out of hatred or dislike for his friend, but only because he felt that his presence weighed on Werther.

Lotte's father, who was confined to his room by sickness, sent his carriage for her and she drove out to see him. It was a fine winter day; the first heavy snow had fallen, covering the whole region.

Werther followed her the next morning to escort her back home in case Albert did not come to fetch her.

The clear weather had little effect on his gloomy state of mind; a heavy weight lay on his heart, sad fancies held his mind in a firm grip, and his spirit could only move from one painful thought to the next.

As he lived in eternal discord with himself, so the state of others only seemed to him the more dubious and confused; he thought he had disturbed the beautiful relationship between Albert and his wife; he reproached himself for it, and into these reproaches there crept a secret ill-will toward the husband.

His thoughts turned to this subject again on the way to Lotte. Yes, yes, he said to himself, secretly grinding his teeth, this intimate, friendly, tender association that exends to everything, this calm, steady loyalty! It is surfeit and indifference! Does not every wretched business matter have more attraction for him than his dear, precious wife? Does he appreciate his good fortune? Is he able to respect her as she deserves? He has her—all right, he has her— I know that, as I know certain other things; I believe I am accustomed to the thought, but it will drive me insane yet; it will destroy me yet.—And has his friendship for me really stood the test? Does he not already regard my attachment to Lotte as an infringement on his rights, my attentions to her as a silent reproach? I know quite well, I feel it, that he does not like to see me, that he wants me to leave, that my presence is a burden to him.

He often slackened his swift pace, often stopped in his tracks as if to turn back; but he always directed his steps

Gang immer wieder vorwärts und war mit diesen Gedanken und Selbstgesprächen endlich gleichsam wider Willen bei dem Jagdhause angekommen.

Er trat in die Tür, fragte nach dem Alten und nach Lotten, er fand das Haus in einiger Bewegung. Der älteste Knabe sagte ihm, es sei drüben in Wahlheim ein Unglück geschehn, es sei ein Bauer erschlagen worden! — Es machte das weiter keinen Eindruck auf ihn. — Er trat in die Stube und fand Lotten beschäftigt, dem Alten zuzureden, der ungeachtet seiner Krankheit hinüberwollte, um an Ort und Stelle die Tat zu untersuchen. Der Täter war noch unbekannt, man hatte den Erschlagenen des Morgens vor der Haustür gefunden, man hatte Mutmaßungen: der Entleibte war Knecht einer Witwe, die vorher einen andern im Dienst gehabt, der mit Unfrieden aus dem Hause gekommen war.

Da Werther dieses hörte, fuhr er mit Heftigkeit auf. — „Ist's möglich!" rief er aus, „ich muß hinüber, ich kann nicht einen Augenblick ruhn." — Er eilte nach Wahlheim zu, jede Erinnerung ward ihm lebendig, und er zweifelte nicht einen Augenblick, daß jener Mensch die Tat begangen, den er so manchmal gesprochen, der ihm so wert geworden war.

Da er durch die Linden mußte, um nach der Schenke zu kommen, wo sie den Körper hingelegt hatten, entsetzt' er sich vor dem sonst so geliebten Platze. Jene Schwelle, worauf die Nachbarskinder so oft gespielt hatten, war mit Blut besudelt. Liebe und Treue, die schönsten menschlichen Empfindungen, hatten sich in Gewalt und Mord verwandelt. Die starken Bäume standen ohne Laub und bereift, die schönen Hecken, die sich über die niedrige Kirchhofmauer wölbten, waren entblättert, und die Grabsteine sahen mit Schnee bedeckt durch die Lücken hervor.

Als er sich der Schenke näherte, vor welcher das ganze Dorf versammelt war, entstand auf einmal ein Geschrei. Man erblickte von fern einen Trupp bewaffneter Männer, und ein jeder rief, daß man den Täter herbeiführe. Werther sah hin und blieb nicht lange zweifelhaft. Ja! es war der Knecht, der jene Witwe so sehr liebte, den er vor einiger

forward again, and finally, engaged in such thoughts and soliloquies, he arrived at the hunting lodge, in spite of himself, as it were.

He stepped into the doorway and asked for the old gentleman and Lotte; he found the house in some commotion. The oldest boy told him that over in Wahlheim there had been an accident, a peasant had been murdered.—This made no special impression on him.—He entered the living room and found Lotte busy dissuading the old gentleman who, in spite of his illness, wanted to go to Wahlheim to investigate the crime on the spot. The criminal was still unknown; the slain man had been found at his own front door in the morning; there was speculation: the murdered man had been in the service of a widow who had formerly had another man in her employ who had left her house in a dissatisfied state.

When Werther heard this he started vehemently. "Is it possible!" he exclaimed, "I must go there, I can't wait a moment."—He hurried toward Wahlheim; his memory became vivid in every detail; he did not doubt for a moment that the murder had been committed by the man with whom he had spoken quite often, and who had become so dear to him.

As he had to walk past the linden trees to get to the tavern where the body had been placed, he was horrified at the appearance of the square which had formerly been so dear to him. The threshold where the neighbor's children had so often played was stained with blood. Love and loyalty, the most beautiful of human emotions, had turned into violence and murder. The powerful trees stood leafless and were covered with hoarfrost; the beautiful hedges which curved over the low churchyard wall were stripped of foliage, and the tombstones covered with snow looked out through the gaps.

As he approached the tavern, in front of which the whole village was assembled, he suddenly heard shouts. From a distance a band of armed men could be seen, and everyone cried that the murderer was being brought. Werther looked, and did not long remain in doubt. Yes, it was the hired man who had loved the widow so passion-

Zeit mit dem stillen Grimme, mit der heimlichen Verzweiflung umhergehend, angetroffen hatte.

„Was hast du begangen, Unglücklicher!" rief Werther
aus, indem er auf den Gefangnen losging. — Dieser sah ihn
still an, schwieg und versetzte endlich ganz gelassen:
„Keiner wird sie haben, sie wird keinen haben." — Man
brachte den Gefangenen in die Schenke, und Werther eilte
fort.

Durch die entsetzliche gewaltige Berührung war alles,
was in seinem Wesen lag, durcheinander geschüttelt
worden. Aus seiner Trauer, seinem Mißmut, seiner gleich-
gültigen Hingegebenheit wurde er auf einen Augenblick
herausgerissen; unüberwindlich bemächtigte sich die Teilnehmung seiner, und es ergriff ihn eine unsägliche Begierde,
den Menschen zu retten. Er fühlte ihn so unglücklich, er
fand ihn als Verbrecher selbst so schuldlos, er setzte sich
so tief in seine Lage, daß er gewiß glaubte, auch andere
davon zu überzeugen. Schon wünschte er für ihn sprechen
zu können, schon drängte sich der lebhafteste Vortrag
nach seinen Lippen; er eilte nach dem Jagdhause und
konnte sich unterwegs nicht enthalten, alles das, was er
dem Amtmann vorstellen wollte, schon halblaut auszusprechen.

Als er in die Stube trat, fand er Alberten gegenwärtig,
dies verstimmte ihn einen Augenblick; doch faßte er sich
bald wieder und trug dem Amtmanne feurig seine Gesinnungen vor. Dieser schüttelte einigemal den Kopf, und
obgleich Werther mit der größten Lebhaftigkeit, Leidenschaft und Wahrheit alles vorbrachte, was ein Mensch zur
Entschuldigung eines Menschen sagen kann, so war doch,
wie sich's leicht denken läßt, der Amtmann dadurch nicht
gerührt. Er ließ vielmehr unsern Freund nicht ausreden,
widersprach ihm eifrig und tadelte ihn, daß er einen Meuchelmörder in Schutz nehme! Er zeigte ihm, daß auf diese
Weise jedes Gesetz aufgehoben, alle Sicherheit des Staates
zugrund gerichtet werde, auch, setzte er hinzu, daß er in
einer solchen Sache nichts tun könne, ohne sich die größte
Verantwortung aufzuladen; es müsse alles in der Ordnung
in dem vorgeschriebenen Gang gehen.

Werther ergab sich noch nicht, sondern bat nur, der

ately, and whom he had encountered some time ago nursing his silent anger, his secret despair.

"What crime have you committed, unhappy man!" Werther exclaimed as he went toward the prisoner.—The latter looked at him silently, then replied quite calmly, "No one will have her, she will have no one."—The prisoner was taken into the tavern and Werther hurried away.

This terrible, violent contact had shaken his whole being. For a moment he was torn out of his sadness, his discontent, his apathetic indifference; an unconquerable feeling of sympathy took possession of him and he was seized by an indescribable desire to save the man. He felt that he was so unhappy, that he found him so innocent even as a criminal, and identified himself so completely with him that he felt certain he could convince others too. Already he wished to be able to speak in his defense, already the most eloquent plea was forming on his lips; he hurried to the hunting lodge and could not refrain from speaking half aloud all that he intended to say before the bailiff.

When he entered the room, he found Albert present; this put him out of sorts for a moment, but he soon recovered himself and spoke his mind passionately to the bailiff. The latter shook his head a few times, and although Werther, with the greatest animation, passion, and truth, said everything that one man can say in defense of another, the bailiff, as can be easily imagined, was not moved by it. On the contrary he interrupted our friend in his discourse, contradicted him warmly and rebuked him for protecting a murderer. He showed him that in this way all law would be annulled, the security of the state destroyed, and he added that in such a matter he could do nothing without incurring the greatest responsibility; everything had to proceed in an orderly manner, and take the prescribed course.

Werther did not give up yet, but merely begged the

Amtmann möchte durch die Finger sehn, wenn man dem Menschen zur Flucht behülflich wäre! Auch damit wies ihn der Amtmann ab. Albert, der sich endlich ins Gespräch mischte, trat auch auf des Alten Seite. Werther wurde überstimmt, und mit einem entsetzlichen Leiden machte er sich auf den Weg, nachdem ihm der Amtmann einigemal gesagt hatte: „Nein, er ist nicht zu retten!"

Wie sehr ihm diese Worte aufgefallen sein müssen, sehn wir aus einem Zettelchen, das sich unter seinen Papieren fand, und das gewiß an dem nämlichen Tage geschrieben worden.

„Du bist nicht zu retten, Unglücklicher! Ich sehe wohl, daß wir nicht zu retten sind."

Was Albert zuletzt über die Sache des Gefangenen in Gegenwart des Amtmanns gesprochen, war Werthern höchst zuwider gewesen; er glaubte, einige Empfindlichkeit gegen sich darin bemerkt zu haben, und wenn gleich bei mehrerem Nachdenken seinem Scharfsinne nicht entging, daß beide Männer recht haben möchten, so war es ihm doch, als ob er seinem innersten Dasein entsagen müßte, wenn er es gestehen, wenn er es zugeben sollte.

Ein Blättchen, das sich darauf bezieht, das vielleicht sein ganzes Verhältnis zu Albert ausdrückt, finden wir unter seinen Papieren.

„Was hilft es, daß ich mir's sage und wieder sage, er ist brav und gut, aber es zerreißt mir mein inneres Eingeweide; ich kann nicht gerecht sein."

Weil es ein gelinder Abend war und das Wetter anfing, sich zum Tauen zu neigen, ging Lotte mit Alberten zu Fuße zurück. Unterwegs sah sie sich hier und da um, eben, als wenn sie Werthers Begleitung vermißte. Albert fing von ihm an zu reden, er tadelte ihn, indem er ihm Gerechtigkeit widerfahren ließ. Er berührte seine unglückliche Leidenschaft und wünschte, daß es möglich sein möchte, ihn zu entfernen. — „Ich wünsch' es auch um unsertwillen", sagte er, „und ich bitte dich", fuhr er fort, „siehe zu,

bailiff to look the other way if the man were helped to escape. But this too the bailiff rejected. Albert, who finally joined the conversation, took the old man's side. Werther was outvoted, and with a horrible sense of pain he went on his way after the bailiff had told him several times: "No, he cannot be saved!"

How deeply these words must have struck him we can see from a note that was found among his papers and which had quite certainly been written on that same day:

"You cannot be saved, unhappy man. I see clearly that we cannot be saved."

What Albert had finally said in the presence of the bailiff about the case of the prisoner had been most repugnant to Werther; he thought he had noticed some resentment against himself in the remarks; and although, upon reflection, his reason told him that the two men might be right, it still seemed to him that he would have to renounce his innermost being if he confessed it, if he admitted it.

A note which refers to this, and which perhaps expresses his whole relationship to Albert, was found among his papers:

"What use is it for me to say to myself over and over again, he is a good and nice man? It tears my heart; I cannot be just."

Because it was a mild evening and the weather was beginning to approach a thaw, Lotte and Albert returned on foot. On the way she looked around here and there, as if she missed Werther's companionship. Albert began to speak of him; he criticized him but was just to him. He touched on his unhappy passion and wished it were possible to send him away. "I wish it for our sake too," he said, "and I beg of you," he continued, "try to give his behavior toward you a different direction and to reduce

seinem Betragen gegen dich eine andere Richtung zu geben, seine öftern Besuche zu vermindern. Die Leute werden aufmerksam, und ich weiß, daß man hier und da drüber gesprochen hat." — Lotte schwieg, und Albert schien ihr Schweigen empfunden zu haben, wenigstens seit der Zeit erwähnte er Werthers[87] nicht mehr gegen sie, und wenn sie seiner erwähnte, ließ er das Gespräch fallen oder lenkte es woanders hin.

Der vergebliche Versuch, den Werther zur Rettung des Unglücklichen gemacht hatte, war das letzte Auflodern der Flamme eines verlöschenden Lichtes; er versank nur desto tiefer in Schmerz und Untätigkeit; besonders kam er fast außer sich, als er hörte, daß man ihn vielleicht sogar zum Zeugen gegen den Menschen, der sich nun aufs Leugnen legte[88], auffordern könnte.

Alles, was ihm Unangenehmes jemals in seinem wirksamen[89]Leben begegnet war, der Verdruß bei der Gesandtschaft, alles was ihm sonst mißlungen war, was ihn je gekränkt hatte, ging in seiner Seele auf und nieder. Er fand sich durch alles dieses wie zur Untätigkeit berechtigt, er fand sich abgeschnitten von aller Aussicht, unfähig, irgendeine Handhabe zu ergreifen, mit denen man die Geschäfte des gemeinen Lebens anfaßt, und so rückte er endlich, ganz seiner wunderbaren Empfindung, Denkart und einer endlosen Leidenschaft hingegeben, in dem ewigen Einerlei eines traurigen Umgangs mit dem liebenswürdigen und geliebten Geschöpfe, dessen Ruhe er störte, in seine Kräfte stürmend, sie ohne Zweck und Aussicht abarbeitend, immer einem traurigen Ende näher.

Von seiner Verworrenheit, Leidenschaft, von seinem rastlosen Treiben und Streben, von seiner Lebensmüde sind einige hinterlassene Briefe die stärksten Zeugnisse, die wir hier einrücken wollen.

„Am 12. Dezember

„Lieber Wilhelm, ich bin in einem Zustande, in dem jene Unglücklichen gewesen sein müssen, von denen man glaubte, sie würden von einem bösen Geiste umhergetrieben. Manchmal ergreift mich's; es ist nicht Angst, nicht

his frequent visits. People are taking notice, and I know that there has been talk about it here and there."—Lotte was silent and Albert seems to have been sensitive to her silence; at least from then on he did not mention Werther to her again and when she mentioned him, he dropped the conversation or changed the subject.

The futile attempt which Werther had made to save the unfortunate man was the last flicker of a dying light; he sank ever deeper into pain and inactivity. He was almost beside himself when he heard that he might be called as a witness against the man, who was now denying everything.

Everything unpleasant that he had experienced in his active life, the annoying incident at the embassy, every one of his other failures, everything that had offended him kept going through his mind. He felt as though justified in his inactivity by all this; he found himself cut off from every prospect, unable to get a grip anywhere, to tackle the affairs of everyday life and so, wholly surrendered to his strange emotion, his way of thinking, and his endless passion—in the eternal monotony of a melancholy association with the charming and beloved creature whose peace he was destroying, ravaging his energies, exhausting them without purpose or prospect— he moved closer and closer to a sorrowful end.

A few letters which have been left are the strongest evidence of his confusion and passion, his restless activity and exertion, of his weariness with life; we will insert them here.

"December 12

"Dear Wilhelm: I am in the state of mind of those unfortunate creatures of whom it was believed that they were possessed of an evil spirit. Sometimes I have a seizure; it is not anxiety, not desire—it is an unfamiliar, inner raging

219

Begier — es ist ein inneres unbekanntes Toben, das meine Brust zu zerreißen droht, das mir die Gurgel zupreßt. Wehe, wehe! Und dann schweife ich umher in den furchtbaren nächtlichen Szenen dieser menschenfeindlichen Jahreszeit.

„Gestern abend mußte ich hinaus. Es war plötzlich Tauwetter eingefallen; ich hatte gehört, der Fluß sei übergetreten, alle Bäche geschwollen und von Wahlheim herunter mein liebes Tal überschwemmt! Nachts nach elf rannte ich hinaus. Ein fürchterliches Schauspiel, vom Fels herunter die wühlenden Fluten in dem Mondlichte wirbeln zu sehen, über Äcker und Wiesen und Hecken und alles, und das weite Tal hinauf und hinab e i n e stürmende See im Sausen des Windes! Und wenn dann der Mond wieder hervortrat und über der schwarzen Wolke ruhte und vor mir hinaus die Flut in fürchterlich herrlichem Widerschein rollte und klang: da überfiel mich ein Schauer und wieder ein Sehnen! Ach mit offenen Armen stand ich gegen den Abgrund und atmete hinab! hinab! und verlor mich in der Wonne, meine Qualen, mein Leiden da hinabzustürmen! dahinzubrausen wie die Wellen! Oh! — und den Fuß vom Boden zu heben vermochtest du nicht, und alle Qualen zu enden! — Meine Uhr ist noch nicht ausgelaufen, ich fühle es! O Wilhelm! wie gern hätte ich mein Menschsein drum gegeben, mit jenem Sturmwinde die Wolken zu zerreißen, die Fluten zu fassen! Ha! und wird nicht vielleicht dem Eingekerkerten einmal diese Wonne zuteil? —

„Und wie ich wehmütig hinabsah auf ein Plätzchen, wo ich mit Lotten unter einer Weide geruht, auf einem heißen Spaziergange, — das war auch überschwemmt, und kaum daß ich die Weide erkannte, Wilhelm! Und ihre Wiesen, dachte ich, die Gegend um ihr Jagdhaus! wie verstört jetzt vom reißenden Strome unsere Laube! dacht' ich. Und der Vergangenheit Sonnenstrahl blickte herein, wie einem Gefangenen ein Traum von Herden, Wiesen und Ehrenämtern! Ich stand! — Ich schelte mich nicht, denn ich habe Mut zu sterben. — Ich hätte — Nun sitze ich hier wie ein altes Weib, das ihr Holz von Zäunen stoppelt und ihr Brot an den Türen, um ihr hinsterbendes, freudeloses Dasein noch einen Augenblick zu verlängern und zu erleichtern."

which threatens to tear my heart asunder and constricts my throat. Woe! Woe! And then I roam about in the terrible nights of this inhuman season.

"Last night I had to go out. A thaw had suddenly set in; I had heard that the river had overflowed its banks, that all the brooks were swollen, and that from Wahlheim down my beloved valley was flooded. After eleven at night I ran out. A fearful spectacle to see the turbulent waters eddying down from the rocks in the moonlight, over fields and meadows and hedges and all, up and down the broad valley, one stormy sea in the roaring of the wind. And then when the moon came out again, resting above the black clouds, and before me the waters rolled and roared in the fearful, splendid reflection, a shudder overcame me and once more I felt a yearning. I stood with open arms facing the abyss, whispering, 'down, down,' and was lost in the bliss of flinging my torments and my suffering down there to roar like the waves! Oh—but you were not able to lift your foot from the ground and put an end to all your torments!—My time has not yet run out, I feel it! Oh Wilhelm, how gladly would I have yielded up my human existence to rend the clouds and grasp the waves like that tempestuous wind! Ha! And will not the imprisoned man some day perhaps experience this bliss?—

"And as I looked down sadly on a little spot where I had rested with Lotte under a willow tree, on a hot walk we took—this too was flooded, and I could barely recognize the willow, Wilhelm. And her meadows, I thought, the country around her hunting lodge, how our arbor, I thought, has now been ruined by the raging river! And the sunshine of the past looked in on me like a dream of flocks, meadows, and honors upon a prisoner. But I stood there.— I do not blame myself, for I have the courage to die.—I might—Now I am sitting here like an old woman who scrounges her wood from fences and begs her bread from door to door to prolong and ease her joyless, waning existence for another moment."

„Was ist das, mein Lieber? Ich erschrecke vor mir selbst! Ist nicht meine Liebe zu ihr die heiligste, reinste, brüderlichste Liebe? Habe ich jemals einen strafbaren Wunsch in meiner Seele gefühlt? — Ich will nicht beteuern — Und nun, Träume! Oh, wie wahr fühlten die Menschen, die so widersprechende Wirkungen fremden Mächten zuschrieben! Diese Nacht! Ich zittere es zu sagen, hielt ich sie in meinen Armen, fest an meinen Busen gedrückt und deckte ihren liebelispelnden Mund mit unendlichen Küssen; mein Auge schwamm in der Trunkenheit des ihrigen! Gott! bin ich strafbar, daß ich auch jetzt noch eine Seligkeit fühle, mir diese glühenden Freuden mit voller Innigkeit zurückzurufen? Lotte! Lotte! — Und mit mir ist es aus! Meine Sinne verwirren sich, schon acht Tage habe ich keine Besinnungskraft mehr, meine Augen sind voll Tränen. Ich bin nirgend wohl und überall wohl. Ich wünsche nichts, verlange nichts. Mir wäre besser, ich ginge."

Der Entschluß, die Welt zu verlassen, hatte in dieser Zeit, unter solchen Umständen in Werthers Seele immer mehr Kraft gewonnen. Seit der Rückkehr zu Lotten war es immer seine letzte Aussicht und Hoffnung gewesen; doch hatte er sich gesagt, es solle keine übereilte, keine rasche Tat sein, er wolle mit der besten Überzeugung, mit der möglichst ruhigen Entschlossenheit diesen Schritt tun.

Seine Zweifel, sein Streit mit sich selbst blicken aus einem Zettelchen hervor, das wahrscheinlich ein angefangener Brief an Wilhelm ist und ohne Datum unter seinen Papieren gefunden worden.

„Ihre Gegenwart, ihr Schicksal, ihre Teilnehmung an dem meinigen preßt noch die letzten Tränen aus meinem versengten Gehirne.

„Den Vorhang aufzuheben und dahinter zu treten! Das ist alles! Und warum das Zaudern und Zagen? Weil man nicht weiß, wie es dahinten aussieht? und man nicht wiederkehrt? Und daß das nun die Eigenschaft unseres Geistes

"What is this, my dear friend? I am afraid of myself! Is not my love for her the holiest, purest, most brotherly love? Have I ever felt a culpable desire in my heart?—I will not assert—And now, dreams! Oh, how rightly those people felt who ascribed these contradictory effects to alien powers. Last night, I tremble to say it, I held her in my arms, pressed her close to my breast and covered her lips, which whispered love to me, with countless kisses; my eyes swam in the intoxication of hers! Heaven! Am I culpable for feeling even now transported when I recall these ardent joys in all their depth? Lotte, Lotte!—It's all over with me! My senses are confused, for a week I have not been able to control my mind. My eyes are filled with tears. I feel happy nowhere and everywhere. I desire nothing and ask for nothing. It would be better for me if I went."

The resolve to leave the world had at this time, under these circumstances, gained more and more power over Werther's mind. Since his return to Lotte it had always been his final prospect and hope; but he had told himself that it must not be a hasty, rash deed; he would take this step with the firmest conviction, with the utmost resolution possible.

His doubts and his inner conflict are revealed by a note which is probably the beginning of a letter to Wilhelm and which was found undated among his papers:

"Her presence, her destiny, her sympathy with mine, press the last tears out of my burning brain.

"To lift the curtain and step behind it, that is everything. And why this hesitation and delay? Because one does not know what it looks like behind the curtain, and because one cannot return, and because it is a characteristic of our

ist, da Verwirrung und Finsternis zu ahnen, wovon wir nichts Bestimmtes wissen."

Endlich ward er mit dem traurigen Gedanken immer mehr verwandt und befreundet und sein Vorsatz fest und unwiderruflich, wovon folgender zweideutige Brief, den er an seinen Freund schrieb, ein Zeugnis abgibt.

„Am 20. Dezember

„Ich danke Deiner Liebe, Wilhelm, daß Du das Wort so aufgefangen hast. Ja, Du hast recht: mir wäre besser, ich ginge. Der Vorschlag, den Du zu einer Rückkehr zu Euch tust, gefällt mir nicht ganz; wenigstens möchte ich noch gern einen Umweg machen, besonders da wir anhaltenden Frost und gute Wege zu hoffen haben. Auch ist mir es sehr lieb, daß Du kommen willst, mich abzuholen; verziehe nur noch vierzehn Tage und erwarte noch einen Brief von mir mit dem Weiteren. Es ist nötig, daß nichts gepflückt werde, ehe es reif ist. Und vierzehn Tage auf oder ab tun viel. Meiner Mutter sollst Du sagen: daß sie für ihren Sohn beten soll, und daß ich sie um Vergebung bitte, wegen alles Verdrusses, den ich ihr gemacht habe. Das war nun mein Schicksal, die zu betrüben, denen ich Freude schuldig war. Leb wohl, mein Teuerster! Allen Segen des Himmels über Dich! Leb wohl!"

Was in dieser Zeit in Lottens Seele vorging, wie ihre Gesinnungen gegen ihren Mann, gegen ihren unglücklichen Freund gewesen, getrauen wir uns kaum mit Worten auszudrucken, ob[90] wir uns gleich davon, nach der Kenntnis ihres Charakters, wohl einen stillen Begriff machen können und eine schöne weibliche Seele[91] sich in die ihrige denken und mit ihr empfinden kann.

So viel ist gewiß, sie war fest bei sich entschlossen, alles zu tun, um Werthern zu entfernen, und wenn sie zauderte, so war es eine herzliche, freundschaftliche Schonung, weil sie wußte, wieviel es ihm kosten, ja daß es ihm beinahe unmöglich sein würde. Doch ward sie in dieser Zeit mehr gedrängt, Ernst zu machen; es schwieg ihr Mann ganz über

mind to suspect confusion and darkness where we know nothing definite."

He finally became more and more familiar and friendly with the sad thought, and his resolution became firm and irrevocable, to which the following ambiguous letter, which he wrote to his friend, bears testimony.

"December 20

"I owe it to your love, Wilhelm, that you take my words in this spirit. Yes, you are right: it would be better for me if I went. Your proposal that I should return to you is not altogether to my liking; at least I should like to make a detour first, especially since we may expect a lasting frost and good roads. I am also very happy that you are willing to come and fetch me; only put it off for another fortnight and wait for one more letter from me with further news. Nothing must be plucked before it is ripe. And a fortnight more or less may make a great difference. Tell my mother to pray for her son and that I beg her forgiveness for all the distress I have caused her. It was simply my destiny to sadden those to whom I owe joy. Farewell, my dearest friend! All the blessings of Heaven upon you. Farewell!"

What was going on in Lotte's mind during this time, her attitude toward her husband and her unhappy friend, we scarcely dare to express in words, although we can form our own ideas of it from our knowledge of her character; a noble feminine soul can appreciate her thoughts and feelings.

This much is certain: she was firmly resolved in her own mind to do her utmost to send Werther away and if she hesitated it was from a warm, friendly desire to spare him, because she knew how hard, in fact almost impossible it would be for him to go. However, at this time she was pressed more urgently to take serious action; her husband

dies Verhältnis, wie sie auch immer darüber geschwiegen hatte, und um so mehr war ihr angelegen, ihm durch die Tat zu beweisen, wie ihre Gesinnungen der seinigen wert seien.

An demselben Tage, als Werther den zuletzt eingeschalteten Brief an seinen Freund geschrieben, es war der Sonntag vor Weihnachten, kam er abends zu Lotten und fand sie allein. Sie beschäftigte sich, einige Spielwerke in Ordnung zu bringen, die sie ihren kleinen Geschwistern zum Christgeschenke zurechtgemacht hatte. Er redete von dem Vergnügen, das die Kleinen haben würden, und von den Zeiten, da einen die unerwartete Öffnung der Tür und die Erscheinung eines aufgeputzten Baumes mit Wachslichtern, Zuckerwerk und Äpfeln in paradiesische Entzückung setzte. — „Sie sollen", sagte Lotte, indem sie ihre Verlegenheit unter ein liebes Lächeln verbarg, „Sie sollen auch beschert kriegen, wenn Sie recht geschickt[92] sind; ein Wachsstöckchen und noch was." — „Und was heißen Sie geschickt sein?" rief er aus; „wie soll ich sein, wie kann ich sein? beste Lotte!" — „Donnerstag abend", sagte sie, „ist Weihnachtsabend, da kommen die Kinder, mein Vater auch, da kriegt jedes das Seinige, da kommen Sie auch — aber nicht eher." — Werther stutzte. — „Ich bitte Sie", fuhr sie fort, „es ist nun einmal so, ich bitte Sie um meiner Ruhe willen, es kann nicht, es kann nicht so bleiben." — Er wendete seine Augen von ihr und ging in der Stube auf und ab und murmelte das: „Es kann nicht so bleiben!" zwischen den Zähnen. Lotte, die den schrecklichen Zustand fühlte, worein ihn diese Worte versetzt hatten, suchte durch allerlei Fragen seine Gedanken abzulenken, aber vergebens. — „Nein, Lotte", rief er aus, „ich werde Sie nicht wieder sehen!" — „Warum das?" versetzte sie, „Werther, Sie können, Sie müssen uns wieder sehen, nur mäßigen Sie sich. Oh, warum mußten Sie mit dieser Heftigkeit, dieser unbezwinglich haftenden Leidenschaft für alles, was Sie einmal anfassen, geboren werden! Ich bitte Sie", fuhr sie fort, indem sie ihn bei der Hand nahm, „mäßigen Sie sich! Ihr Geist, Ihre Wissenschaften, Ihre Talente, was bieten die Ihnen für mannigfaltige Ergötzungen dar! Seien Sie ein Mann! Wenden Sie diese traurige Anhänglichkeit von

was completely silent about the relationship, as she too had always kept silent about it, and she was all the more anxious to prove to him by her actions that her attitude was worthy of his.

On the same day on which Werther had written the above letter to his friend—it was the Sunday before Christmas—he came to Lotte in the evening and found her alone. She was busy finishing some toys which she had put together as a Christmas gift for her brothers and sisters. He talked of the joy the children would feel and of the time when the unexpected opening of the door and the sight of a decorated tree with wax candles, candy, and apples was heavenly ecstasy. "You too," said Lotte, concealing her embarrassment behind a lovely smile, "you will get a gift too if you are really nice; a little roll of wax tapers and something else." "And what do you call being nice?" he exclaimed. "How am I to be, how can I be, my dearest Lotte?" "Thursday evening is Christmas Eve," she said, "the children will come and father too, and everyone will get his gift. You may come too, but not before then." Werther was taken aback.—"Please," she continued, "that's the way things are. I beg of you for the sake of my peace of mind, things cannot, cannot go on this way."—He averted his gaze from her, walked up and down the room muttering between his teeth, "Things cannot go on this way." Lotte, who sensed the terrible state into which these words had plunged him, sought to divert his thoughts by all sorts of questions, but in vain.—"No Lotte!" he exclaimed, "I shall not see you again!" "Why?" she replied, "Werther, you can, you must see us again, but control yourself. Oh, why did you have to be born with this vehemence, this unconquerable, clinging passion for everything you touch? I beg you," she continued, taking him by the hand, "control yourself. Your intelligence, your knowledge, your talents, what a variety of delights they offer you! Be a man! Turn this sad attachment away from a creature who can do nothing but feel sorry for you." He ground his teeth and looked at her gloomily. She held his hand. "Calm your mind just for one moment, Werther," she said. "Don't you feel that you are deceiving yourself, de-

einem Geschöpf, das nichts tun kann als Sie bedauern." —
Er knirrte[93] mit den Zähnen und sah sie düster an. Sie hielt
seine Hand: „Nur einen Augenblick ruhigen Sinn, Werther!" sagte sie. „Fühlen Sie nicht, daß Sie sich betrügen,
sich mit Willen zugrunde richten! Warum denn mich,
Werther? just mich, das Eigentum eines andern? just das?
Ich fürchte, ich fürchte, es ist nur die Unmöglichkeit, mich
zu besitzen, die Ihnen diesen Wunsch so reizend macht." —
Er zog seine Hand aus der ihrigen, indem er sie mit einem
starren, unwilligen Blich ansah. — „Weise[94]!" rief er, „sehr
weise! Hat vielleicht Albert diese Anmerkung gemacht?
Politisch[95]! sehr politisch!" — „Es kann sie jeder machen",
versetzte sie drauf. „Und sollte denn in der weiten Welt
kein Mädchen sein, das die Wünsche Ihres Herzens er-
füllte? Gewinnen Sie's über sich, suchen Sie danach, und
ich schwöre Ihnen, Sie werden sie finden; denn schon
lange ängstet mich, für Sie und uns, die Einschränkung, in
die Sie sich diese Zeit her[96] selbst gebannt haben. Gewinnen Sie es über sich! Eine Reise wird Sie, muß Sie zerstreuen! Suchen Sie, finden Sie einen werten Gegenstand
Ihrer Liebe, und kehren Sie zurück und lassen Sie uns
zusammen die Seligkeit einer wahren Freundschaft genießen."

„Das könnte man", sagte er mit einem kalten Lachen,
„drucken lassen und allen Hofmeistern empfehlen. Liebe
Lotte! Lassen Sie mir noch ein klein wenig Ruh, es wird
alles werden!" — „Nur das, Werther, daß Sie nicht eher
kommen als Weihnachtsabend!" — Er wollte antworten,
und Albert trat in die Stube. Man bot sich einen frostigen
Guten Abend und ging verlegen im Zimmer nebeneinander
auf und nieder. Werther fing einen unbedeutenden Diskurs
an, der bald aus war, Albert desgleichen, der sodann seine
Frau nach gewissen Aufträgen fragte, und als er hörte, sie
seien noch nicht ausgerichtet, ihr einige Worte sagte, die
Werthern kalt, ja gar hart vorkamen. Er wollte gehen, er
konnte nicht und zauderte bis acht, da sich denn sein Unmut und Unwillen immer vermehrte, bis der Tisch gedeckt
wurde und er Hut und Stock nahm. Albert lud ihn zu
bleiben, er aber, der nur ein unbedeutendes Kompliment zu
hören glaubte, dankte kalt dagegen[97] und ging weg.

liberately destroying yourself? Why me, Werther? Why just me, who belongs to another man? Why just this? I fear, I fear, it is only the impossibility of possessing me that makes your desire for me so strong."—He withdrew his hand from hers, and looked at her with a rigid, angry stare.—"Wise!" he cried, "very wise! Did Albert perhaps make this remark? Politic! Very politic!" "Anyone might say it," she replied. "And is there no girl in the whole world who could fulfill the desires of your heart? Bring yourself to do it, to look for her, and I swear to you that you'll find her; for I have long been unhappy, both for your sake and ours, with the way you have confined yourself within this circumscribed sphere lately. Bring yourself to do it! A journey will and must distract you. Seek and find an object worthy of your love, and then return and let us enjoy together the happiness of a true friendship."

"This could be printed," he said with a cold laugh, "and recommended to all schoolmasters. Dear Lotte, give me a little more peace and everything will turn out well."—"Only one thing, Werther, do not come back before Christmas Eve."—He was about to reply but Albert entered the room. They bade each other a frosty good evening and paced up and down the room side by side in embarrassment. Werther began a trivial conversation, which soon came to an end. Albert did the same, and then asked his wife about certain domestic matters; when he heard that they had not been attended to yet, he said a few words to her which to Werther seemed cold, even harsh. He wanted to go but could not, and stayed there till eight o'clock, his displeasure and irritability growing all the time. At length the table was set and he took his hat and cane. Albert invited him to stay, but thinking that he heard only meaningless politeness in his voice, Werther thanked him

Er kam nach Hause, nahm seinem Burschen, der ihm leuchten wollte, das Licht aus der Hand und ging allein in sein Zimmer, weinte laut, redete aufgebracht mit sich selbst, ging heftig die Stube auf und ab und warf sich endlich in seinen Kleidern aufs Bett, wo ihn der Bediente fand, der es gegen elf wagte, hineinzugehn, um zu fragen, ob er dem Herrn die Stiefel ausziehen sollte? das[98] er denn zuließ und dem Bedienten verbot, den andern Morgen ins Zimmer zu kommen, bis er ihm rufen würde.

Montags früh, den einundzwanzigsten Dezember, schrieb er folgenden Brief an Lotten, den man nach seinem Tode versiegelt auf seinem Schreibtische gefunden und ihr überbracht hat, und den ich absatzweise hier einrücken will, so wie aus den Umständen erhellt, daß er ihn geschrieben habe.

„Es ist beschlossen, Lotte, ich will sterben, und das schreibe ich Dir ohne romantische Überspannung, gelassen, an dem Morgen des Tages, an dem ich Dich zum letzten Male sehen werde. Wenn du dieses liesest, meine Beste, deckt schon das kühle Grab die erstarrten Reste des Unruhigen, Unglücklichen, der für die letzten Augenblicke seines Lebens keine größere Süßigkeit weiß, als sich mit Dir zu unterhalten. Ich habe eine schreckliche Nacht gehabt, und ach! eine wohltätige Nacht. Sie ist es, die meinen Entschluß befestiget, bestimmt hat: ich will sterben! Wie ich mich gestern von Dir riß, in der fürchterlichen Empörung meiner Sinne, wie sich alles das nach meinem Herzen drängte, und mein hoffnungsloses freudeloses Dasein neben Dir in gräßlicher Kälte mich anpackte — ich erreichte kaum mein Zimmer, ich warf mich außer mir auf meine Knie, und o Gott! du gewährtest mir das letzte Labsal der bittersten Tränen! Tausend Anschläge, tausend Aussichten wüteten durch meine Seele, und zuletzt stand er da, fest, ganz, der letzte einzige Gedanke: Ich will sterben! — Ich legte mich nieder, und morgens, in der Ruhe des Erwachens, steht er noch fest, noch ganz stark in meinem Herzen: ich will sterben! — Es ist nicht Verzweiflung, es ist Gewißheit, daß ich ausgetragen[99] habe, und daß ich

coldly and went away.

He returned home, took the candle from the hand of his boy, who wanted to light the way for him, and went to his room alone. He wept aloud, talked excitedly to himself, walked up and down the room impetuously, and finally threw himself fully dressed on the bed, where the servant found him when he dared to go in about eleven o'clock to ask if he should take his master's boots off. Werther permitted this and forbade the servant to enter the room the next morning before he was summoned.

On Monday morning, the twenty-first of December, he wrote the following letter to Lotte. It was found, sealed, on his desk after his death, and was delivered to her. I shall insert it here in instalments, just as he seems to have written it, to judge by the circumstances.

"My mind is made up, Lotte, I want to die. I am writing this to you without romantic exaggeration, calmly, on the morning of the day on which I shall see you for the last time. When you read this, my dearest one, the cool grave will already cover the rigid remains of the restless, unhappy man who knows of no sweeter delight in the last moments of his life than to converse with you. I have had a frightful night, and ah! a beneficent night. It is this night which has confirmed and fixed my resolution: I want to die! When I tore myself from you yesterday, in the fearful rebellion of my senses, with everything pressing to my heart, and my hopeless, joyless existence near you gripped me with a gruesome coldness—I was scarcely able to reach my room; I threw myself on my knees, beside myself, and Thou, God, didst grant me the final comfort of the bitterest tears! A thousand plans, a thousand prospects raged in my mind, and finally it stood there, fixed, whole, the final and single thought: I want to die!—I lay down, and in the morning, in the calm of awakening it still stands firm, still strong in my heart: I want to die!—It is not despair, it is the certainty that I have reached the end of my suffering, that I sacrifice myself for you. Yes, Lotte! Why should I conceal it? One of us three must go, and I am willing to

mich opfere für Dich. Ja, Lotte! warum sollte ich es verschweigen? Eins von uns dreien muß hinweg, und das will
ich sein! O meine Beste! In diesem zerrissenen Herzen ist
es wütend herumgeschlichen, oft — Deinen Mann zu
ermorden! — Dich! — mich! — So sei es denn! — Wenn
Du hinaufsteigst auf den Berg, an einem schönen Sommer-
abende, dann erinnere Dich meiner, wie ich so oft das Tal
heraufkam, und dann blicke nach dem Kirchhofe hinüber,
nach meinem Grabe, wie der Wind das hohe Gras im
Scheine der sinkenden Sonne hin- und herwiegt. — Ich
war ruhig, da ich anfing, nun, nun weine ich wie ein Kind,
da alles das so lebhaft um mich wird. —"

Gegen zehn Uhr rief Werther seinem Bedienten, und
unter dem Anziehen sagte er ihm: wie er in einigen Tagen
verreisen würde; er solle daher die Kleider auskehren und
alles zum Einpacken zurecht machen; auch gab er ihm
Befehl, überall Kontos zu fordern, einige ausgeliehene
Bücher abzuholen und einigen Armen, denen er wöchentlich etwas zu geben gewohnt war, ihr Zugeteiltes auf zwei
Monate voraus zu bezahlen.

Er ließ sich das Essen auf die Stube bringen, und nach
Tische ritt er hinaus zum Amtmanne, den er nicht zu
Hause antraf. Er ging tiefsinnig im Garten auf und ab und
schien noch zuletzt alle Schwermut der Erinnerung auf
sich häufen zu wollen.

Die Kleinen ließen ihn nicht lange in Ruhe, sie verfolgten ihn, sprangen an ihm hinauf, erzählten ihm; daß,
wenn morgen und wieder morgen und noch ein Tag wäre,
sie die Christgeschenke bei Lotten holten, und erzählten
ihm Wunder, die sich ihre kleine Einbildungskraft versprach. — „Morgen!" rief er aus, „und wieder morgen!
und noch ein Tag!" — und küßte sie alle herzlich und
wollte sie verlassen, als ihm der Kleine noch etwas in das
Ohr sagen wollte. Der verriet ihm, die großen Brüder hätten schöne Neujahrswünsche geschrieben, so groß! und
einen für den Papa, für Albert und Lotten einen und auch
einen für Herrn Werther; die wollten sie am Neujahrs-
tage früh überreichen. Das übermannte ihn, er schenkte

be that one. Oh, my dearest one! In this torn heart the frenzied thought has often slunk about, often—to murder your husband—you—myself!—So be it, then.—When you climb the mountain on a beautiful summer evening, remember me, the way I often came up the valley; and then look over toward the churchyard at my grave, see how the wind makes the tall grass sway back and forth in the light of the setting sun.—I was calm when I began, but now, when all this becomes so vivid to me, I am weeping like a child."—

Toward ten o'clock Werther called his servant and, while dressing, told him that he would leave on a journey in a few days; he was therefore to take out his clothes and prepare everything for packing; he also ordered him to call in all his bills, get back books he had lent, and pay some poor people, to whom he usually gave a weekly allowance, their allotted share for two months in advance.

He had his meal brought to his room, and after eating it he rode out to visit the bailiff, whom he did not find at home. He walked up and down the garden deep in thought, as if, in the end, he wished to heap on himself the full measure of melancholy memories.

The children did not leave him long in peace; they pursued him, jumped upon him, told him that after tomorrow and another tomorrow and one more day they would fetch their Christmas gifts from Lotte; and they told him all the wonderful things they pictured in their childish imaginations.—"Tomorrow!" he exclaimed, "and another tomorrow, and one more day"—and kissed them all heartily and was about to leave them when the little fellow wanted to whisper something in his ear. He confided to him that his big brothers had written beautiful New Year's greetings, So Big! and one for Papa, one for Albert and Lotte, and one for Herr Werther too; they were going to present them early on New Year's day. This overwhelmed him. He gave

jedem etwas, setzte sich zu Pferde, ließ den Alten grüßen, und ritt mit Tränen in den Augen davon.

Gegen fünf kam er nach Hause, befahl der Magd, nach dem Feuer zu sehen und es bis in die Nacht zu unterhalten. Den Bedienten hieß er Bücher und Wäsche unten in den Koffer packen und die Kleider einnähen. Darauf schrieb er wahrscheinlich folgenden Absatz seines letzten Briefes an Lotten.

„Du erwartest mich nicht! Du glaubst, ich würde gehorchen und erst Weihnachtsabend Dich wieder sehn. O Lotte! heut oder nie mehr. Weihnachtsabend hältst Du dieses Papier in Deiner Hand, zitterst und benetzest es mit Deinen lieben Tränen. Ich will, ich muß! Oh, wie wohl ist es mir, daß ich entschlossen bin."

Lotte war indes in einen sonderbaren Zustand geraten. Nach der letzten Unterredung mit Werthern hatte sie empfunden, wie schwer es ihr fallen[100] werde, sich von ihm zu trennen, was er leiden würde, wenn er sich von ihr entfernen sollte.

Es war wie im Vorübergehn in Alberts Gegenwart gesagt worden, daß Werther vor Weihnachtsabend nicht wiederkommen werde, und Albert war zu einem Beamten in der Nachbarschaft geritten, mit dem er Geschäfte abzutun hatte, und wo er über Nacht ausbleiben mußte.

Sie saß nun allein; keins von ihren Geschwistern war um sie, sie überließ sich ihren Gedanken, die stille über ihren Verhältnissen herumschweiften. Sie sah sich nun mit dem Mann auf ewig verbunden, dessen Liebe und Treue sie kannte, dem sie von Herzen zugetan war, dessen Ruhe, dessen Zuverlässigkeit recht vom Himmel dazu bestimmt zu sein schien, daß eine wackere Frau das Glück ihres Lebens darauf gründen sollte; sie fühlte, was er ihr und ihren Kindern auf immer sein würde. Auf der andern Seite war ihr Werther so teuer geworden; gleich von dem ersten Augenblick ihrer Bekanntschaft an hatte sich die Übereinstimmung ihrer Gemüter so schön gezeigt, der lange dauernde Umgang mit ihm, so manche durchlebten Situationen hatten einen unauslöschlichen Eindruck auf ihr

something to each of them, mounted his horse, left regards for the old gentleman, and rode off with tears in his eyes.

He arrived home at about five o'clock, gave orders to the maid to attend to the fire and to keep it going into the night. He told his servant to pack books and linen into the bottom of the trunk, and to sew his outer clothes up in a bundle. Then he probably wrote the following paragraph of his last letter to Lotte:

"You are not expecting me. You believe I will obey you and not see you before Christmas Eve. O Lotte! It's today or never. On Christmas Eve you will hold this paper in your hand; you will tremble and moisten it with your precious tears. I will, I must! Oh how good I feel in my resolution."

Lotte had meanwhile fallen into a strange mental state. After her last conversation with Werther she had felt how difficult it would be for her to part from him, how much he would suffer if he left her.

It had been mentioned in Albert's presence, as though in passing, that Werther would not come again before Christmas Eve, and Albert had gone on horseback to see an official in the district with whom he had some business to transact; he was to stay overnight.

She now sat alone; none of her brothers or sisters was with her, and she abandoned herself to her thoughts, which silently revolved about her situation. She now saw herself tied forever to the man whose love and loyalty she knew, to whom she was devoted with all her heart, whose tranquillity and trustworthiness really seemed destined by Heaven to serve as the basis for a good woman's lifelong happiness; she felt what he would always be to her and the children. On the other hand, Werther had become very dear to her; from the first moment of their acquaintance the harmony of their minds had revealed itself so beautifully, her long and continuous association with him, the many situations they had experienced together had made an indelible impression on her heart. Every interesting thing she felt and

Herz gemacht. Alles, was sie Interessantes fühlte und dachte, war sie gewohnt, mit ihm zu teilen, und seine Entfernung drohte, in ihr ganzes Wesen eine Lücke zu reißen, die nicht wieder ausgefüllt werden konnte. Oh, hätte sie ihn in dem Augenblick zum Bruder umwandeln können, wie glücklich wäre sie gewesen! — Hätte sie ihn einer ihrer Freundinnen verheiraten dürfen, hätte sie hoffen können, auch sein Verhältnis gegen Albert ganz wieder herzustellen!

Sie hatte ihre Freundinnen der Reihe nach durchgedacht und fand bei einer jeglichen[101] etwas auszusetzen, fand keine, der sie ihn gegönnt hätte.

Über allen diesen Betrachtungen fühlte sie erst tief, ohne sich es deutlich zu machen, daß ihr herzliches heimliches Verlangen sei, ihn für sich zu behalten, und sagte sich daneben, daß sie ihn nicht behalten könne, behalten dürfe; ihr reines, schönes, sonst so leichtes und leicht sich helfendes Gemüt empfand den Druck einer Schwermut, dem die Aussicht zum Glück verschlossen ist. Ihr Herz war gepreßt, und eine trübe Wolke lag über ihrem Auge.

So war es halb sieben geworden, als sie Werthern die Treppe heraufkommen hörte und seinen Tritt, seine Stimme, die nach ihr fragte, bald erkannte. Wie schlug ihr Herz, und wir dürfen fast sagen zum erstenmal, bei seiner Ankunft. Sie hätte sich gern vor ihm verleugnen lassen, und als er hereintrat, rief sie ihm mit einer Art von leidenschaftlicher Verwirrung entgegen: „Sie haben nicht Wort gehalten." — „Ich habe nichts versprochen", war seine Antwort. — „So hätten Sie wenigstens meiner Bitte stattgeben sollen", versetzte sie, „ich bat Sie um unser beider Ruhe."

Sie wußte nicht recht, was sie sagte, ebensowenig was sie tat, als sie nach einigen Freundinnen schickte, um nicht mit Werthern allein zu sein. Er legte einige Bücher hin, die er gebracht hatte, fragte nach andern, und sie wünschte, bald daß ihre Freundinnen kommen, bald daß sie wegbleiben möchten. Das Mädchen kam zurück und brachte die Nachricht, daß sich beide entschuldigen ließen.

Sie wollte das Mädchen mit ihrer Arbeit in das Nebenzimmer sitzen[102] lassen; dann besann sie sich wieder an-

thought, she was accustomed to share with him, and his departure threatened to open a gap in her entire existence which could never be filled. Oh, if at that moment she could have transformed him into a brother, how happy she would have been!—If she could have married him off to one of her friends, she might have hoped to restore his relationship to Albert completely to its former state.

She had thought of her friends one after the other, but found something to object to in every one of them and found none to whom she would gladly have yielded him.

Amid all these reflections she felt deeply for the first time, without realizing it clearly, that the secret longing of her heart was to keep him for herself, but she also told herself that she could not, must not keep him; her pure, beautiful spirit, usually so light and so ready to solve difficulties, felt the oppressive melancholy to which the prospect of happiness is closed. Her heart was heavy, and a cloud of gloom hung over her eyes.

It was half past six when she heard Werther coming up the stairs and she soon recognized his step and his voice, which asked for her. How her heart pounded at his approach—one might almost say for the first time. She would have liked to deny him her presence, and when he came in she cried out to him with a sort of passionate confusion: "You have not kept your word." "I promised nothing," was his answer. "Then you should at least have granted my wish," she replied, "I begged you for peace of mind for us both."

She did not quite know what she was saying, and just as little what she was doing, when she sent out for some friends so that she would not have to be alone with Werther. He put down some books which he had brought, asked about others, and she wished at one moment that her friends would come, the next that they would not. The maid came back and reported that they both sent their regrets.

She wanted to have the maid sit in the next room over her sewing; then she changed her mind. Werther paced up

ders. Werther ging in der Stube auf und ab, sie trat ans Klavier und fing ein Menuett an, es wollte nicht fließen. Sie nahm sich zusammen und setzte sich gelassen zu Werthern, der seinen gewöhnlichen Platz auf dem Kanapee eingenommen hatte.

„Haben Sie nichts zu lesen?" sagte sie. — Er hatte nichts. — „Da drin in meiner Schublade", fing sie an, „liegt Ihre[103] Übersetzung einiger Gesänge Ossians; ich habe sie noch nicht gelesen, denn ich hoffte immer, sie von Ihnen zu hören; aber zeither[104] hat sich's nicht finden, nicht machen wollen." — Er lächelte, holte die Lieder, ein Schauer überfiel ihn, als er sie in die Hände nahm, und die Augen standen ihm voll Tränen, als er hineinsah. Er setzte sich nieder und las.

Stern[105] der dämmernden Nacht, schön funkelst du in Westen, hebst dein strahlend[106] Haupt aus deiner Wolke, wandelst stattlich deinen Hügel hin. Wonach blickst du auf die Heide? Die stürmenden Winde haben sich gelegt; von ferne kommt des Gießbachs Murmeln; rauschende Wellen spielen am Felsen ferne; das Gesumme der Abendfliegen schwärmet übers Feld. Wornach siehst du, schönes Licht? Aber du lächelst und gehst, freudig umgeben dich die Wellen und baden dein liebliches Haar. Lebe wohl, ruhiger Strahl. Erscheine, du herrliches Licht von Ossians Seele!

Und es erscheint in seiner Kraft. Ich sehe meine geschiedenen Freunde, sie sammeln sich auf Lora, wie in den Tagen, die vorüber sind. — Fingal kommt wie eine feuchte Nebelsäule; um ihn sind seine Helden, und, siehe! die Barden des Gesanges: Grauer Ullin! stattlicher Ryno! Alpin, lieblicher Sänger! und du, sanft klagende Minona! — Wie verändert seid ihr, meine Freunde, seit den festlichen Tagen auf Selma, da wir buhlten um die Ehre des Gesangs, wie Frühlingslüfte den Hügel hin wechselnd beugen das schwach lispelnde Gras.

Da trat Minona hervor in ihrer Schönheit, mit niedergeschlagenem Blick und tränenvollem Auge, schwer floß ihr Haar im unsteten Winde, der von dem Hügel herstieß. — Düster ward's in der Seele der Helden, als sie die liebliche Stimme erhob; denn oft hatten sie das Grab Salgars gesehen, oft die finstere Wohnung der weißen Colma. Colma, verlassen auf dem Hügel, mit der harmonischen Stimme; Salgar ver-

and down the room, and she went to the piano and began to play a minuet, but it refused to come smoothly. She pulled herself together and sat down calmly beside Werther, who had taken his usual place on the sofa.

"Have you nothing to read?" she said.—He had nothing. —"There in my drawer," she said, "is your translation of some songs of Ossian; I haven't read them yet, for I kept hoping to hear them from you; but since then I have never been able to find or make the opportunity."—He smiled, fetched the songs, a shudder possessing him as he took them in his hands, and his eyes filled with tears as he looked at them. He sat down and read:

Star of descending night! fair is thy light in the west! thou liftest thy unshorn head from thy cloud; thy steps are stately on thy hill. What dost thou behold in the plain? The stormy winds are laid. The murmur of the torrent comes from afar. Roaring waves climb the distant rock. The flies of evening are on their feeble wings; the hum of their course is on the field. What dost thou behold, fair light? But thou dost smile and depart. Thy waves come with joy around thee: they bathe thy lovely hair. Farewell, thou silent beam! Let the light of Ossian's soul arise!

And it does arise in its strength! I behold my departed friends. Their gathering is on Lora, as in the days of other years. Fingal comes like a watery column of mist; his heroes are around. And see the bards of song, grey-haired Ullin! stately Ryno! Alpin, with the tuneful voice! the soft complaint of Minona! How are ye changed, my friends, since the days of Selma's feast? when we contended like gales of spring, as they fly along the hill, and bend by turns the feebly-whistling grass.

Minona came forth in her beauty; with down-cast look and tearful eye. Her hair flew slowly on the blast, that rushed unfrequent from the hill. The souls of the heroes were sad when she raised the tuneful voice. Often had they seen the grave of Salgar, the dark dwelling of white-bosomed Colma. Colma left alone on the hill, with all her voice of song! Salgar promised to come: but the night descended around. Hear the voice of

sprach zu kommen; aber ringsum zog sich die Nacht. Höret
Colmas Stimme, da sie auf dem Hügel allein saß.

Colma

Es ist Nacht! — Ich bin allein, verloren auf dem stürmischen Hügel. Der Wind saust im Gebirge. Der Strom heult
den Felsen hinab. Keine Hütte schützt mich vor dem Regen,
mich Verlaßne auf dem stürmischen Hügel.

Tritt, o Mond, aus deinen Wolken! Erscheinet, Sterne der
Nacht! Leite[107] mich irgendein Strahl zu dem Orte, wo meine
Liebe[108] ruht von den Beschwerden der Jagd, sein Bogen
neben ihm abgespannt, seine Hunde schnobend[109] um ihn!
Aber hier muß ich sitzen allein auf dem Felsen des ver-
wachsenen Stroms. Der Strom und der Sturm saust[110], ich höre
nicht die Stimme meines Geliebten.

Warum zaudert mein Salgar? Hat er sein Wort vergessen?
— Da ist der Fels und der Baum und hier der rauschende
Strom! Mit einbrechender Nacht versprachst du hier zu sein:
ach! wohin hat sich mein Salgar verirrt? Mit dir wollt' ich
fliehen, verlassen Vater und Bruder, die Stolzen! Lange sind
unsere Geschlechter Feinde, aber wir sind keine Feinde, o
Salgar!

Schweig eine Weile, o Wind, still eine kleine Weile, o
Strom! daß meine Stimme klinge durchs Tal, daß mein Wanderer mich höre. Salgar! ich bin's, die ruft! Hier ist der Baum
und der Fels! Salgar! mein Lieber! hier bin ich; warum
zauderst du zu kommen?

Sieh, der Mond erscheint, die Flut glänzt im Tale, die
Felsen stehen grau den Hügel hinauf; aber ich seh' ihn nicht
auf der Höhe, seine Hunde vor ihm her verkündigen nicht
seine Ankunft. Hier muß ich sitzen allein.

Aber wer sind, die[111] dort unten liegen auf der Heide?
— Mein Geliebter? Mein Bruder? Redet, o meine Freunde!
Sie antworten nicht. Wie geängstet ist meine Seele! — Ach
sie sind tot! Ihre Schwerter rot vom Gefechte! O mein Bruder,
mein Bruder! warum hast du meinen Salgar erschlagen? O
mein Salgar! warum hast du meinen Bruder erschlagen? Ihr
wart mir beide so lieb! Oh, du warst schön an dem Hügel
unter Tausenden! Er war schrecklich in der Schlacht. Ant-
wortet mir! hört meine Stimme, meine Geliebten! Aber ach!
sie sind stumm! stumm auf ewig! Kalt, wie die Erde, ist ihr
Busen!

Oh, von dem Felsen des Hügels, von dem Gipfel des
stürmenden Berges, redet, Geister der Toten! Redet! mir soll

Colma, when she sat alone on the hill!

Colma

It is night; I am alone, forlorn on the hill of storms. The wind is heard in the mountain. The torrent pours down the rock. No hut receives me from the rain, forlorn on the hill of winds

Rise, moon! from behind thy clouds. Stars of the night, arise! Lead me, some light, to the place where my love rests from the chase alone! his bow near him, unstrung: his dogs panting around him. But here I must sit alone, by the rock of the mossy stream. The stream and the wind roar aloud. I hear not the voice of my love!

Why delays my Salgar, why the chief of the hill, his promise? Here is the rock, and here the tree! here is the roaring stream! Thou didst promise with night to be here. Ah! whither is my Salgar gone? With thee I would fly from my father; with thee, from my brother of pride. Our race have long been foes; we are not foes, O Salgar!

Cease a little while, O wind! stream, be thou silent a while! let my voice be heard around. Let my wanderer hear me! Salgar! it is Colma who calls. Here is the tree, and the rock. Salgar, my love! I am here. Why delayest thou thy coming?

Lo! the calm moon comes forth. The flood is bright in the vale. The rocks are gray on the steep. I see him not on the brow. His dogs come not before him, with tidings of his near approach. Here I must sit alone!

Who lie on the heath beside me? Are they my love and my brother? Speak to me, O my friends! To Colma they give no reply. Speak to me: I am alone! My soul is tormented with fears! Ah, they are dead! Their swords are red from the fight. O my brother! my brother! why hast thou slain my Salgar? why, O Salgar! hast thou slain my brother? Dear were ye both to me! what shall I say in your praise? Thou wert fair on the hill among thousands! he was terrible in fight. Speak to me; hear my voice; hear me, sons of my love! They are silent; silent for ever! Cold, cold are their breasts of clay!

Oh! from the rock on the hill; from the top of the windy steep, speak, ye ghosts of the dead! speak, I will not be afraid!

es nicht grausen! — Wohin seid ihr zur Ruhe gegangen? In welcher Gruft des Gebirges soll ich euch finden! — Keine schwache Stimme vernehme ich im Winde, keine wehende Antwort im Sturme des Hügels.

Ich sitze in meinem Jammer, ich harre[112] auf den Morgen in meinen Tränen. Wühlet das Grab, ihr Freunde der Toten; aber schließt es nicht, bis ich komme. Mein Leben schwindet wie ein Traum, wie sollt' ich zurückbleiben. Hier will ich wohnen mit meinen Freunden an dem Strome des klingenden Felsens — Wenn's Nacht wird auf dem Hügel und Wind kommt über die Heide, soll mein Geist im Winde stehn und trauern den Tod meiner Freunde. Der Jäger hört mich aus seiner Laube, fürchtet meine Stimme und liebt sie; denn süß soll meine Stimme sein um meine Freunde, sie waren mir beide so lieb!

Das war dein Gesang, o Minona, Tormans sanft errötende Tochter. Unsere Tränen flossen um Colma, und unsere Seele ward düster.

Ullin trat auf mit der Harfe und gab uns Alpins Gesang — Alpins Stimme war freundlich, Rynos Seele ein Feuerstrahl. Aber schon ruhten sie im engen Hause, und ihre Stimme war verhallet in Selma. Einst kehrte Ullin zurück von der Jagd, ehe die Helden noch fielen. Er hörte ihren Wettegesang[113] auf dem Hügel. Ihr Lied war sanft, aber traurig. Sie klagten Morars Fall, des Ersten der Helden. Seine Seele war wie Fingals Seele, sein Schwert wie das Schwert Oskars[114] — Aber er fiel, und sein Vater jammerte, und seiner Schwester Augen waren voll Tränen, Minonas Augen waren voll Tränen, der Schwester des herrlichen Morars. Sie trat zurück vor Ullins Gesang wie der Mond in[115] Westen, der den Sturmregen voraussieht und sein schönes Haupt in eine Wolke verbirgt. — Ich schlug die Harfe mit Ullin zum Gesange des Jammers.

Ryno

Vorbei sind Wind und Regen, der Mittag ist so heiter, die Wolken teilen sich. Fliehend bescheint den Hügel die unbeständige Sonne. Rötlich fließt der Strom des Bergs im Tale hin. Süß ist dein Murmeln, Strom; doch süßer die Stimme, die ich höre. Es ist Alpins Stimme, er bejammert den Toten. Sein Haupt ist vor Alter gebeugt und rot sein tränendes Auge. Alpin, trefflicher Sänger! warum allein auf dem schweigenden Hügel? Warum jammerst du wie ein Windstoß im Wald, wie eine Welle am fernen Gestade?

Whither are ye gone to rest? In what cave of the hill shall I find the departed? No feeble voice is on the gale; no answer half-drowned in the storm!

I sit in my grief! I wait for morning in my tears! Rear the tomb, ye friends of the dead. Close it not till Colma come. My life flies away like a dream! why should I stay behind? Here shall I rest with my friends, by the stream of the sounding rock. When night comes on the hill; when the loud winds arise; my ghost shall stand in the blast, and mourn the death of my friends. The hunter shall hear from his booth. He shall fear, but love my voice! For sweet shall my voice be for my friends: pleasant were her friends to Colma!

Such was thy song, Minona, softly-blushing daughter of Torman. Our tears descended from Colma, and our souls were sad!

Ullin came with his harp; he gave the song of Alpin. The voice of Alpin was pleasant; the soul of Ryno was a beam of fire! But they had rested in the narrow house: their voice had ceased in Selma. Ullin had returned, one day, from the chase, before the heroes fell. He heard their strife on the hill; their song was soft but sad. They mourned the fall of Morar, first of mortal men! His soul was like the soul of Fingal; his sword like the sword of Oscar. But he fell, and his father mourned: his sister's eyes were full of tears. Minona's eyes were full of tears, the sister of car-borne Morar. She retired from the song of Ullin, like the moon in the west, when she foresees the shower, and hides her fair head in a cloud. I touched the harp, with Ullin; the song of mourning rose!

Ryno

The wind and the rain are past: calm is the noon of day. The clouds are divided in heaven. Over the green hills flies the inconstant sun. Red through the stony vale comes down the stream of the hill. Sweet are thy murmurs, O stream! but more sweet is the voice I hear. It is the voice of Alpin, the son of song, mourning for the dead! Bent is his head of age; red his tearful eye. Alpin, thou son of song, why alone on the silent hill? why complainest thou, as a blast in the woods; as a wave on the lonely shore?

Meine Tränen, Ryno, sind für den Toten, meine Stimme für die Bewohner des Grabs. Schlank bist du auf dem Hügel, schön unter den Söhnen der Heide. Aber du wirst fallen wie Morar und auf deinem Grabe der Trauernde sitzen. Die Hügel werden dich vergessen, deine Bogen in der Halle liegen ungespannt.

Du warst schnell, o Morar, wie ein Reh auf dem Hügel, schrecklich wie die Nachtfeuer am Himmel. Dein Grimm war ein Sturm, dein Schwert in der Schlacht wie Wetterleuchten über der Heide. Deine Stimme glich dem Waldstrome nach dem Regen, dem Donner auf fernen Hügeln. Manche fielen vor deinem Arm, die Flamme deines Grimmes verzehrte sie. Aber wenn du wiederkehrtest vom Kriege, wie friedlich war deine Stirne! Dein Angesicht war gleich der Sonne nach dem Gewitter, gleich dem Monde in der schweigenden Nacht, ruhig deine Brust wie der See, wenn sich des Windes Brausen gelegt hat.

Eng ist nun deine Wohnung, finster deine Stätte! Mit drei Schritten mess' ich dein Grab, o du, der du ehe[116] so groß warst! Vier Steine mit moosigen Häuptern sind dein einziges Gedächtnis, ein entblätterter Baum, langes Gras, das im Winde wispelt[117], deutet dem Auge des Jägers das Grab des mächtigen Morars. Keine Mutter hast du, dich zu beweinen, kein Mädchen mit Tränen der Liebe. Tot ist, die dich gebar, gefallen die Tochter von Morglan.

Wer auf seinem Stabe ist das? Wer ist es, dessen Haupt weiß ist vor Alter, dessen Augen rot sind von Tränen? Es ist dein Vater, o Morar! der Vater keines Sohnes außer dir. Er hörte von deinem Ruf in der Schlacht, er hörte von zerstobenen Feinden; er hörte Morars Ruhm! Ach! nichts von seiner Wunde? Weine, Vater Morars, weine! Aber dein Sohn hört dich nicht. Tief ist der Schlaf der Toten, niedrig ihr Kissen von Staube. Nimmer achtet er auf die Stimme, nie erwacht er auf deinen Ruf. Oh, wann wird es Morgen im Grabe, zu bieten dem Schlummerer: Erwache!

Lebe wohl, edelster der Menschen, du Eroberer im Felde! Aber nimmer wird dich das Feld sehen, nimmer der düstere Wald leuchten vom Glanze deines Stahls. Du hinterließest keinen Sohn; aber der Gesang soll deinen Namen erhalten, künftige Zeiten sollen von dir hören, hören von dem gefallenen Morar.

Laut war die Trauer der Helden, am lautesten Armins ber-

My tears, O Ryno! are for the dead; my voice for those that have passed away. Tall thou art on the hill; fair among the sons of the vale. But thou shalt fall like Morar; the mourner shall sit on thy tomb. The hills shall know thee no more; thy bow shall lie in thy hall unstrung!

Thou wert swift, O Morar! as a roe on the desert; terrible as a meteor of fire. Thy wrath was as the storm. Thy sword in battle, as lightning in the field. Thy voice was a stream after rain; like thunder on distant hills. Many fell by thy arm; they were consumed in the flames of thy wrath. But when thou didst return from war, how peaceful was thy brow! Thy face was like the sun after rain; like the moon in the silence of night; calm as the breast of the lake when the loud wind is laid.

Narrow is thy dwelling now! dark the place of thine abode! With three steps I compass thy grave, O thou who wast so great before! Four stones, with their heads of moss are the only memorial of thee. A tree with scarce a leaf, long grass which whistles in the wind, mark to the hunter's eye the grave of the mighty Morar. Morar! thou art low indeed. Thou hast no mother to mourn thee; no maid with her tears of love. Dead is she that brought thee forth. Fallen is the daughter of Morglan.

Who on his staff is this? who is this, whose head is white with age? whose eyes are red with tears? who quakes at every step? It is thy father, O Morar! the father of no son but thee. He heard of thy fame in war; he heard of foes dispersed. He heard of Morar's renown; why did he not hear of his wound? Weep, thou father of Morar! weep; but thy son heareth thee not. Deep is the sleep of the dead; low their pillow of dust. No more shall he hear thy voice; no more awake at thy call. When shall it be morn in the grave, to bid the slumberer awake?

Farewell, thou bravest of men! thou conqueror in the field! but the field shall see thee no more; nor the dark wood be lightened with the splendor of thy steel. Thou hast left no son. The song shall preserve thy name. Future times shall hear of thee; they shall hear of the fallen Morar!

The grief of all arose, but most the bursting sigh of Armin.

245

stender Seufzer. Ihn erinnerte es an den Tod seines Sohnes, er fiel in den Tagen der Jugend. Carmor saß nah bei dem Helden, der Fürst des hallenden Galmal. „Warum schluchzet der Seufzer Armins?" sprach er, „was ist hier zu weinen? Klingt nicht Lied und Gesang, die Seele zu schmelzen und zu ergötzen? Sie sind wie sanfter Nebel, der steigend vom See aufs Tal sprüht, und die blühenden Blumen füllet das Naß; aber die Sonne kommt wieder in ihrer Kraft und der Nebel ist gegangen. Warum bist du so jammervoll, Armin, Herrscher des seeumflossenen Gorma?"

„Jammervoll! Wohl das bin ich, und nicht gering die Ursache meines Wehs. — Carmor, du verlorst keinen Sohn, verlorst keine blühende Tochter; Colgar, der Tapfere, lebt, und Annira, die schönste der Mädchen. Die Zweige deines Hauses blühen, o Carmor; aber Armin ist der Letzte seines Stammes. Finster ist dein Bett, o Daura, dumpf ist dein Schlaf in dem Grabe — Wann erwachst du mit deinen Gesängen, mit deiner melodischen Stimme? Auf! ihr Winde des Herbstes! Auf! stürmt über die finstere Heide! Waldströme, braust! Heult, Stürme, im Gipfel der Eichen! Wandle durch gebrochene Wolken, o Mond, zeige wechselnd dein bleiches Gesicht! Erinnre mich der schrecklichen Nacht, da meine Kinder umkamen, da Arindal, der Mächtige, fiel, Daura, die Liebe, verging.

„Daura, meine Tochter, du warst schön! Schön wie der Mond auf den Hügeln von Fura, weiß wie der gefallene Schnee, süß wie die atmende Luft! Arindal, dein Bogen war stark, dein Speer schnell auf dem Felde, dein Blick wie Nebel auf der Welle, dein Schild eine Feuerwolke im Sturme!

„Armar, berühmt im Kriege, kam und warb um Dauras Liebe; sie widerstand nicht lange. Schön waren die Hoffnungen ihrer Freunde.

„Erath, der Sohn Ogdals, grollte, denn sein Bruder lag erschlagen von Armar. Er kam, in einen Schiffer verkleidet. Schön war sein Nachen auf der Welle, weiß seine Locken vor Alter, ruhig sein ernstes Gesicht. ‚Schönste der Mädchen,' sagte er, ‚liebliche Tochter von Armin, dort am Felsen, nicht fern in der See, wo die rote Frucht vom Baume herblinkt, dort wartet Armar auf Daura; ich komme, seine Liebe zu führen über die rollende See.'

„Sie folgt' ihm und rief nach Armar; nichts antwortete als die Stimme des Felsens. ‚Armar! mein Lieber! Mein Lieber! warum ängstest du mich so? Höre, Sohn Arnarths, höre! Daura ist's, die dich ruft!'

He remembers the death of his son, who fell in the days of his youth. Carmor was near the hero, the chief of the echoing Galmal. Why bursts the sigh of Armin? he said. Is there a cause to mourn? The song comes, with its music, to melt and please the soul. It is like soft mist, that, rising from a lake, pours on the silent vale; the green flowers are filled with dew, but the sun returns in his strength, and the mist is gone. Why art thou sad, O Armin! chief of sea-surrounded Gorma?

Sad I am! nor small is my cause of woe! Carmor, thous hast lost no son; thou hast lost no daughter of beauty. Colgar the valiant lives; and Annira, fairest maid. The boughs of thy house ascend, O Carmor! but Armin is the last of his race. Dark is thy bed, O Daura! deep thy sleep in the tomb! When shalt thou awake with thy songs? with all thy voice of music? Arise, winds of Autumn, arise; blow along the heath! streams of the mountains, roar! roar, tempests, in the groves of my oaks! walk through broken clouds, O moon! show thy pale face, at intervals! bring to my mind the night, when all my children fell; when Arindal the mighty fell; when Daura the lovely failed!

Daura, my daughter! thou wert fair; fair as the moon on Fura; white as the driven snow; sweet as the breathing gale. Arindal, thy bow was strong. Thy spear was swift in the field. Thy look was like mist on the wave; thy shield, a red cloud in a storm.

Armar, renowned in war, came, and sought Daura's love. He was not long refused: fair was the hope of their friends!

Erath, son of Odgal, repined; his brother had been slain by Armar. He came disguised like a son of the sea: fair was his skiff on the wave; white his locks of age; calm his serious brow. Fairest of women, he said, lovely daughter of Armin! a rock not distant in the sea bears a tree on its side; red shines the fruit afar. There Armar waits for Daura. I come to carry his love!

She went; she called on Armar. Nought answered, but the son of the rock, Armar, my love! my love! why tormentest thou me with fear? hear, son of Arnart, hear: it is Daura who calleth thee!

„Erath, der Verräter, floh lachend zum Lande. Sie erhob ihre Stimme, rief nach ihrem Vater und Bruder: ‚Arindal; Armin! Ist keiner, seine Daura zu retten?‘

„Ihre Stimme kam über die See. Arindal, mein Sohn, stieg vom Hügel herab, rauh in der Beute der Jagd, seine Pfeile rasselten an seiner Seite, seinen Bogen trug er in der Hand, fünf schwarzgraue Doggen waren um ihn. Er sah den kühnen Erath am Ufer, faßte und band ihn an die Eiche, fest umflocht er seine Hüften, der Gefesselte füllt mit Ächzen die Winde.

„Arindal betritt die Wellen in seinem Boote, Daura herüber zu bringen. Armar kam in seinem Grimme, drückt' ab den grau befiederten Pfeil, er klang, er sank in dein Herz, o Arindal, mein Sohn! Statt Eraths, des Verräters, kamst du um, das Boot erreichte den Felsen, er sank dran nieder und starb. Zu deinen Füßen floß deines Bruders Blut, welch war dein Jammer, o Daura!

„Die Wellen zerschmettern das Boot. Armar stürzt sich in die See, seine Daura zu retten oder zu sterben. Schnell stürmt ein Stoß vom Hügel in die Wellen, er sank und hob sich nicht wieder.

„Allein auf dem seebespülten Felsen hörte ich die Klagen meiner Tochter. Viel und laut war ihr Schreien, doch konnte sie ihr Vater nicht retten. Die ganze Nacht stand ich am Ufer, ich sah sie im schwachen Strahle des Mondes, die ganze Nacht hörte ich ihr Schreien, laut war der Wind, und der Regen schlug scharf nach der Seite des Berges. Ihre Stimme ward schwach, ehe der Morgen erschien; sie starb weg wie die Abendluft zwischen dem Grase der Felsen. Beladen mit Jammer starb sie und ließ Armin allein! Dahin ist meine Stärke[118] im Kriege, gefallen mein Stolz unter den Mädchen.

„Wenn die Stürme des Berges kommen, wenn der Nord die Wellen hochhebt, sitze ich am schallenden Ufer, schaue nach dem schrecklichen Felsen. Oft im sinkenden Monde sehe ich die Geister meiner Kinder, halb dämmernd wandeln sie zusammen in trauriger Eintracht.“

Ein Strom von Tränen, der aus Lottens Augen brach und ihrem gepreßten Herzen Luft machte, hemmte Werthers Gesang. Er warf das Papier hin, faßte ihre Hand und weinte die bittersten Tränen. Lotte ruhte auf der andern und verbarg ihre Augen ins Schnupftuch. Die Bewegung beider war fürchterlich. Sie fühlten ihr eigenes

Erath the traitor fled laughing to the land. She lifted up her voice; she called for her brother and her father. Arindal! Armin! none to relieve your Daura!

Her voice came over the sea. Arindal my son descended from the hill; rough in the spoils of the chase. His arrows rattled by his side; his bow was in his hand: five dark gray dogs attend his steps. He saw fierce Erath on the shore: he seized and bound him to an oak. Thick wind the thongs of the hide around his limbs; he loads the wind with his groans.

Arindal ascends the deep in his boat, to bring Daura to land. Armar came in his wrath, and let fly the grey-feathered shaft. It sung; it sunk in thy heart, O Arindal, my son! for Erath the traitor thou diedst. The oar is stopped at once; he panted on the rock and expired. What is thy grief, O Daura, when round thy feet is poured thy brother's blood!

The boat is broken in twain. Armar plunges into the sea, to rescue his Daura, or die. Sudden a blast from the hill came over the waves. He sank and he rose no more.

Alone, on the sea-beat rock, my daughter was heard to complain. Frequent and loud were her cries. What could her father do? All night I stood on the shore. I saw her by the faint beam of the moon. All night I heard her cries. Loud was the wind; the rain beat hard on the hill. Before morning appeared her voice was weak. It died away, like the evening-breeze among the grass of the rocks. Spent with grief she expired; and left thee, Armin, alone. Gone is my strength in war! fallen my pride among women!

When the storms aloft arise; when the north lifts the wave on high; I sit by the sounding shore, and look on the fatal rock. Often by the setting moon, I see the ghosts of my children. Half viewless, they walk in mournful conference together.

A flood of tears which fell from Lotte's eyes and relieved her bursting heart checked Werther's recitation. He threw the papers down, grasped her hand and wept the bitterest tears. Lotte supported herself on the other hand and covered her eyes with her handkerchief. Both showed a fearful emotion. They felt their own misery in the destiny of the

Elend in dem Schicksale der Edlen, fühlten es zusammen, und ihre Tränen vereinigten sie. Die Lippen und Augen Werthers glühten an Lottens Arme; ein Schauer überfiel sie; sie wollte sich entfernen und Schmerz und Anteil lagen betäubend wie Blei auf ihr. Sie atmete, sich zu erholen, und bat ihn schluchzend, fortzufahren, bat mit der ganzen Stimme des Himmels! Werther zitterte, sein Herz wollte bersten, er hob das Blatt auf und las halb gebrochen.

Warum[119] weckst du mich, Frühlingsluft? Du buhlst und sprichst: „Ich betaue mit Tropfen des Himmels!" Aber die Zeit meines Welkens ist nahe, nahe der Sturm, der meine Blätter herabstört! Morgen wird der Wanderer kommen, kommen der mich sah in meiner Schönheit; ringsum wird sein Auge im Felde mich suchen und wird mich nicht finden. —

Die ganze Gewalt dieser Worte fiel über den Unglücklichen. Er warf sich vor Lotten nieder in der vollen Verzweiflung, faßte ihre Hände, drückte sie in seine Augen, wider seine Stirn, und ihr schien eine Ahnung seines schrecklichen Vorhabens durch die Seele zu fliegen. Ihre Sinne verwirrten sich, sie drückte seine Hände, drückte sie wider ihre Brust, neigte sich mit einer wehmütigen Bewegung zu ihm, und ihre glühenden Wangen berührten sich. Die Welt verging ihnen. Er schlang seine Arme um sie her, preßte sie an seine Brust und deckte ihre zitternden, stammelnden Lippen mit wütenden Küssen. — „Werther!" rief sie mit erstickter Stimme, sich abwendend, „Werther!" —und drückte mit schwacher Hand seine Brust von der ihrigen; — „Werther!" rief sie mit dem gefaßten Tone des edelsten Gefühles. — Er widerstand nicht, ließ sie aus seinen Armen und warf ich unsinnig vor sie hin. Sie riß sich auf, und in ängstlicher Verwirrung, bebend zwischen Liebe und Zorn, sagte sie: „Das ist das letztemal! Werther! Sie sehn mich nicht wieder." — Und mit dem vollsten Blick der Liebe auf den Elenden eilte sie ins Nebenzimmer und schloß hinter sich zu. Werther streckte ihr die Arme nach, getraute sich nicht, sie zu halten. Er lag an der Erde, den Kopf auf dem Kanapee, und in dieser Stellung blieb er

heroes, felt it together, and their tears mingled. Werther's lips and eyes burned on Lotte's arms; a shudder possessed her and she wanted to withdraw; pain and sympathy lay upon her like a leaden weight, numbing her senses. She took a deep breath, hoping to compose herself, and, sobbing, begged him to continue, begged him with the full voice of Heaven. Werther trembled and, his heart ready to burst, picked up the sheets and read in a broken voice:

"Why dost thou awake me, O gale!" it seems to say, "I am covered with the drops of heaven! The time of my fading is near, the blast that shall scatter my leaves. Tomorrow shall the traveler come; he that saw me in my beauty shall come. His eyes will search the field, but they will not find me."—

The whole force of these words descended on the unhappy man. He threw himself down before Lotte in all his despair, grasped her hands, pressed them to his eyes, against his forehead, and a premonition of his terrible resolve seemed to fly through her mind. Her senses became confused, she pressed his hands, pressed them against her breast, leaned toward him with a melancholy movement, and their burning cheeks touched. The world ceased to exist for them. He threw his arms about her, pressed her to his breast, and covered her trembling, stammering lips with violent kisses.—"Werther!" she cried in a choking voice, turning from him, "Werther!" and with a weak hand she pushed his body away from hers. "Werther!" she cried in the steady tone of the noblest emotion—He did not resist, released her from his arms and threw himself before her, senseless. She jumped up, and in confusion and anxiety, quivering between love and anger, she said, "This is the last time, Werther. You shall not see me again."—And with the warmest look of love at the wretched man she hurried into the next room and locked the door behind her. Werther stretched out his arms after her, but did not dare to hold her back. He lay on the floor, his head on the sofa, and remained in this position for more than half

über eine halbe Stunde, bis ihn ein Geräusch zu sich selbst rief. Es war das Mädchen, das den Tisch decken wollte. Er ging im Zimmer auf und ab, und da er sich wieder allein sah, ging er zur Türe des Kabinetts und rief mit leiser Stimme: „Lotte! Lotte! Nur noch ein Wort! ein Lebewohl!" — Sie schwieg. Er harrte und bat und harrte; dann riß er sich weg und rief: „Lebe wohl, Lotte! auf ewig lebe wohl!"

Er kam ans Stadttor. Die Wächter, die ihn schon gewohnt waren, ließen ihn stillschweigend hinaus. Es stiebte[120] zwischen Regen und Schnee, und erst gegen elf klopfte er wieder. Sein Diener bemerkte, als Werther nach Hause kam, daß seinem Herrn der Hut fehlte. Er getraute sich nicht, etwas zu sagen, entkleidete ihn, alles war naß. Man hat nachher den Hut auf einem Felsen, der an dem Abhange des Hügels ins Tal sieht, gefunden, und es ist unbegreiflich, wie er ihn in einer finstern feuchten Nacht, ohne zu stürzen, erstiegen hat.

Er legte sich zu Bette und schlief lange. Der Bediente fand ihn schreibend, als er ihm den andern Morgen auf sein Rufen den Kaffee brachte. Er schrieb folgendes am Briefe an Lotten.

„Zum letzten Male denn, zum letzten Male schlage ich diese Augen auf. Sie sollen ach! die Sonne nicht mehr sehen, ein trüber neblichter[121] Tag hält sie bedeckt. So traure denn, Natur! Dein Sohn, dein Freund, dein Geliebter naht sich seinem Ende. Lotte, das ist ein Gefühl ohnegleichen, und doch kommt es dem dämmernden Traum am nächsten, zu sich zu sagen: Das ist der letzte Morgen. Der letzte! Lotte, ich habe keinen Sinn für das Wort der letzte! Stehe ich nicht da in meiner ganzen Kraft, und morgen liege ich ausgestreckt und schlaff am Boden. Sterben! Was heißt das? Siehe, wir träumen, wenn wir vom Tode reden. Ich habe manchen sterben sehen; aber so eingeschränkt ist die Menschheit, daß sie für ihres Daseins Anfang und Ende keinen Sinn hat. Jetzt noch mein, Dein! Dein, o Geliebte! Und einen Augenblick — getrennt, geschieden — vielleicht auf ewig? — Nein, Lotte, nein — Wie kann ich vergehen? Wie kannst Du vergehen? Wir *sind* ja! — Vergehen! —

an hour, until a noise brought him back to consciousness. It was the maid who wanted to set the table. He paced up and down the room, and when he found himself alone again, he went to the door of the study and called in a low voice: "Lotte! Lotte! just one more word, a word of farewell."—She was silent. He waited and begged and waited; then he tore himself away and cried: "Farewell, Lotte! Farewell forever!"

He came to the city gate. The guards, who were used to him, let him out without a word. A mixture of rain and snow was falling, and he did not knock at the door again till about eleven. His servant noticed that his master was without his hat when he came home. He did not venture to say anything; he helped him undress; all his clothes were wet. Later his hat was found on a rock which overhangs the valley from the slope of the hill; it is beyond comprehension how he could have climbed this rock on a dark, wet night without falling.

He went to bed and slept long. Next morning, when he answered Werther's call and brought him his coffee, the servant found him writing. He added the following to his letter to Lotte:

"For the last time, then, for the last time I open these eyes. They shall, alas, never see the sun again, for a gloomy, foggy day obscures it. Mourn then, O Nature! Your son, your friend, your lover is approaching his end. Lotte, this is an incomparable feeling, and yet it comes closest to a twilit dream to say to oneself: this is the last morning. The last! Lotte, I have no feeling for that word: last. Do I not stand here in all my strength, and tomorrow I shall lie on the ground stretched out and limp. To die: what does that mean? Behold, we dream when we talk of death. I have seen many die; but so limited is human nature that it has no feeling for the beginning or end of its existence. At this moment there is still mine and yours— yours, O my beloved. And in another moment—separated, parted—perhaps forever?—No, Lotte, no—How can I perish? How can you perish? For we *exist!*—Perish—what does that mean? It is just another word, an empty sound,

Was heißt das? Das ist wieder ein Wort! Ein leerer Schall! ohne Gefühl für mein Herz. — — Tot, Lotte! eingescharrt der kalten Erde, so eng! so finster! — Ich hatte eine Freundin[122], die mein Alles war meiner hilflosen Jugend; sie starb, und ich folgte ihrer Leiche und stand an dem Grabe, wie sie den Sarg hinunterließen und die Seile schnurrend unter ihm weg und wieder heraufschnellten, dann die erste Schaufel hinunterschollerte und die ängstliche Lade einen dumpfen Ton wiedergab, und dumpfer und immer dumpfer, und endlich bedeckt war! — Ich stürzte neben das Grab hin — ergriffen, erschüttert, geängstet, zerrissen mein Innerstes; aber ich wußte nicht, wie mir geschah — wie mir geschehen wird — Sterben! Grab! Ich verstehe die Worte nicht!

„O vergib mir! vergib mir! Gestern! Es hätte der letzte Augenblick meines Lebens sein sollen. O Du Engel! Zum ersten Male, zum ersten Male ganz ohne Zweifel durch mein innig Innerstes durchglühte mich das Wonnegefühl: sie liebt mich! sie liebt mich! Es brennt noch auf meinen Lippen das heilige Feuer, das von den Deinigen strömte; neue warme Wonne ist in meinem Herzen. Vergib mir! Vergib mir!

„Ach, ich wußte, daß Du mich liebtest, wußte es an den ersten seelenvollen Blicken, an dem ersten Händedruck, und doch, wenn ich wieder weg war, wenn ich Alberten an Deiner Seite sah, verzagte ich wieder in fieberhaften Zweifeln.

„Erinnerst Du Dich der Blumen, die Du mir schicktest, als Du in jener fatalen Gesellschaft mir kein Wort sagen, keine Hand reichen konntest? Oh, ich habe die halbe Nacht davor gekniet, und sie versiegelten mir Deine Liebe. Aber ach! diese Eindrücke gingen vorüber, wie das Gefühl der Gnade seines Gottes allmählich wieder aus der Seele des Gläubigen weicht, die ihm mit ganzer Himmelsfülle in heiligen sichtbaren Zeichen gereicht ward.

„Alles das ist vergänglich; aber keine Ewigkeit soll das glühende Leben auslöschen, das ich gestern auf Deinen Lippen genoß, das ich in mir fühle! Sie liebt mich! Dieser Arm hat sie umfaßt, diese Lippen haben auf ihren Lippen

which does not touch my heart.—Dead, Lotte! Buried in the cold ground, so confined, so dark!—I had a friend who was everything to me in my helpless youth; she died and I followed her corpse, and stood at her grave when they let the coffin down; the ropes whirred under it, then bobbed up again; and the first shovelful of earth pattered down, and the frightened box reverberated with a dull sound which grew duller and duller until at last it was completely covered.—I threw myself down beside the grave—moved, shaken, frightened, my insides torn, but I did not know what was happening to me—what will happen to me—Dying! Grave! I don't understand these words.

"Oh forgive me, forgive me! Yesterday! It should have been the last moment of my life. Oh you angel! For the first time, for the first time without any doubt whatever, the joyful feeling burned through my innermost depths: she loves me! She loves me! The sacred fire that streamed from your lips is still burning on mine; a new, warm joy is in my heart. Forgive me! Forgive me!

"Oh, I knew that you loved me, knew it from the first soulful looks, from the first handclasp, and yet, when I was away from you, when I saw Albert at your side, again I despaired in feverish doubts.

"Do you remember the flowers you sent me when you could not say a word to me at that awful party, and could not give me your hand? Oh, I knelt before them half the night, and they confirmed your love for me. But, alas, those impressions passed, as the soul of the believer gradually loses the feeling of grace given him by his God with all the fullness of Heaven, with a sacred, visible symbol.

"All this is transitory, but no eternity shall extinguish the glowing life which I savored yesterday on your lips, and which I feel within me now. She loves me! This arm has embraced her, these lips have trembled on hers, this

gezittert, dieser Mund hat an dem ihrigen gestammelt. Sie ist mein! Du bist mein! ja, Lotte, auf ewig.

„Und was ist das, daß Albert Dein Mann ist? Mann! das wäre[123] denn für diese Welt — und für diese Welt Sünde, daß ich Dich liebe, daß ich Dich aus seinen Armen in die meinigen reißen möchte? Sünde? Gut, und ich strafe mich dafür; ich habe sie in ihrer ganzen Himmelswonne geschmeckt, diese Sünde, habe Lebensbalsam und Kraft in mein Herz gesaugt. Du bist von diesem Augenblicke mein! mein, o Lotte! Ich gehe voran! gehe zu meinem Vater, zu Deinem Vater. Dem will ich's klagen, und er wird mich trösten bis Du kommst, und ich fliege Dir entgegen und fasse Dich und bleibe bei Dir vor dem Angesichte des Unendlichen in ewigen Umarmungen.

„Ich träume nicht, ich wähne[124] nicht! Nahe am Grabe wird mir es heller. Wir werden sein[125]! wir werden uns wieder sehen! Deine Mutter sehen! Ich werde sie sehen, werde sie finden, ach und vor ihr mein ganzes Herz ausschütten! Deine Mutter, Dein Ebenbild."

Gegen elf fragte Werther seinen Bedienten, ob wohl Albert zurückgekommen sei? Der Bediente sagte: ja, er habe dessen Pferd dahin führen sehen. Drauf gibt ihm der Herr ein offenes Zettelchen des Inhalts:

„Wollten Sie[126] mir wohl zu einer vorhabenden Reise Ihre Pistolen leihen? Leben Sie recht wohl!"

Die liebe Frau hatte die letzte Nacht wenig geschlafen; was sie gefürchtet hatte, war entschieden, auf eine Weise entschieden, die sie weder ahnen noch fürchten konnte. Ihr sonst so rein und leicht fließends Blut war in einer fieberhaften Empörung, tausenderlei Empfindungen zerrütteten das schöne Herz. War es das Feuer von Werthers Umarmungen, das sie in ihrem Busen fühlte? War es Unwille über seine Verwegenheit? War es eine unmutige Vergleichung ihres gegenwärtigen Zustandes mit jenen Tagen ganz unbefangener, freier Unschuld und sorglosen Zutrauens an sich selbst? Wie sollte sie ihrem Manne entge-

mouth has stammered words on hers. She is mine! You are mine! Yes, Lotte, forever.

"And what does it mean that Albert is your husband? Husband! That is something for this world—and for this world it is a sin that I love you, that I should like to snatch you out of his arms into mine. Sin? Very well! And I am punishing myself for it; I have tasted this sin in all its heavenly bliss, I have sucked the balm of life and strength into my heart. From this moment on, you are mine. Mine, Lotte! I am going ahead, going to my Father, to your Father. I will complain to Him and He will comfort me until you come, and I will fly to meet you, clasp you and remain with you in eternal embrace before the countenance of the Infinite.

"I am not dreaming, I am not delusional; so near the grave the light grows brighter for me. We shall be! We shall see each other again! See your mother! I shall see her, shall find her, ah, and pour out my whole heart to her! Your mother, your image."

Toward eleven o'clock Werther asked his servant whether Albert had returned yet. The servant replied: yes, he had seen his horse being led home. Thereupon his master gave him an unsealed note with the following content:

"Will you loan me your pistols for a journey I am planning? Farewell."

The dear woman had slept little that night; what she had feared had been realized in a way which she could neither have suspected nor dreaded. Her blood, which usually flowed so pure and light, was in a feverish rebellion; a thousand different emotions rent her fair heart. Was it the fire of Werther's embraces she felt in her bosom? Was it anger at his boldness? Was it an irritating comparison between her present state and the days of perfectly natural, naïve innocence and carefree confidence in herself? How was she to face her husband? How confess to him a scene which she might well confess but which she yet did not

gengehen? Wie ihm eine Szene bekennen, die sie so gut gestehen durfte und die sie sich doch zu gestehen nicht getraute? Sie[127] hatten so lange gegeneinander geschwiegen, und sollte sie die erste sein, die das Stillschweigen bräche und eben zur unrechten Zeit ihrem Gatten eine so unerwartete Entdeckung machte? Schon fürchtete sie, die bloße Nachricht von Werthers Besuch werde ihm einen unangenehmen Eindruck machen, und nun gar diese unerwartete Katastrophe! Konnte sie wohl hoffen, daß ihr Mann sie ganz im rechten Lichte sehen, ganz ohne Vorurteil aufnehmen würde? Und konnte sie wünschen, daß er in ihrer Seele lesen möchte? Und doch wieder, konnte sie sich verstellen gegen den Mann, vor dem sie immer wie ein kristallhelles Glas offen und frei gestanden war, und dem sie keine ihrer Empfindungen jemals verheimlicht noch verheimlichen können? Eins und das andre machte ihr Sorgen und setzte sie in Verlegenheit; und immer kehrten ihre Gedanken wieder zu Werthern, der für sie verloren war, den sie nicht lassen konnte, den sie leider! sich selbst überlassen mußte, und dem, wenn er sie verloren hatte, nichts mehr übrig blieb.

Wie schwer lag jetzt, was sie sich in dem Augenblick nicht deutlich machen konnte, die Stockung auf ihr, die sich unter ihnen festgesetzt hatte! So verständige, so gute Menschen fingen wegen gewisser heimlicher Verschiedenheiten untereinander zu schweigen an, jedes dachte seinem Recht und dem Unrechte des andern nach, und die Verhältnisse verwickelten und verhetzten sich dergestalt, daß es unmöglich ward, den Knoten eben in dem kritischen Momente, von dem alles abhing, zu lösen. Hätte eine glückliche Vertraulichkeit sie früher wieder einander näher gebracht, wäre Liebe und Nachsicht wechselweise unter ihnen lebendig worden und hätte ihre Herzen aufgeschlossen, vielleicht wäre unser Freund noch zu retten gewesen.

Noch ein sonderbarer Umstand kam dazu. Werther hatte, wie wir aus seinen Briefen wissen, nie ein Geheimnis daraus gemacht, daß er sich diese Welt zu verlassen sehnte. Albert hatte ihn[128] oft bestritten, auch war zwischen Lotten und ihrem Mann manchmal die Rede davon gewesen. Dieser,

dare confess? They had been silent toward each other so long. Was she to be the first to break the silence and make such an unexpected revelation to her husband at so inopportune a time? She was afraid that the mere report of Werther's visit would make an unpleasant impression on him, how much more this unexpected catastrophe! Could she really hope that her husband would see it in exactly the right light and accept it without prejudice? Dare she wish that he might read her soul? But then again could she dissimulate before the man whom she had always faced, open and free like a glass of clear crystal, and from whom she never had, nor could have, concealed any of her feelings? Either alternative was a cause of anxiety and embarrassment to her; and always her thoughts returned to Werther, who was lost to her, whom she could not give up, whom she must, unfortunately, abandon to himself and for whom there was nothing left when he had lost her.

How heavily the estrangement that had settled over them now weighed on her, she could not clearly understand herself at that moment. Such intelligent, such good people began to observe a silence toward each other because of certain secret differences, each pondering his right and the other's wrong, and the relationship became so entangled and so harassed that it became impossible to loosen the knot at the critical moment on which everything depended. If a happy intimacy had re-established their former closeness sooner, if their mutual love and understanding had flourished and opened their hearts, perhaps there might still have been help for our friend.

Another strange circumstance was added to the situation. Werther, as we know from his letters, had never made a secret of the fact that he yearned to leave this world. Albert had often challenged him on the subject; Lotte and her husband had sometimes discussed the subject too.

wie er einen entschiedenen Widerwillen gegen die Tat empfand, hatte auch gar oft mit einer Art von Empfindlichkeit, die sonst ganz außer seinem Charakter lag, zu erkennen gegeben, daß er an dem Ernst eines solchen Vorsatzes sehr zu zweifeln Ursach finde; er hatte sich sogar darüber einigen Scherz erlaubt und seinen Unglauben Lotten mitgeteilt. Dies beruhigte sie zwar von einer Seite, wenn ihre Gedanken ihr das traurige Bild vorführten, von der andern aber fühlte sie sich auch dadurch gehindert, ihrem Manne die Besorgnisse mitzuteilen, die sie in dem Augenblicke quälten.

Albert kam zurück, und Lotte ging ihm mit einer verlegenen Hastigkeit entgegen, er war nicht heiter, sein Geschäft war nicht vollbracht, er hatte an dem benachbarten Amtmanne einen unbiegsamen kleinsinnigen Menschen gefunden. Der üble Weg auch hatte ihn verdrießlich gemacht.

Er fragte, ob nichts vorgefallen sei, und sie antwortete mit Übereilung: Werther sei gestern abends dagewesen. Er fragte, ob Briefe gekommen, und er erhielt zur Antwort, daß ein Brief und Pakete auf seiner Stube lägen. Er ging hinüber, und Lotte blieb allein. Die Gegenwart des Mannes, den sie liebte und ehrte, hatte einen neuen Eindruck in ihr Herz gemacht. Das Andenken seines Edelmuts, seiner Liebe und Güte hatte ihr Gemüt mehr beruhigt, sie fühlte einen heimlichen Zug, ihm zu folgen, sie nahm ihre Arbeit und ging auf sein Zimmer, wie sie mehr[129] zu tun pflegte. Sie fand ihn beschäftigt, die Pakete zu erbrechen und zu lesen. Einige schienen nicht das Angenehmste zu enthalten. Sie tat einige Fragen an ihn, die er kurz beantwortete, und sich an den Pult stellte[130] zu schreiben.

Sie waren auf diese Weise eine Stunde nebeneinander gewesen, und es ward immer dunkler in Lottens Gemüt. Sie fühlte, wie schwer es ihr werden würde, ihrem Mann, auch wenn er bei dem besten Humor wäre, das zu entdecken, was ihr auf dem Herzen lag; sie verfiel in eine Wehmut, die ihr um desto ängstlicher ward, als sie solche zu verbergen und ihre Tränen zu verschlucken suchte.

Die Erscheinung von Werthers Knaben setzte sie in die

Albert, who felt a decided aversion to the act, had quite often, with a sort of irritation that was quite out of character, made it quite clear that he had reason to doubt the seriousness of such an intention; he had even allowed himself to joke about the matter and had communicated his skepticism to Lotte. This, to be sure, calmed her when her thoughts presented the sad picture to her; on the other hand it made her feel reluctant to inform her husband of the anxiety which tormented her at the moment.

Albert returned and Lotte went to meet him with an embarrassed haste; he was not in a cheerful mood; his business had not been completed and he had found in the neighboring bailiff an unbending, petty man. The bad road too had spoiled his temper.

He asked whether anything had happened, and she answered overhastily that Werther had been there the night before. He asked if any letters had arrived and received the reply that a letter and some packages were lying in his room. He went in and Lotte remained alone. The presence of the man whom she loved and honored had made a new impression on her heart. The memory of his noble-mindedness, his love and kindness had somewhat calmed her mind, and she felt a secret impulse to follow him; she took her sewing and went into his room as she was accustomed to do. She found him occupied opening his packages and reading. Some of the contents did not seem to be of the most agreeable sort. She put some questions to him, which he answered curtly, and he took his position at his desk to write.

They had been together like this for an hour and Lotte's heart sank lower and lower. She felt how difficult it would be for her to reveal to her husband what weighed on her heart, even if he were in the best of humors; she lapsed into a state of melancholy which became all the more frightening to her as she sought to conceal it and to choke back her tears.

The appearance of Werther's servant threw her into the

größte Verlegenheit; er überreichte Alberten das Zettelchen, der sich gelassen nach seiner Frau wendete und sagte: „Gib ihm die Pistolen." — „Ich lasse ihm glückliche Reise wünschen," sagte er zum Jungen. — Das fiel auf sie wie ein Donnerschlag, sie schwankte aufzustehen, sie wußte nicht, wie ihr geschah. Langsam ging sie nach der Wand, zitternd nahm sie das Gewehr herunter, putzte den Staub ab und zauderte und hätte noch lange gezögert, wenn nicht Albert durch einen fragenden Blick sie gedrängt hätte. Sie gab das unglückliche Werkzeug dem Knaben, ohne ein Wort vorbringen zu können, und als der zum Hause hinaus war, machte sie ihre Arbeit zusammen, ging in ihr Zimmer, in dem Zustande der unaussprechlichsten Ungewißheit. Ihr Herz weissagte ihr alle Schrecknisse. Bald war sie im Begriffe, sich zu den Füßen ihres Mannes zu werfen, ihm alles zu entdecken, die Geschichte des gestrigen Abends, ihre Schuld und ihre Ahnungen. Dann sah sie wieder keinen Ausgang des Unternehmens, am wenigsten konnte sie hoffen, ihren Mann zu einem Gange nach Werthern zu bereden. Der Tisch ward gedeckt, und eine gute Freundin, die nur etwas zu fragen kam, gleich gehen wollte — und blieb, machte die Unterhaltung bei Tische erträglich; man zwang sich, man redete, man erzählte, man vergaß sich.

Der Knabe kam mit den Pistolen zu Werthern, der sie ihm mit Entzücken abnahm, als er hörte, Lotte habe sie ihm gegeben. Er ließ sich Brot und Wein[131] bringen, hieß den Knaben zu Tische gehen und setzte sich nieder zu schreiben.

„Sie sind durch Deine Hände gegangen, Du hast den Staub davon geputzt, ich küsse sie tausendmal, Du hast sie berührt! Und Du, Geist des Himmels, begünstigst meinen Entschluß! und Du, Lotte, reichst mir das Werkzeug. Du, von deren Händen ich den Tod zu empfangen wünschte, und ach, nun empfange. Oh, ich habe meinen Jungen ausgefragt. Du zittertest, als Du sie ihm reichtest, Du sagtest kein Lebewohl! — Wehe! wehe! kein Lebewohl! — Solltest Du Dein Herz für mich verschlossen haben, um des Augenblicks willen, der mich ewig an Dich befestigte? Lotte, kein Jahrtausend vermag den Eindruck auszu-

greatest embarrassment; he handed the note to Albert, who turned calmly to his wife and said: "Give him the pistols."—"I wish him a happy journey," he said to the boy. The words struck her like a thunderbolt; she staggered to her feet, not knowing what she was doing. She went slowly to the wall, trembling she took down the weapons, dusted them off, and hesitated; she would have hesitated longer still if Albert had not pressed her with a questioning look. She gave the boy the fatal weapons without being able to utter a word, and when the boy had left the house she gathered up her work and went to her room in a state of the most indescribable uncertainty. Her heart foretold her every possible terror. She was soon on the point of throwing herself at her husband's feet and disclosing everything to him, the events of the previous evening, her guilt and her premonitions. Then again she saw no way out in the matter, least of all could she hope to persuade her husband to go to Werther. The table was set and a good friend, who had merely come in to ask a question, intended to go at once—but stayed on, made the dinner conversation endurable. They made an effort, talked, told stories and forgot themselves.

The boy came back to Werther with the pistols; he took them from him with great delight when he heard that Lotte had given them to him. He had bread and wine brought up, told the boy to have his dinner, and sat down to write:

"They have passed through your hands, you dusted them off; I kiss them a thousand times, for you have touched them; and you, heavenly spirit, favor my resolve! And you, Lotte, hand me the tools, you, from whose hands I wished to receive death, and, ah, to receive it now. Oh, I questioned my boy. You were trembling when you handed them to him, you did not say farewell.—Woe, woe, no farewell!—Can you have closed your heart to me for the sake of the moment which tied me to you forever? Lotte, not even a thousand years can efface the impression! And I feel it, you cannot hate the man who burns so passionately

löschen! und ich fühle es, Du kannst den nicht hassen, der so für Dich glüht."

Nach Tische hieß er den Knaben alles vollends einpacken, zerriß viele Papiere, ging aus und brachte noch kleine Schulden in Ordnung. Er kam wieder nach Hause, ging wieder aus vors Tor, ungeachtet des Regens, in den gräflichen Garten, schweifte weiter in der Gegend umher und kam mit anbrechender Nacht zurück und schrieb.

"Wilhelm, ich habe zum letzten Male Feld und Wald und den Himmel gesehen. Lebe wohl auch Du! Liebe Mutter, verzeiht mir! Tröste sie, Wilhelm! Gott segne Euch! Meine Sachen sind alle in Ordnung. Lebt wohl! wir sehen uns wieder und freudiger."

"Ich habe Dir übel gelohnt, Albert, und Du vergibst mir. Ich habe den Frieden Deines Hauses gestört, ich habe Mißtrauen zwischen Euch gebracht. Lebe wohl! Ich will es enden. Oh, daß ihr glücklich wäret durch meinen Tod! Albert! Albert! Mache den Engel glücklich! Und so wohne Gottes Segen über Dir!"

Er kramte den Abend noch viel in seinen Papieren, zerriß vieles und warf es in den Ofen, versiegelte einige Päcke mit den Adressen an Wilhelm. Sie enthielten kleine Aufsätze, abgerissene Gedanken, deren ich verschiedene gesehen habe; und nachdem er um zehn Uhr Feuer hatte nachlegen und sich eine Flasche Wein geben lassen, schickte er den Bedienten, dessen Kammer wie auch die Schlafzimmer der Hausleute weit hinten hinaus waren, zu Bette, der sich dann in seinen Kleidern niederlegte, um frühe bei der Hand zu sein; denn sein Herr hatte gesagt, die Postpferde würden vor sechs vors Haus kommen.

"Nach elf

"Alles ist so still um mich her, und so ruhig meine Seele. Ich danke dir, Gott, der du diesen letzten Augenblicken diese Wärme, diese Kraft schenkest.

for you."

After dinner he ordered the boy to finish packing, tore up many papers, and went out to take care of some small debts. He came home again, then went out once more, through the town gate, heedless of the rain, into the Count's garden, roamed about in the area, returned home as night descended, and wrote:

"Wilhelm, I have seen the fields and the woods and the sky for the last time. Farewell to you too! Dear Mother, forgive me. Comfort her, Wilhelm. God bless you both. All my affairs are in order. Farewell! We shall see each other again, in happier circumstances."

"I have ill rewarded you, Albert, but you will forgive me. I have disturbed the peace of your home, I have brought distrust between you. Farewell; I will end it. Oh I wish that my death may restore your happiness. Albert, Albert, make the angel happy! And so may God's blessing rest upon you."

That evening he continued to rummage among his papers, tore up many of them, threw them into the stove, and sealed some packages addressed to Wilhelm. They contained short essays and fragmentary thoughts, some of which I have seen. At ten o'clock he had the fire replenished and a bottle of wine brought in. He then sent his servant to his bedroom, which, like those of the other servants, was far to the rear of the house. The boy slept in his clothes so that he could be at hand early next morning; for his master had told him that the post horses would be in front of the house before six.

"After 11 o'clock

"Everything is so quiet round about me, and my mind is so quiet too. I thank Thee, Lord, for giving me such warmth, such strength, in these last moments.

„Ich trete an das Fenster, meine Beste! und sehe und sehe noch durch die stürmenden, vorüberfliehenden Wolken einzelne Sterne des ewigen Himmels! Nein, ihr werdet nicht fallen! Der Ewige trägt euch an seinem Herzen, und mich. Ich sehe die Deichselsterne des Wagens, des liebsten unter allen Gestirnen. Wenn ich nachts von Dir ging, wie ich aus Deinem Tore trat, stand er gegen mir über[132]. Mit welcher Trunkenheit habe ich ihn oft angesehen! oft mit aufgehabenen[133] Händen ihn zum Zeichen, zum heiligen Merksteine meiner gegenwärtigen Seligkeit gemacht! und noch — O Lotte, was erinnert mich nicht an Dich! Umgibst Du mich nicht! Und habe ich nicht, gleich einem Kinde, ungenügsam allerlei Kleinigkeiten zu mir gerissen, die Du Heilige berührt hattest!

„Liebes Schattenbild! Ich vermache Dir es zurück, Lotte, und bitte Dich, es zu ehren. Tausend, tausend Küsse habe ich drauf gedrückt, tausend Grüße ihm zugewinkt, wenn ich ausging oder nach Hause kam.

„Ich habe Deinen Vater in einem Zettelchen gebeten, meine Leiche zu schützen. Auf dem Kirchhofe sind zwei Lindenbäume, hinten in der Ecke nach dem Felde zu; dort wünsche ich zu ruhen. Er kann, er wird das für seinen Freund tun. Bitte ihn auch. Ich will frommen Christen nicht zumuten, ihren Körper neben einen armen Unglücklichen zu legen[134]. Ach, ich wollte, ihr begrübt mich am Wege oder im einsamen Tale, daß Priester und Levit[135] vor dem bezeichneten Steine sich segnend vorübergingen und der Samariter eine Träne weinte.

„Hier, Lotte! Ich schaudere nicht, den kalten, schrecklichen Kelch zu fassen, aus dem ich den Taumel des Todes trinken soll! Du reichtest mir ihn und ich zage nicht. All! all! So sind alle die Wünsche und Hoffnungen meines Lebens erfüllt! So kalt, so starr an der ehernen Pforte des Todes anzuklopfen.

„Daß ich des Glückes hätte teilhaftig werden können, für Dich zu sterben! Lotte, für Dich mich hinzugeben! Ich wollte mutig, ich wollte freudig sterben, wenn ich Dir die Ruhe, die Wonne Deines Lebens wieder schaffen könnte. Aber ach! das ward nur wenigen Edeln gegeben, ihr Blut für die Ihrigen zu vergießen und durch ihren Tod

"I go to the window, my dearest one, and I can see individual stars in the eternal sky, even through the passing storm clouds. No, you will not fall! The Eternal One bears you on His heart and me too. I saw the handle of the Great Wain, which I love best of all the constellations. When I went from you at night, as I left your gate, it stood right before me. With what intoxication have I often looked at it! Often, with uplifted hands, I have made it the symbol, the sacred milestone of my present happiness; and even now—O Lotte, doesn't everything remind me of you? Do you not surround me? And have I not, like a child, greedily snatched up every trifle, which your sacred hands had touched?

"Precious silhouette! I bequeath it back to you, Lotte, and beg you to revere it. I have pressed a thousand kisses on it, waved a thousand greetings to it when I went out or came home.

"I have asked your father, in a note I sent, to protect my body. In the churchyard there are two linden trees, at the rear in the corner toward the field; there I wish to rest. He can, he will do this for his friend. You ask him too. I do not expect God-fearing Christians to lay their bodies near that of a poor, unfortunate man like me. Ah, I wish you would bury me beside the road or in some lonesome valley, so that the priest and the Levite might pass the stone marker and bless themselves, and the Samaritan might shed a tear.

"See, Lotte, I do not shudder to take the cold terrible cup into my hand, from which I shall drink the intoxication of death. You handed it to me, and I do not hesitate. All! All! Thus are all the wishes and hopes of my life fulfilled—to knock so coldly, so rigidly at the brazen portals of death.

"If I could have partaken of the joy of dying for you, Lotte, of sacrificing myself for you! I would die bravely, die joyfully, if I could restore to you the peace, the bliss of your life. But alas, it is granted only to a few noble souls to shed their blood for their dear ones, and by their death to kindle a new, hundredfold life for their friends.

ein neues hundertfältiges Leben ihren Freunden anzufachen.

„In diesen Kleidern, Lotte, will ich begraben sein, Du hast sie berührt, geheiligt; ich habe auch Deinen Vater darum gebeten. Meine Seele schwebt über dem Sarge. Man soll meine Taschen nicht aussuchen. Diese blaßrote Schleife, die Du am Busen hattest, als ich Dich zum ersten Male unter Deinen Kindern fand — Oh, küsse sie tausendmal und erzähle ihnen das Schicksal ihres unglücklichen Freundes. Die Lieben! Sie wimmeln um mich. Ach wie ich mich an Dich schloß! seit dem ersten Augenblicke Dich nicht lassen konnte! — Diese Schleife soll mit mir begraben werden. An meinem Geburtstage schenktest Du mir sie! Wie ich das alles verschlang! — Ach ich dachte nicht, daß mich der Weg hierher führen sollte! — — Sei ruhig! ich bitte Dich, sei ruhig! —

„Sie sind geladen — Es schlägt zwölf! So sei es denn! — Lotte! Lotte, lebe wohl! lebe wohl!"

Ein Nachbar sah den Blick[136] vom Pulver und hörte den Schuß fallen; da aber alles stille blieb, achtete er nicht weiter drauf.

Morgens um sechs tritt der Bediente herein mit dem Lichte. Er findet seinen Herrn an der Erde, die Pistole und Blut. Er ruft, er faßt ihn an; keine Antwort, er röchelte nur noch. Er läuft nach den Ärzten, nach Alberten. Lotte hört die Schelle ziehen, ein Zittern ergreift alle ihre Glieder. Sie weckt ihren Mann, sie stehen auf, der Bediente bringt heulend und stotternd die Nachricht, Lotte sinkt ohnmächtig vor Alberten nieder.

Als der Medikus zu dem Unglücklichen kam, fand er ihn an der Erde ohne Rettung, der Puls schlug, die Glieder waren alle gelähmt. Über dem rechten Auge hatte er sich durch den Kopf geschossen, das Gehirn war herausgetrieben. Man ließ ihm zum Überfluß eine Ader[137] am Arme, das Blut lief, er holte noch immer Atem.

Aus dem Blut auf der Lehne des Sessels konnte man schließen, er habe sitzend vor dem Schreibtische die Tat vollbracht, dann ist er herunter gesunken, hat sich konvulsivisch um den Stuhl herumgewälzt. Er lag gegen das

"I wish to be buried in these clothes, Lotte; you have touched them, hallowed them; I have requested this too of your father. My soul hovers over my coffin. My pockets are not to be emptied. This pale pink ribbon which you wore at your breast when I saw you for the first time among the children—O kiss them a thousand times and tell them the fate of their unhappy friend. The dear ones! They are crowding about me. Oh, how I clung to you! I could not leave you from the first moment.—This ribbon shall be buried with me. You gave it to me on my birthday. How I devoured all this.—Ah, I did not think that my road was to lead me here.—Be calm, I beg you, be calm!—

"They are loaded—the clock strikes twelve. So be it then! Lotte, Lotte, farewell, farewell."

A neighbor noticed the flash of the powder and heard the shot; but since a silence followed, he paid no attention to it.

At six in the morning the servant came in with a light. He found his master on the floor, the pistol and blood. He called, and touched him; no answer, only the death rattle. He ran for a doctor, to Albert. Lotte heard the bell and was seized with a trembling in all her limbs. She awakened her husband and they got up; the servant gave them the news, weeping and stuttering. Lotte sank down unconscious at Albert's feet.

When the doctor came to the unhappy man, he found him on the floor beyond rescue, his pulse still beating, but all his limbs paralyzed. The bullet had entered his head above the right eye; his brains were protruding. A vein was needlessly opened in his arm; the blood flowed, and he was still breathing.

From the blood on the arm of the chair one could infer that he had done the deed as he sat before his desk, then slumped down thrashing about convulsively in his chair. He lay on his back near the window, exhausted. He was

Fenster entkräftet auf dem Rücken, war in völliger Kleidung, gestiefelt, im blauen Frack mit gelber Weste.

Das Haus, die Nachbarschaft, die Stadt kam in Aufruhr. Albert trat herein. Werthern hatte man auf das Bette gelegt, die Stirn verbunden, sein Gesicht schon wie eines Toten, er rührte kein Glied. Die Lunge röchelte noch fürchterlich, bald schwach, bald stärker; man erwartete sein Ende.

Von dem Weine hatte er nur ein Glas getrunken. Emilia Galotti[138] lag auf dem Pulte aufgeschlagen.

Von Alberts Bestürzung, von Lottens Jammer laßt mich nichts sagen.

Der alte Amtmann kam auf die Nachricht hereingesprengt, er küßte den Sterbenden unter den heißesten Tränen. Seine ältesten Söhne kamen bald nach ihm zu Fuße, sie fielen neben dem Bette nieder im Ausdruck des unbändigsten Schmerzes, küßten ihm die Hände und den Mund, und der älteste, den er immer am meisten geliebt, hing an seinen Lippen, bis er verschieden war und man den Knaben mit Gewalt wegriß. Um zwölf mittags starb er. Die Gegenwart des Amtmannes und seine Anstalten tuschten einen Auflauf. Nachts gegen elf ließ er ihn an die Stätte begraben, die er sich erwählt hatte. Der Alte folgte der Leiche und die Söhne, Albert vermocht's nicht. Man fürchtete für Lottens Leben. Handwerker trugen ihn. Kein Geistlicher hat ihn begleitet[139].

fully dressed, wearing his boots, his blue coat and yellow vest.

The house, the neighborhood, the whole town was in an uproar. Albert came in. Werther had been placed on the bed, his forehead bandaged; his face already touched with the look of death, he was unable to move a limb. A horrible rattle came from his lungs, now weak, now stronger; the end was expected momentarily.

He had drunk only one glass of the wine. *Emilia Galotti* lay open on his desk.

I shall say nothing of Albert's consternation nor of Lotte's grief.

The old bailiff, upon hearing the news, came rushing in; he kissed the dying man, shedding the most passionate tears. His oldest sons soon followed after him on foot; they fell down beside the bed with an expression of the most uncontrollable pain, and kissed his hands and lips; and the oldest, whom he had always liked best, clung to his lips until he had died, and the boy had to be removed by force. He died at noon. The presence of the bailiff, and the measures he had taken, quelled a disturbance. At about eleven o'clock at night he had him buried at the spot which he had selected for himself. The old man and his sons followed the body; Albert was unable to do so. Lotte's life was feared to be in danger. Workmen carried him. No clergyman accompanied him.

NOTES

BOOK ONE

1. Leonore plays the same role in this novel as Rosaline in Shakespeare's *Romeo and Juliet:* she is the object of a former superficial love, in contrast to the deep love to come.
2. *konnte ich dafür,* could I help it.
3. *der Schmerzen,* genitive depending on *minder.*
4. The world of the *Sturm und Drang* is revealed here in the preference for the natural or "English" garden over the geometrically pruned "French" garden of the baroque period; in the contrast between the intellect and the heart; in the cult of ruins (*verfallen*); in the tears which Werther sheds so frequently.
5. An instance of the romantic emphasis on inspiration, inner vision, rather than on concrete performance.
6. *dämmern,* a favorite word of the *Sturm und Drang,* more "romantic" than the full light, which is a symbol of consciousness and intellect.
7. *unendlich,* another romantic word, expressing the urge to transcend the limitations of this existence.
8. The well, the patriarchs, the princesses fetching water—all these conjure up Rousseau's world of primitive life in contrast to modern artificial and degenerate urban civilization. This contrast is one of the leitmotifs of the novel.
9. *Melusine,* the legendary mermaid who married a mortal. Her story is told in a *Volksbuch.*
10. *anzüglich,* suggestive, offensive; used for *anziehend,* attractive.
11. An allusion to Genesis 24 and 29.
12. Homer, symbol of simplicity and the naïve (Rousseau's "nature"), which to the "sentimental" man connotes happiness.
13. The simple folk and children are symbols of Rousseauistic "nature."
14. *Flüchtlinge,* i.e., people who defect from their higher social status to go slumming among the lower classes.
15. older form for *Ihnen.*

16. *ward,* older form of *wurde.*
17. *Kringen,* a cushion of cloth, stuffed with horsehair, to soften the weight of the load borne on the head.
18. Cf. Erich Fromm's "escape from freedom."
19. *Freundin,* an older woman who acted as a spiritual mentor to Werther (cf. page 254, line 4 ff.), as Susanne von Klettenberg did to the young Goethe. Such mentors of either sex were common in the life and literature of the eighteenth century.
20. i.e., if I had not actually had such a friend.
21. *Seele* is much broader in meaning than the English word "soul" and must on occasion be rendered by "heart" or "mind."
22. *Genie,* one of the key words of the *Sturm und Drang,* also known as the *Genieperiode* because it glorified genius—i.e., deep emotion or wild inspiration—over dull regularity.
23. Werther's contempt for theory is characteristic of the romantic revolt against the *Aufklärung.* Charles Batteux (1713–1780), French writer on aesthetics, author of *Les beaux arts réduits à un même principe.* Robert Wood (1717–1775), Scottish archaeologist, author of *Essay on the Original Genius and Writings of Homer.* Roger de Piles (1635–1709), painter, and writer on aesthetics, author of *Abrégé de la vie des peintres.* Johann Joachim Winckelmann (1717–1768), archaeologist, art historian, one of the great minds of the eighteenth century. Johann Georg Sulzer (1720–1779), author of a much read encyclopedia of art, *Theorie der schönen Künste* (1774). Christian Heyne (1729–1812), philologist, professor at the University of Göttingen.
24. *Manuskript,* lecture notes from one of his courses.
25. *gar einen,* more usual: *einen gar.*
26. *viel Wesens machen,* make much of.
27. *historisch,* i.e., it gives factual material instead of emotional effusions.
28. *Ahnung,* literally: presentiment; *Darstellung,* literally: representation.
29. *gelahrt,* older form of *gelehrt,* here used sarcastically; *Hofmeister,* private tutor.
30. *hierauf,* in reply to this.
31. *Hüttchen,* a favorite word of the time, symbolizing idyllic bliss in nature. Goethe used it frequently in his *Sturm und Drang* period.
32. *heimlich,* homely, i.e., characteristic of home life; simple, unpretentious.
33. *interessant,* another characteristic "period" word, like "picturesque," associated with the new romantic feeling. Cf. page 46, line 2. In modern usage the word has lost the vivid tone it had for the later eighteenth century.

34. The conflict between nature and the "rules" is central in the rise of romantic sensibility.

35. *Philister*, Philistine, Babbitt, "square"; the smug, conventional opponent of culture.

36. *los* indicates vigorous motion.

37. *irden = irdenes;* the omission of the adjective ending is older usage.

38. *Kreuzer*, a copper coin of small denomination.

39. *inkommodieren.* The foreign word suggests the deference which the simple woman feels toward the "gentleman."

40. *teil.* Modern usage requires: *teilnehmen sollen.*

41. *gezeichnet.* On page 46, line 21 we are told that Werther was sitting on the plow while he sketched. This letter was not in the first version of *Werther*.

42. *schelte,* more normal: *schilt.*

43. *Junius,* the Latin form for *Juni.*

44. *Frauenzimmer,* now used with slight disparagement.

45. *dumpficht,* normally: *dumpfig.*

46. *Treppe,* staircase: for *Stufe,* step.

47. *darin,* for *worin.*

48. *das,* more usual: *was,* since the antecedent is an idea.

49. Allusion to either *Histoire de Miss Jenny Glanville* by Marie-Jeanne Riccoboni, which appeared in a German translation in 1764, or to the novel by J. T. Hermes, *Miss Fanny Wilkes* (1766), whose heroine is a Miss Jenny.

50. Oliver Goldsmith's *The Vicar of Wakefield* (1766) was popular in Germany soon after its appearance. Goethe was introduced to it by Herder in Strassburg; it remained a favorite throughout his life.

51. *daran* for *woran.*

52. *dämmernd,* see note 6 above.

53. The three types of dance mentioned here are: the French minuet, the English country or square dance, and the German waltz *(allemande).*

54. *Chapeau,* dancing partner.

55. *Plan,* field of battle.

56. *Achte,* the big eight, a figure in the square dance.

57. *Promenade,* the grand march, another figure in the square dance.

58. *der ersten,* of the first woman.

59. *Schlucker = Schlemmer,* roisterer, playboy.

60. *Vortrag = Vorschlag,* proposal.

61. *Mäulchen. Maul* is insulting—the mouth of an animal. The diminutive adds a touch of quaintness.

62. *Zählens,* older genitive after *spielen.*

63. *gen = gegen.*

64. *der,* older genitive after *sich erinnern,* which now requires *an* with the accusative.

65. *Ode,* allusion to *Die Frühlingsfeier* (1759) by Friedrich

Gottlieb Klopstock (1724–1803). Klopstock was the herald of the *Sturm und Drang* through his epic poem *Der Messias* and his odes, which vibrated with passion and were couched in free rhythms. The ode alluded to here was occasioned by a thunderstorm and records the protagonist's emotional response to the storm.

66. *Tag*, i.e., opportunity.
67. *Penelope*, allusion to Homer's *Odyssey* 20,251.
68. *Kräusel*, frill of the shirt.
69. *der* adds a touch of contempt: that [fellow] Werther.
70. Matthew 18:3.
71. *Quakelchen* (Frankfurt dialect), pet synonym for baby.
72. *Karlsbad* in Bohemia (now Czechoslovakia), a famous medicinal bathing resort.
73. *es hieß*, he was told.
74. *Jungfer*, Miss; i.e., the parson's daughter.
75. *die kurze Zeit über*, throughout the brief time.
76. *aßen* indicates that it is sour milk or yoghurt they are eating.
77. *der*, genitive after *wenig* and *viel*.
78. allusion to *Predigten über das Buch Jonas* (1773) by Johann Kaspar Lavater (1741–1801), theologian and physiognomist, whose work Goethe esteemed highly. The sermon in question is entitled: "Mittel gegen Unzufriedenheit und üble Laune."
79. *seine*, i.e., his own wife.
80. *mich deucht* (from *dünken*), methinks; it seems to me.
81. *gegenwärtig*, i.e., who was there when she was needed.
82. *Schulden*, literally: guilty acts.
83. *einem etwas weismachen*, tell a person tales; fool one.
84. *daß ich kurz bin*, let me be brief.
85. *resigniert*, devoted.
86. *Ossian*, see note 56 of Book Two.
87. The identity of this friend is not clear.
88. *rangig* (Frankfurt dialect), greedy.
89. *was rechts*, something awful.
90. *Gulden*, an old coin worth two marks.
91. *eins*, a person (popular speech).
92. *Ölkrüglein*, I Kings 17: 14–16.
93. *Kraft*, i.e., magic power.
94. *geistvoll*, i.e., full of soul or feeling.
95. *Zauberlaterne*. The magic lantern and the peep show (*Raritätenkasten*—See note 13 of Book Two) are favorite images of the early Goethe.
96. *Bononisch*. Bononia is the Latin name of Bologna.
97. *um*, for.
98. *Taler*, an old coin worth three marks.
99. The *zu* is now unnecessary.
100. *sich prostituieren*, waste one's time, bungle.

101. *das*, more normally *was*, since the antecedent is an idea.

102. *im Treffen*, i.e., in getting a likeness.

103. *Sand*, used for blotting.

104. *einmal* emphasizes the intention: you *will*, or: for once.

105. *Sünde*. One would expect *Laster*, vice, as on page 84, line 8. But there, too, the vice was discussed in a theological context.

106. *erzählt* . . . , let the matter speak for itself.

107. *Strohmann*, i.e., man without feeling.

108. *getan*, i.e., settled.

109. *vernachlässigt*. The omission of the auxiliary in a subordinate clause is frequent in German.

110. *ehrlich*, here used in a slightly patronizing tone, perhaps: "respectable," as on page 100, line 31.

111. *das Terzerol –e*, pocket pistol.

112. *sitze*. The transition to the present tense (the historic present) is for rhetorical purposes, to achieve greater narrative power. The device is used frequently in the novel.

113. *lasse*. The present tense is used to express an action which began in the past and is still continuing.

114. *läßt sich nicht*, does not allow itself, i.e., cannot.

115. *dir*, the "ethical dative"; not translatable.

116. *was soll das* [*heißen* or *bedeuten*]?

117. *ganz was anders* = *etwas ganz anderes*.

118. *Priester*, Luke 10: 31; *Pharisäer*, Luke 18: 11.

119. *Gemeinspruch*, normally *Gemeinplatz*.

120. *sechsen*. Numbers were formerly declined.

121. *Ehre*, here: right.

122. *moralisch*, in the older sense of "mental."

123. *Krankheit zum Tode*, John 11: 4.

124. *von*, more usually *auf*.

125. *Ahnung*, i.e., an idea as to what it all means, or what she may do.

126. *in die Enge pressen*, drive into a corner.

127. *Säfte*, the "humors" or juices in the body which, according to the old physiology, regulate the proper functioning of the system.

128. *andern*, more usual: *anderem*.

129. *Hauptstückchen*, chapter, story.

130. *Inzidentpunkt* (legal term), minor incident.

131. *Schnürchen*, i.e., like counting beads on a rosary—mechanically.

132. *gleitete*, usually: *glitt, geglitten*.

133. *mutig* = *mutwillig*, gaily.

134. *vergöttern*, idolize; here: turn into a god.

135. *wirken*, produce; for Herder and the young Goethe equivalent to *schaffen*, create.

136. *sich zusammen sichern*, seek security in living together.

137. *etliche* = *einige*.

138. *Fabel*. The horse asks man to help him in his battle against

277

the stag, but finds that he loses his freedom as a result of the help offered.

139. August 28 is Goethe's birthday.
140. *vorhatte,* wore in front [of her dress].
141. *Duodez, duodecimo,* i.e., small in size (because the sheet is folded twelve times). J. H. Wetstein was the printer of the duodecimo edition, which appeared in Amsterdam in 1707; J. A. Ernesti was the editor of the five-volume quarto edition, published at Leipzig (1759–1764).
142. *Erscheinungen,* appearances, i.e., unrealities.
143. *Gipfel,* mountain peak; here used for *Wipfel,* treetop.
144. *wären.* The subjunctive introduces a note of conjecture into the statement.
145. *Garten,* the Count's garden described on page 32, line 33.
146. *mir* for me. Werther unconsciously assumes proprietorship over nature and the places that attract him. This is not arrogance, but indicative of a high degree of intimacy.
147. *Kunst,* i.e., although the garden was made by man (=*Kunst*), it was romantic, i.e., natural.
148. *Kabinett,* small room; here: garden house.
149. The sentiment, though not the precise wording, is that of Klopstock's ode *An Fanny.*
150. *hingegeben* = *ergeben,* resigned.
151. *erweckt,* i.e., out of my spell.
152. *Gestalten,* i.e., in the next world.

BOOK TWO

1. *idealisch,* i.e., born in our imagination.
2. *übersieht,* i.e., he is not a pedant who can see only the small details of the job to be done.
3. *Base,* literally: cousin; here: old woman.
4. *leicht weg,* casually.
5. *Partikel.* Conjunctions are meant, as Werther explains in the sentence after the next. This stylistic unorthodoxy and the use of inversions (i.e., beginning a sentence with an adverbial or adjectival phrase rather than with the subject) were characteristic of the young *Sturm und Drang* rebels. Goethe's early letters are full of them, whereas his legal writings of the same period are entirely free from them.
6. *des Teufels werden,* go mad.
7. *außenbleiben* = *ausbleiben.*
8. *Perioden,* now feminine: *die Periode.*
9. *von* usually *an.*
10. *Eigensinn,* stubbornness; here: capriciousness.
11. *Jahrhundert,* age. Classical writers divided history into four periods or ages: the golden, silver, bronze, and iron; each age was regarded as being inferior to the preceding one. This scheme is here applied to individual man's existence.

278

12. *Dichten,* here: inventiveness.
13. *Raritätenkasten,* peep show: a box with a hole in front; peeping through the hole, one sees tiny figures moving about, illustrating some story. These boxes were hawked about at German fairs.
14. *eine.* One would expect *ein,* since *Fräulein* is neuter. But Goethe uses the feminine consistently.
15. *mir,* usually: *mich.*
16. *Eingeweide,* intestines, common eighteenth-century synonym for heart, mind, feelings.
17. *Subalterne,* subaltern, subordinate.
18. *Obrist = Oberst.*
19. *en passant,* in passing.
20. Francis I was crowned emperor of the Holy Roman Empire in 1745.
21. *in qualitate,* i.e., by virtue of being admitted to this aristocratic society, he was addressed with a title.
22. The following letter tells us that Werther spoke to Fräulein B. on March 16, i.e., the next day.
23. *Ulyß.* The eighteenth century used the Latin names of the Greek gods and heroes.
24. *etwas auf die leichte Achsel nehmen,* make light of something.
25. *Hundegeschwätz,* wretched chatter.
26. Werther places the incident as occurring two days ago. It would therefore seem likely that the aunt would belabor Fräulein B. that same evening (March 14) or the following morning (March 15). But in the final sentence of this paragraph Fräulein B. tells Werther that her aunt raised the matter *gestern nacht* and *heute früh*—i.e., March 15 and 16. An instance of Homer nodding?
27. *gestern nacht,* usually: *gestern abend.*
28. *trätschen,* pour; here for *tratschen,* gossip.
29. *nun einmal,* simply.
30. *Säftchen,* syrup; as one gives children a bitter medicine in syrup.
31. *Geheimenrat = Geheimrat.* Goethe declines the first component like an adjective, which it really is.
32. *Halte,* stop.
33. *auf gut Glück,* on the off-chance, or hoping for the best.
34. *Pilgrim,* now: *Pilger.*
35. *es läßt sich,* one can.
36. *davon = wovon.*
37. *hält,* treats.
38. *Lage,* i.e., in my normal situation or condition.
39. *Wesen,* stuff.
40. *gestempelt,* bearing the stamp of authority: or perhaps "rubber stamped," stereotyped.
41. *sich weismachen,* make oneself believe.

42. *das,* more usual: *was;* cf. note 101 above. The position of the verb *verließ* is unusual.
43. *kränkt.* According to Trunz the word means "sickens" rather than the usual "offends." He refers to page 114, line 22 and page 126, line 15.
44. *sein,* genitive of *er.*
45. *verbilden,* miseducate, deform.
46. *schwer halten,* be difficult.
47. *tut,* behaves.
48. *eins ist doch dabei,* there's this about it.
49. *Zutrauen.* Some commentators consider this a misprint for *Zutragen,* contribution. However, it may mean: sign of confidence or affection.
50. *Kanon.* Eighteenth-century liberal theology examined the books of the Bible critically to determine which of them are canonical, i.e., divine and authoritative; *melieren,* mix.
51. Lavater's general position in theology is antirationalist. He was a friend of Hamann, Herder, and the young Goethe. The rationalistic Frau Pfarrerin would therefore shrug her shoulders at his "enthusiasms."
52. *ich komme nicht zu mir,* I cannot regain my equanimity.
53. Benjamin Kennicott (1718–83), British scholar, who wrote critically on the text of the Old Testament; J. S. Semler (1725–91) tried to establish a canon of the Biblical books; J. D. Michaelis (1717–91) published a critical translation of the Old Testament.
54. *Frauen,* the old genitive.
55. *ihm die Suppen fett machen,* i.e., bring him in much.
56. *Ossian,* the legendary Gaelic bard of the third century A.D. Supposed translations from his works were published by James Macpherson (1736–96): *Fragments of Ancient Poetry* (1760), *Fingal* (1762), *Temora* (1763), in a collected edition (1765). These gloomy ballads and songs were taken for genuine translations and acclaimed throughout Europe. Macpherson's imposture was not proven till 1840, though some (e.g., Samuel Johnson) had their suspicions. Klopstock, Herder, and the young Goethe were Ossian enthusiasts. Goethe translated some of the Ossian songs into German. See note 103 of Book Two.
57. The quotation is from the passage of Ossian quoted on page 250.
58. *Sinne,* i.e., inner senses.
59. *der ganze Kerl,* i.e., my total personality.
60. *verlecht* from *lechen* (Biblical and dialect), to leak. Modern German: *lecken,* adj. *leck.*
61. This letter is rich in Biblical allusions, comparing Werther's suffering to that of Christ on the Cross. See Introduction.
62. *Müdseligkeit.* The word is Goethe's own coinage.
63. *verschmachten,* be parched with thirst.

64. *sagt,* John 6: 37, 44, 66.
65. Werther is not justifying his fear of death, but his condemnation of life. "Shall I lack the courage to say at the last moment: life is not worth living, when Jesus Himself said as much?"
66. Psalms 104: 2.
67. *Mitleiden* is stronger than *Mitleid;* it implies that Lotte suffers with him and this suffering shows itself on her face.
68. *schwur,* alternate form of *schwor.*
69. *untergegangen.* The participle is equivalent to an imperative.
70. *darin = worin.*
71. *Nadeln = Haarnadeln,* hairpins.
72. *haußen = hier außen,* out here.
73. *Er,* older form of address (singular of the modern *Sie*), used both as a deferential form to superiors and condescendingly to inferiors. Werther uses it in the latter sense, the insane man in the former.
74. *Seinen = the modern Ihren.*
75. *Generalstaaten.* The Netherlands government is meant: it was considered to be fabulously rich.
76. *Euer = the modern Ihr.*
77. *nichts.* The double negative is characteristic of common speech.
78. *von sich,* out of his mind.
79. *mir auf = auf mich.*
80. *Hindernis,* now neuter.
81. *müsse,* subjunctive of wish (optative), stronger than the more usual *möge.*
82. *das heilige Grab,* the Holy Sepulchre.
83. *Tränen des Weinstocks,* i.e., wine.
84. *Melodie.* See page 94, line 34.
85. *Lieblingsgerichte,* favorite dishes, i.e., melodies.
86. *Abscheidenden,* the man who was in the process of departing.
87. *Werthers.* The verb *erwähnen* now governs the accusative case.
88. *sich legen,* apply oneself, stick to.
89. *wirksam,* i.e., when he held an office.
90. *ob* and *gleich* belong together.
91. *schöne Seele,* a popular phrase of the period, used also by Rousseau (*belle âme*). It denoted a person who enjoys a natural harmony between his intellect and instincts, between duty and desires. With its roots in Plato and Plotinus, the conception was given classic formulation by Schiller in his essay *Über Anmut und Würde* (1793) and by Goethe in the sixth book of *Wilhelm Meisters Lehrjahre* (1795).
92. *geschickt,* capable; here: good, nice.
93. *knirren = knirschen,* gnash.
94. *weise,* i.e., worldly wise.
95. *politisch,* i.e., diplomatic, clever.

281

96. *diese Zeit her,* recently.
97. *dagegen,* in return.
98. *das = was.*
99. *ausgetragen* refers to the mother who has borne her child the full nine months. So Werther has reached his time.
100. *schwer fallen,* be hard.
101. *jeglichen = jeden.*
102. *sitzen = sich setzen* (southwest German).
103. *Ihre,* i.e., Goethe's. The passage which follows is from *Songs of Selma,* one of the shorter poems of Macpherson-Ossian. Goethe translated it in Strassburg during his first enthusiasm for Ossian; the present version was made especially for *Werther.*
104. *zeither,* since then.
105. The situation presented in the passage is rather complex. The hoary bard Ossian sings a song to the evening star (page 238, lines 15–24). He then recalls the feast of Selma, held at Lora, the royal hall of his father Fingal, King of the Caledonians on the northwestern coast of Scotland. Ossian then sings three songs which he once heard at Selma's feast. The first of these was sung by Minona; its theme is the lament of Colma, who waited in vain for the appearance of her lover Salgar who did not come to her because he and Colmar's brother had killed each other (page 240, line 2— page 242, line 18). The second song is sung by the bard Ullin. Its theme is the death of Minona's brother Morar; in form it is a dialogue between Ryno and Alpin. In Ullin's recitation the role of Alpin was sung by Ullin, that of Ryno by Ossian himself (page 242, lines 32–33). The third song is sung by Armin, who laments the death of his children. His daughter Dama had been abducted and taken overseas by Erath, who was captured by her brother Arindal. Dama's lover, Armar, mistakes Arindal for the abductor Erath and kills him. He then leaps into the water to rescue Dama but is drowned. Dama dies on a rock from grief, in view of her father Armin (page 244, line 42—page 248, line 36). The text is that of Macpherson; it shows how freely Goethe translated. Goethe has used virtually the whole poem, omitting only the last paragraph.
106. *strahlend = strahlendes.*
107. *leite.* Third person present subjunctive of command or request.
108. *Liebe,* i.e., lover.
109. *schnobend,* modern: *schnobernd.*
110. *saust.* A singular verb with two subjects is not uncommon in German, when the subjects are felt to be closely linked.
111. *die = diejenigen, die.*
112. *harren = warten.*
113. *Wettegesang,* competitive song.

114. Oskar, the son of Ossian; he figures in many of the Ossianic poems.
115. *in = im.*
116. *ehe = ehedem*, formerly.
117. *wispeln = wispern = flüstern*, whisper.
118. *Stärke . . . Stolz*, i.e., his son and daughter, respectively.
119. This pasage is from a different poem of Macpherson: *Berrathon*. It concentrates into a few lines the motif of death which now haunts Werther.
120. *stiebte*, more commonly strong: *stieben o o.*
121. *neblicht = nebelig.*
122. *Freundin*. See page 40, line 16 ff.
123. *wäre*. See note 144 of Book One.
124. *wähnen*, be delusional.
125. Werther refers to Lotte's words on page 132, lines 32 ff.
126. The use of the formal *Sie* to Albert conforms to eighteenth-century epistolary style.
127. This contradiction to the statement on page 216, line 31 results from additions which Goethe made in the second version of *Werther*.
128. *bestreiten*, usually with the dative of person.
129. *mehr = oft.*
130. *stellte*. For the position of the verb, see note 42 above; *Pult* is now neuter.
131. *Brot und Wein*, possibly an allusion to the Last Supper, in line with Werther's vision of himself as a Christlike martyr.
132. *gegen mir über = mir gegenüber.*
133. *aufgehaben = aufgehoben* (Biblical).
134. Orthodox Christians refuse burial to a suicide in consecrated ground.
135. Allusion to Luke 10: 31–33.
136. *Blick = Blitz.*
137. *eine Ader lassen*, to bleed.
138. *Emilia Galotti*, a tragedy by Lessing, published in 1772. While the detail is taken over from Kestner's report about Jerusalem's suicide, there is a literary justification for including it here. The heroine of Lessing's tragedy seeks death from a sense of guilt.
139. Burial at night was usual in the eighteenth century; also that the coffin should be borne by the members of some guild. The absence of a clergyman at the burial is explained by the fact that Werther was a murderer in the eyes of the Church. But it also underlines Werther's religious independence.

QUESTIONNAIRE

Pages 30–48

1. In welchem Verhältnis stand Leonore zu Werther?
2. Was entdeckte Werther über seine Tante?
3. Was fühlt man gleich beim Eintritt in den gräflichen Garten?
4. Welche Erinnerungen erweckt der Brunnen in Werther?
5. Welche sozialen Ideen drückt Werther im Brief vom 15. Mai aus?
6. Wie leben die meisten Menschen?
7. Welches Mitglied der Familie des Amtmanns wird besonders gelobt?
8. Beschreiben Sie das Bild, das Werther zeichnete?

Pages 50–68

9. Was erfährt Werther über die junge Mutter, mit der er sich unterhält?
10. Was erfährt Werther vom Bauerburschen?
11. Warum hat Werther gezögert, an seinen Freund Wilhelm zu schreiben?
12. Ist ihm das Schreiben dieses Briefes leicht gefallen?
13. Wovor sollte sich Werther in acht nehmen?
14. Was erblickte Werther, als er in die Tür trat?
15. Welchen Auftrag gab Lotte ihrer Schwester?
16. Welchen Eindruck machte Lotte auf Werther?
17. Welches Ereignis brachte die Gesellschaft in Verwirrung?

Pages 70–88

18. Worüber war der Arzt entrüstet?
19. Welche Eigenschaft bewundert Werther an Lotte in diesen Zeilen?
20. Was betrübte Werther an Herrn Schmidt?
21. Mit welchem Thema befaßt sich dieser ganze Brief?
22. Welche Wirkung übte die Erinnerung an diese Szene auf Werther aus!

Pages 90–108

23. Warum nimmt Werther Anstoß an dem Wort „gefällt"?
24. Was ist der Sinn der Anekdote, die in diesem Brief erzählt wird?

25. Wie wirkt Lottes Klavierspielen auf Werther?
26. Warum will Werther kein Amt annehmen?
27. Warum beschließt Werther wegzugehen?
28. Vor welchem Entweder—Oder steht Werther?
29. Welche Geschichte war Werther neugierig zu hören?

Pages 110–128

30. Was ärgert Werther an der Geschichte?
31. Wie äußert sich Werther über Anstrengung und Überspannung?
32. Was will Werther mit der Geschichte vom Mädchen beweisen?
33. Was konnte Albert nicht begreifen?
34. Worin findet Werther die Quelle des menschlichen Elends?
35. Werther sieht überall Zerstörung. Geben Sie einige Beispiele davon.
36. Was war in dem Päckchen, das Werther von Albert erhielt?

Pages 130–158

37. Welchen Wunsch drückt Werther am Schluß dieses Briefes aus?
38. Welches Ereignis beschreibt dieser Brief?
39. Worüber spricht Lotte mit tiefem Gefühl?
40. Was versprach Lotte der sterbenden Mutter?
41. Warum fühlt sich Werther mit seiner Lage zufrieden?
42. Was ärgert Werther an dem Gesandten?
43. Auf wen wälzt er die Schuld für seinen Mißstand?
44. Welche menschliche Schwäche tadelt Werther in diesem Brief?
45. Wo schreibt Werther diesen Brief?
46. Was schrieb der Minister im Privatbrief an Werther?
47. Welche Beleidigung erleidet Werther von der Gesellschaft beim Grafen von C.?
48. Was kann Werther nicht dulden?

Pages 160–178

49. Welchen Plan kündet der Brief vom 5. Mai an?
50. Welche Erinnerungen erweckt der Besuch in Werther?
51. Welche Bedeutung mißt Werther dem Herzen bei?
52. Aus welchem Grunde glaubt Werther einen Anspruch auf Lottes Liebe zu haben?
53. Warum hat Werther die Geschichte des Bauerburschen erzählt?

Pages 180–198

54. Was is die „Werthertracht"?
55. Wer hat die Nußbäume abhauen lassen?
56. Welchen Dichter liest Werther jetzt statt des Homer?
57. Gegen welche Versuchung muß Werther kämpfen?
58. Mit welchem Wunsch geht Werther oft zu Bett?
59. Warum war Werther früher glücklich?

60. Erwartet Werther Trost von der Religion?
61. In welchem Sinne empfindet Werther sein Schicksal als einzigartig?

Pages 200–218

62. Was suchte der Irrsinnige auf dem Berge?
63. Wann fühlte er sich am glücklichsten?
64. Wie betrachtet Werther an dieser Stelle den Selbstmord?
65. In welchen Zustand war Werther allmählich geraten?
66. Was tadelt Werther an Albert?
67. Wer war der Mann, der den Mord begangen hatte?
68. Wie faßt Werther die Worte des Amtmanns auf?

Pages 220–248

69. In welchem Zustand findet Werther die Landschaft um Wahlheim?
70. Was hatte in Werthers Seele immer mehr Kraft gewonnen?
71. Womit beschäftigte sich Lotte, als Werther zu ihr ins Haus kam?
72. Begeht Werther Selbstmord aus Verzweiflung?
73. Was fühlte Lotte seit ihrer letzten Unterredung mit Werther?
74. Aus welchem Dichter las Werther vor?
75. Welchen Eindruck machte die Lektüre auf Lotte?

Pages 250–270

76. In welchem Zustand kam Werther nach Hause?
77. In welcher Überzeugung geht Werther aus der Welt?
78. In welcher Stimmung war Albert, als er nach Hause kam?
79. Wo wünschte Werther begraben zu sein?
80. Welches Buch lag auf seinem Pult?

VOCABULARY

This vocabulary omits words which should be familiar to students who have had one year of college or two years of high school German. Where a verb is given, the noun that is easily derived from it is omitted, and vice versa. The same is true of adjectives that are easily derived from nouns.

Past participles of weak (modern) verbs are not given unless they have a special meaning.

Strong verbs are listed exactly as they occur in the text: *gab aus, vorgeschoben, tritt zusammen.*

The plural of weak feminine nouns is omitted, as it is always formed by adding -n or -en to the singular.

A

sich ab-arbeiten wear oneself out, slave
ab-brechen a o break off
ab-büßen atone
das Abendbrot supper
abenteuerlich strange, adventurous
der Aberglaube –ns superstition
ab-fädmen shell
der Abfall ⸗e gradation
ab-fertigen dispatch, snub
ab-geben yield; **sich —** busy oneself, affect
ab-gehen come off, work
abergrissen (reißen) fragmentary
der Abgeschiedene –n deceased one
abgeschmackt in bad taste
abgeschnitten (schneiden) cut off
abgeschrieben copied
abgespannt unstrung
abgesprochen denied, taken away
abgetan removed
ab-gewinnen a o win from, get ahead
der Abgrund ⸗e abyss
ab-halten hold back, restrain
ab-handeln discuss, debate

der Abhang ⸗e slope
ab-hängen depend
ab-hauen hieb gehauen cut, chop down
abhing (hängen) depended
ab-holen fetch
ab-legen take off
ab-leiten channel
ab-lenken divert
ab-nehmen take away
die Abneigung dislike
ab-passen watch for
ab-putzen clean off
der Absatz ⸗e paragraph; **–weise** in installments
ab-scheiden ie ie depart
abscheulich horrible
der Abschied –e departure, farewell, resignation
abschüttelnd shaking
abseitwärts to one side
die Absicht intention
ab-spiegeln mirror, reflect
ab-spülen rinse away
ab-sterben wither, die out, fade
ab-trocknen dry
ab-tun finish, remove, relieve, subtract
ab-wechseln alternate

289

ab-wehren ward off, avert
ab-weisen ie ie reject
ab-wenden avert
ab-werfen a o throw off
die Abwesenheit absence
ab-wiegen o o weigh
ab-ziehen subtract
ab-zwingen a u obtain by force
die Achsel shoulder
die Acht heed, attention; sich in
— nehmen be careful
die Achtung respect, esteem
das Ächzen groaning
der Acker ╪ field
der Ackersmann –leute farmer
der Adel nobility
die Ader vein, artery
ahnen suspect, have a premonition
die Ahnung presentiment, light
ähnlich similar
die Akte document
albern silly, foolish
das All universe
allbelebend animating everything
die Allee avenue, walk
allerhand all sorts
allerlei all sorts
der Allmächtige –n Almighty
allmählich gradually
alsdann then
von alters her from long ago
altfränkisch old-fashioned
der Altvater ╪ patriarch, ancient
die Ameise ant
das Amthaus ╪er official residence
der Amtmann –leute steward
der Amtschreiber — magistrate's
clerk
an-bauen establish
anbefohlen (befehlen) commended
an-beten worship
der Anblick –e sight
an-bringen produce, apply
die Andacht devotion, reverence
das Andenken — remembrance
ander next
anderthalb one and a half
an-ekeln disgust
an-erkennen recognize
an-fachen kindle
an-fassen grip, take hold
an-feuern inspire
anfuhren drove up
angegriffen (greifen) attacked, affected
an-gehen concern, be possible

angelegen concerned, entreated,
urged
die Angelegenheit occasion
angenommen accepted
das Angesicht –er countenance
angestochen (stechen) nettled
angezogen attracted; jogging
an-greifen affect
ängsten frighten
ängstigen frighten, alarm, worry,
torment
ängstlich causing anxiety, painful
an-halten apply
anhaltend steady, perpetual
die Anhänglichkeit attachment
an-kommen arrive, depend
an-künden announce
die Ankunft ╪e arrival
an-langen arrive
der Anlaß ╪e cause, occasion
an-legen lay out
anmaßlich pretentious
die Anmerkung comment
die Annäherung approach
an-nisten nest
an-ordnen arrange
an-packen grip
an-reden address
das Anschauen contemplation
anschaulich clear, vivid
der Anschein –e appearance, sign,
indication
der Anschlag ╪e proposal, value,
account
anschmieden chain
an-schreiben ascribe
an-sehen regard, observe
das Ansehen appearance, look
ansehnlich substantial
an-setzen begin, sprout
an-spannen harness
der Anspruch ╪e claim
die Anstalt preparation, measure
anstand suited
anständig respectable, decent
an-stellen arrange
an-stimmen strike up, sing
der Anstoß ╪e objection
an-strengen strain
der Anteil share, participation, interest, sympathy
die Antike classical antiquity
antrifft (treffen) meets
an-wandeln seize
an-weisen ie ie assign
an-wenden apply

290

an-ziehen attract
anzüglich attractive, suggestive
ärger worse
ärgern annoy
sich ärgern aggravate oneself
argwohnen suspect
der Ärmel — sleeve
die Armut poverty
die Art sort, kind, type
artig nice, tidy, well-behaved; —
   tun be attentive
die Arznei medicine
der Ast ˸e branch, limb, bough
der Atemzug ˸e breath
atmen breathe, whisper
auf-arbeiten soar
auf-brechen depart, leave
auf-dämmern loom up, half-waken
auf-drücken imprint
der Aufenthalt stay, sojourn
auffahrend vehement
auf-fassen understand
auf-finden discover
auf-fordern summon, invite (to
   dance)
die Aufführung conduct
auf-gären ferment, rise up
aufgebracht excited
aufgefahren occurred
aufgefallen occurred
aufgefangen interpreted
aufgefunden turned up
auf-gehen expand, swell
aufgehoben annulled
aufgejagt excited
aufgeschlagen opened
aufgespannt tense
aufgetragen ordered
auf-hetzen stir up
sich aufhielt stayed, stopped
der Auflauf ˸e uproar, disturbance
auf-leben revive
das Auflodern flickering
aufmerksam attentive
auf-nehmen take in, admit
auf-opfern sacrifice
auf-passen watch out, be alert
auf-putzen decorate
aufrichtig frankly
der Aufruhr –e uproar
der Aufsatz ˸e composition, essay,
   document
der Aufschlag ˸e facings, lapel
auf-schlagen set up
sich auf-schwingen a u soar
aufspringend bounding

auf-suchen ferret out, search for
der Auftrag ˸e task, commission
der Aufwand ˸e expenditure
auf-zeichnen write down
auf-zehren consume
sich aus-bitten win, be granted
aus-breiten extend
der Ausbruch ˸e outburst
aus-brüten hatch
aus-dauern endure, bear
der Ausdruck ˸e expression
ausdrücklich definitely
aus-dulden suffer to the end
auseinander-gehen part
aus-erzählen finish telling
aus-flicken patch up
aus-fragen question
die Ausführung execution, accom-
   plishment
aus-füllen, fill out, occupy
die Ausgabe expense, edition
der Ausgang ˸e way out, issue
ausgebrannt (brennen) burnt-out
ausgebreitet spread out
ausgehauen (hauen) thinned out
ausgelassen wild
ausgeliehen (leihen) lent
ausgestanden endured
ausgoß (gießen) poured out
aus-kehren shake out
aus-kommen make do, get along
   with
das Auskommen income
aus-kramen display
aus-kratzen scratch out, erase
das Ausleben dying
aus-legen interpret
aus-leiden suffer out
aus-lernen finish learning
aus-löschen extinguish
aus-machen agree, arrange
die Ausnahme exception
aus-reden finish talking
aus-richten carry out, attend to
aus-rotten eradicate
die Aussage assertion, view
aus-schlürfen drain
aus-schreien ie ie decry
aus-schütten pour out
die Ausschweifung extravagance
aus-sehen look, appear
die Außenseite exterior
außer sich beside oneself
äußern express
außerordentlich extraordinary
aus-setzen object

die Aussicht view, prospect
aus-sparen spare, put aside
aus-sprechen express
aus-statten equip
aus-stechen a o dig out
aus-stehen endure
aus-strecken stretch out
aus-tilgen destroy
aus-toben have one's fling
aus-trocknen desiccate
der Ausweg –e way out
sich aus-weinen have a good cry

B

der Bach ⸚e brook
die Backe cheek
der Balken —— log
band (binden) bound
bang(e) wretched, fearful, harrowing
bannen confine, hold spellbound
der Barde –n bard
die Barmherzigkeit mercy
der Bart ⸚e beard
die Base cousin
der Bauerbursch –en peasant lad
die Bauernherberge peasant inn
das Baumstück –e orchard
der Beamte –n official
beängstigt in anguish
beben quiver
der Becher —— cup
bedauern pity
bedenklich dubious
die Bedenklichkeit pedantry
sich bedienen make use
der Bediente –n servant
die Bedingung condition
die Bedrängnis –se depression
die Bedrängte lady in distress
das Bedürfnis –se need
befahl (befehlen) ordered
befallen seized, attacked
sich befassen concern oneself
der Befehl –e order, command
befestigen strengthen
befiedert feathered
sich befinden find oneself, feel
befindlich existing
die Beförderung promotion, furthering
befreien free
die Befriedigung satisfaction

begangen committed
sich begeben go, enter
begehren desire
die Begier desire
die Begierde desire
begleiten accompany, escort
begoß (gießen) watered
begraben u a bury
im Begriff sein be about to
begrübt (begraben) would bury
begünstiger favor
behalten retain
behandeln treat
behaupten maintain, assert
behilflich helpful
bei-bringen impart, tell
der Beifall approval
bei-fügen add
die Beinkleider trousers
beiseite aside
beißen i i bite
bei-wohnen witness
bejahen affirm
bejammern bewail
bekennen confess
beklagen complain
bekleiden clothe
die Beklemmung oppression, anxiety
bekränzt decorated, wreathed
sich bekümmern concern oneself
beladen laden, spent
beleben animate, inspire
die Beleidigung insult
der Belletrist –en man of letters
sich bemächtigen take possession
bemalen paint, decorate
sich bemühen strive
beneiden envy
benetzen moisten
berauben rob of
berechnen assess
berechtigen justify
bereden persuade
bereift covered with hoarfrost
bereiten prepare
das Bergwerk –e mine
bersten a o burst
beruhigen calm
die Beruhigung equanimity
berühren touch
besann sich anders (besinnen) changed her mind
beschäftigen occupy
beschatten shade
beschneiden clip, cut

292

bescheren bestow upon, make a present of
beschien (scheinen) illuminated
beschlossen resolved
beschränkt limited
die Beschwerde complaint
beschwerlich offensive
die Beschwerlichkeit difficulty
besetzen occupy, set
die Besinnungskraft presence of mind, power of reflection
der Besitz possession
besorgen attend to
die Besorgnis concern, anxiety
die Besserung improvement
bestärken strengthen, confirm
bestehen auf insist (upon)
die Bestellung order, direction
bestimmen determine, designate, strengthen
bestimmt definite, certain
die Bestimmung determination, destiny
die Bestreitung defraying
bestritten (streiten) challenged
bestürmen besiege
die Bestürzung consternation
besudeln stain
betäubend numbing
betauen bedew
beten pray
beteuern protest
die Betrachtung view, respect
das Betragen manner, conduct
betrat (treten) trod
betreiben ie ie look after
betreten mount, ride
betroffen taken aback, shocked
betrüben distress, sadden
der Bertrug illusion
betrügen o o deceive, cheat
die Betstunde prayer-time
betteln beg
beugen bend
beurteilen judge, appreciate
die Beute spoils, booty
bevölkern populate
bewaffnet armed
bewahren protect, preserve
der Beweggrund ̈e motive
die Bewegung commotion
beweinen mourn
beweisen ie ie prove
sich bewerben a o apply for
bewillkommen welcome
bewirten entertain

bewog (bewegen) induced
die Bewunderung admiration
das Bewußtsein consciousness
bezeichnen mark, characterize
bezeigen show, express
sich beziehen refer
bilden form, shape
das Billet –s note
das Bindwörtchen conjunction
das Birkenreis –er birch rod
bis auf except for
blaß pale
das Blättchen slip of paper
das Blei lead
bleich pale
blendend brilliant, splendid
der Blick –e flash
blies (blasen) blew
blühend flourishing
die Blüte blossom, flower
der Bogen — bow
bohren plunge
borgen lend
bösartig vicious
böse disagreeable
der Bösewicht –e villain
die Bosheit malice
das Boskett –e shrubbery, copse
bosseln tinker
bot (bieten) offered
die Bouteille bottle
bräche (brechen) should break
brachte auf aroused
brachte hervor produced
braten roast
brauchbar useful
brausen bubble, roar
der Bräutigam –e fiancé .
brav good, fine, nice, worthy
der Brei porridge
das Breipfännchen — cereal dish
das Brett –er plank, board
bringen um deprive of
die Brosame bread crumb
der Brunnen — well, spring, fountain
der Bube –n boy
die Buchenwand ̈e wall of beech
buhlen contend, strive, woo
bunt colorful, bright, gay
die Bürde burden
bürgerlich bourgeois
der Bursche –n boy, servant
buschig wooded
der Busen — bosom, heart, mind

C

der **Chapeau** –s partner
das **Christgeschenk** –e Christmas gift
der **Chronikenschreiber** — chronicler

D

daher therefore
dahin gone, done for, away; **mußte — had to die**
dahinaus to the point
dahin-brausen roar away
dahingestellt undecided
dahin-hängen be prone to
dahlen dally, toy
damalig former, of that time
dämmen dam
dämmern become dusky or misty
dämmernd half-lit, twilit
der **Dämmerschein** twilight
die **Dämmerung** twilight
dampfen steam
daneben besides
darauf thereupon
darben starve
dar-bieten o o offer, present
darein into it
darinnen in which
dar-legen present, show
dar-stellen convey, represent
das **Dasein** existence, being
der **Daumen** — thumb
davon away
dazu in addition; **noch — in addition**
dazu-kommen succeed
der **Deckel** — lid
der **Degen** — sword
die **Demut** humility
das **Deraisonnement** twaddle
dergestalt in such a way, so much
dergleichen such things
desgleichen likewise
desto all the more
deuten mark, signify
deutlich clear
die **Dichtkunst** literature
die **Dichtung** poetry
der **Diebstahl** ⸗e theft
das **Dienstmädchen** — servant girl
der **Diskurs** –e conversation
die **Dogge** large dog

der **Dolchstoß** dagger thrust
der **Donnerschlag** ⸗e thunderclap
der **Dorn** –es –e and –en thorn
die **Drahtpuppe** puppet
der **Drang** ⸗e urge, impulse
drängen force
drauß(en) outside, out there
drein in
dringend urgent
drohen threaten
drücken press
drunter und drüber upside down
sich **ducken** submit
dulden endure
dumpf dull, vague
dumpficht hazy
dumpfig damp
dünken seem, fancy, imagine
durchdrang (dringen) pierced
das **Durchdringen** penetration
durcheinander in confusion; **— arbeiten** churn
durchgezogen reviewed
sich **durch-helfen** manage, get on
durch-setzen survive
durch-treiben ie ie carry through, effect
dürr bleak
düster dark, gloomy

E

das **Ebenbild** –er image
die **Ebene** plain
der **Edelmut** high-mindedness
ehedem once, formerly
ehegestern day before yesterday
eh(e) mals formerly
der **Ehemann** ⸗er husband
eher sooner, rather
ehern bronze, brazen
die **Ehre** honor, credit
das **Ehrenamt** ⸗er dignity
ehrenhalben politely
die **Ehrfurcht** respect
ehrlich respectable
ehestens at the earliest opportunity
die **Eiche** oak tree
die **Eifersüchtelei** petty jealousy
eifrig zealously
eigen characteristic, true
eigenhändig original
die **Eigenschaft** characteristic
der **Eigensinn** stubbornness, obstinacy, capriciousness

294

das Eigentum ⸚er property
eilfertig hasty
der Eimer — pail
sich ein-bilden fancy, imagine
die Einbildungskraft imagination
der Eindruck ⸚e impression
ein-engen cramp, confine
einerlei one and the same
das Einerlei monotony
einfach simple
der Einfall ⸚e idea
ein-fallen occur
die Einfalt simplicity
die Einfassung bordering, framework
ein-flößen impart, instill
einförmig uniform, monotonous
der Eingang ⸚e entrance, introduction
der Eingekerkerte –n imprisoned man
eingenommen possessed
eingeschlossen enclosed
die Eingeschränktheit limitedness
ein-gestehen admit
das Eingeweide intestines
der Eingriff –e infringement
sich ein-halten stay in
ein-hauchen breathe into, inspire
einmal: auf — suddenly
ein-nähen sew up
ein-nicken nod, fall asleep
die Einöde wasteland
das Einpacken packing
ein-räumen grant
ein-reden persuade of
ein-rücken insert
einsam lonely
ein-saugen o o suck in
ein-schalten insert
ein-scharren bury roughly
ein-schieben o o wedge in
ein-schlürfen sip in
die Einschränkung limitation, restriction
ein-sehen realize
die Einsiedelei hermitage
ein-sperren confine, imprison
ein-stoßen ie o bash in
ein-teilen divide up
die Eintracht harmony
einzig, einzigartig unique
das Eisenwerk iron[work]
die Eitelkeit vanity
elend wretched
der Ell[en]bogen — elbow

der Empfang ⸚e reception
sich empfehlen a o take leave
empfindlich sensitive
die Empfindung feeling, emotion
empfingen (fangen) received
empor-streben strive, struggle
empört revolted, seething
die Empörung rebellion
die Emsigkeit zeal, diligence
sich endigen end, terminate
eng cozy
der Engel — angel
entblättert leafless
entdecken discover, reveal
entfahren escape
entfalten unfold
die Entfernung distance
entgegen toward
entgegen-schallen resound
entgehen escape, lose
sich enthalten refrain
entkleiden undress
entkräftet exhausted
die Entlassung release
der Entleibte –n murdered man
entrüstet indignant
entsagen renounce
entschieden (scheiden) decided
sich entschließen o o decide
entschlossen resolute
entschlüpfen escape, elude
der Entschluß ⸚e decision, resolution
entsetzen suspend, depose, strip; horrify
entsetzlich dreadful
entstand arose
entweihen desecrate
entwickeln unfold, develop
entzogen (ziehen) withdrawn
entzücken delight, enrapture
entzünden kindle
erbärmlich pitiable, wretched
erblicken glimpse
der Erbprinz –en heir to the throne
die Erbschaft inheritance
der Erbschaftsanteil –e share of the inheritance
erbrechen open up
die Erbse pea
das Erdbeben — earthquake
der Erdboden soil, earth
die Erdscholle clod of earth
erforschen investigate
erfrischt refreshed
erfuhr learned, discovered

295

die **Erfüllung** fulfillment
erfunden invented
sich **ergeben** yield, submit, surrender
ergötzen delight
ergreifen move, seize, grasp, engulf
erhalten maintain, support
erhaschen seize, snatch
erhellen become clear
erhitzen heat up
erhob (erheben) raised
sich **erholen** recover, rest
die **Erholungsstunden** leisure time
die **Erinnerung** memory
erklang (klingen) resounded
sich **erkundigen** inquire
erlassen spare
erleben experience, live to see
erleiden erlitt erlitten suffer
erleuchten illuminate
erliegen succumb
ermangeln fail, be lacking
sich **ermannen** take heart, pull oneself together
das **Ermatten** weakness, fatigue
ermattend wearying
ermattet weary
ermorden murder
ermuntern encourage; **sich —** awake fully
ernähren support
erniedrigen humiliate
der **Eroberer** — conqueror
erquicken refresh
erregen cause, excite
erretten rescue
errötend blushing
die **Erscheinung** phenomenon
sich **erschießen o o** shoot oneself
erschlagen murder
erschrecken frighten
erschuf (schaffen) created
erschüttern astonish, shake
erschweren make difficult
ersetzen replace, compensate for
erstarrt numbed
erstaunen be astonished
ersticken stifle, choke
ertragen endure
der **Erwachsene –n** adult
erwählen choose
erwähnen mention
sich **erwehren** refrain, resist
etabliert settled
erweitern broaden

etwa approximately, about, possibly, perhaps
die **Ewigkeit** eternity
das **Ewigschaffende** Eternal Creation

F

der **Fächer** — fan
der **Faden** ≃ thread
fallen: leicht be easy
in Falten legen — fold
fassen catch, grasp; **sich —** pull oneself together, compose oneself
die **Fassung** composure
fatal disagreeable
fehlgeschlagen frustrated, disappointed
feierlich solemn
feige cowardly
fein subtle, nice
die **Ferne** distance
fesseln chain, fetter
das **Fest –e** holiday
die **Festigkeit** firmness
fest-setzen establish
feurig ardent, warm
das **Fieber** — fever
fiel auf astonished, surprised
fiel ein interrupted
der **Filz –e** miser, skinflint
sich **finden** turn up
die **Finsternis –se** darkness
der **Fittich –e** wing
flach flat
flattern flutter
der **Fleck –e** spot
der **Fleiß** zeal, diligence
sich **flüchten** take refuge
die **Flüchtigkeit** lightness
der **Flüchtling –e** fugitive, refugee
der **Flügel** — wing
flüstern whisper
die **Flut** wave
focht (fechten) fought
die **Folge** sequence; **in der —** subsequently
folgen obey
fordern demand, request
forschend contemplative, searching
fort-fahren continue
fortgerissen (reißen) swept along
fort-keuchen pant, gasp ahead

fortschreitend steady
fortwusch (waschen) washed on
fourniert equipped
der Frack ⸗e dress coat
frappant striking
der Fratze –n fool, child
die Fratze nonsense
das Frauenzimmer — woman
freien court, woo
der Freier suitor
freilich to be sure
freimütig naturally, frankly
freiwillig voluntarily
die Freudigkeit joy
die Freundschaftsbezeigung dem-
  onstration of friendship
frisch brisk, lively, eager
fromm God-fearing
frösteln freeze up
fruchtbar fertile
fügen join, weave together
die Fühlbarkeit sensitivity, suscep-
  tibility
die Fülle abundance
der Funke –ns –n spark
funkeln glitter, twinkle
fuhr auf started
fürchten fear
fürchterlich frightful, dreadful
furchtsam timid, fearful
fürstlich princely, of a prince
der Fußpfad –e footpath
die Fußstapfe footstep
der Fußtritt –e footstep

G

die Gabe talent, gift
die Galeere galley
die Galle gall, rancor
der Gang ⸗e procedure, course
die Gans ⸗e goose
gar quite, most
die Garderobe wardrobe
garstig horrid, nasty
die Gaststube parlor (of an inn)
der Gatte –n husband
die Gattin –nen spouse, wife
das Gäulchen little horse
gebar (gebären) gave birth to
die Gebärde gesture
das Gebet –e prayer
gebieten o o command
das Gebrüll roaring
gedacht said

das Gedächtnis memory
der Gedankenstrich –e dash
gedrungen (dringen) penetrated,
  compelled
sich gefallen lassen accept
gefällig pleasant, kind
die Gefälligkeit kindness, favor
gefangen (fangen) imprisoned
das Gefäß –e vessel, pitcher
gefaßt steady
das Gefecht –e battle, fight
gefesselt fettered
geflochten (flechten) plaited
die Gegend region
der Gegensatz ⸗e contrast
der Gegenstand ⸗e subject, object
das Gegenteil –e the opposite
die Gegenwart present, presence,
  presence of mind
geheim secret, mysterious
der Geheimrat –e privy councillor
das Gehirn –e brain
das Gehör hearing
gehorchen obey
gehörig properly
der Gehorsam obedience
geil luxuriant, rank
der Geistliche –n clergyman
geizen nach covet, be greedy
das Gelächter laughter
gelassen calm, sedate, composed,
  comfortable
gelegen concerned; — sein matter
die Gelehrsamkeit scholarship
gelehrt learned
der Geliebte –n lover
gelind mild
gelitten (leiden) suffered, allowed
der Gemahl –e husband, consort
gemein common, low
der Gemeinspruch ⸗e platitude
das Gemüt –er spirit, disposition,
  feelings
gen toward
genießen o o enjoy
das Geniste shrubbery
genoß (genießen) enjoyed
genötigt obliged
genügen suffice
die Genügsamkeit contentment
der Genuß ⸗e enjoyment
gepriesen (preisen) boasted, glorified
geraten ie a get (into)
das Geräusch –e noise
gerecht righteous

297

das Gericht-e court of justice, judgment

gering slight, small, simple, poor; **—achten** slight

die Geringschätzung contempt, scorn

geruhig calmly

die Gesandtschaft embassy

der Gesang ˫e song, canto

der Gesandte –n ambassador

geschaffen (schaffen) created

der Geschäftsauftrag ˫e business matter

es geschähe it would happen

gescheit intelligent, sensible

das Geschenk –e gift

das Geschick –e fate, destiny

geschieden (scheiden) departed

das Geschlecht –er family

der Geschmack ˫e taste, liking

das Geschöpf –e creature

das Geschrei uproar

das Geschwärm confusion

geschwind fast

geschwollen (schwellen) swollen up

sich gesellen associate oneself

der Gesellschafter — social companion

die Gesichtsbildung facial features, shape of the face

der Gesichtspunkt –e viewpoint

der Gesichtszug ˫e feature

die Gesinnung mind, frame of mind, point of view

gespannt strained

das Gestade — shore

gestand ein (gestehen) conceded

gestand zu (gestehen) granted

gestatten permit, grant

gestehen confess

gestiefelt in boots

das Gestirn –e constellation

gestrig of yesterday

das Gesumme humming, buzzing

sich getrauen dare, venture

getreu loyal

getrost confident

das Getümmel turmoil

gewähren grant

die Gewalt power

gewaltsam violent, forcible

das Gewand ˫er vestment, shirt

das Gewäsch –e twaddle, rubbish

das Gewehr –e weapon

das Gewerbe — business, property

gewiesen (weisen) expelled

gewissenhaft conscientiously

die Gewissensbisse twinges of conscience

die Gewißheit certainty

das Gewitter — thunderstorm

die Gewohnheit habit

gewöhnt accustomed

das Gewölbe — arch

das Gezänk quarrel

gezogen grown

der Gießbach ˫e torrent

das Gift –e poison

gilt (gelten a o) applies to

ging an began

der Gipfel — summit

der Glanz splendor

glänzend splendid

der Gläubige –n believer

gleichgültig indifferent

das Gleichnis –se image, symbol, simile, parallel

gleichsam as it were

das Gleis –e groove

gleiten glide

glich (gleichen) resembled

das Glied –er limb, member

das Glück: auf gut — at random, on the off-chance

glücklicherweise fortunately

die Glückseligkeit happiness

glühen glow

die Gnade grace

gönnen grant

das Grab ˫er grave

grad = gerade

der Grad –e degree, stage

der Graf –en Count

die Gräschen grasses

grausen cause horror

gräßlich gruesome

greifen iff iff grasp, strike, touch

grenzen border

die Grille whim, moodiness

der Grimm anger

grob brusque

grolen resent

groß-tun affect greatness

die Gruft ˫e cave

gründen establish, found

die Gurgel throat, gullet

gut sein like

H

die Habichtsnase aquiline nose

haften cling
hager lean
der Halbgott ⁼er demigod
halbweg halfway
hallen echo
der Halm –e stalk, blade
sich halten stick
die Händel (pl.) quarrels
handeln act, behave
die Handhabe hold
die Handlung action, behavior
die Handlungsweise behavior, attitude
der Handwerker — workman, artisan
hängen nach be attached to
hären hairy
die Harfe harp
harmlos innocent
harren wait
die Haselgerte hazel switch
hassen hate
häßlich ugly
die Hastigkeit haste
der Hauch –e breath
der Hauf(e) –n heap; zu — in droves
häufen pile up
das Haupt ⁼er head
der Hauptzug ⁼e main feature
die Haushaltung housekeeping
die Hausleute servants
häuslich domestic
das Hauswesen housekeeping
die Hecke hedge
heftig vigorous, impetuous
die Heftigkeit vehemence, temperament
die Heide heath
das Heil salvation
heilig sacred
heiligen sanctify
das Heiligtum ⁼er sanctuary
heimlich secret, mysterious, private, homely, homelike
heißen urge, bid, tell, call
heiter calm, serene, cheerful
der Held –en hero
hemmen check, restrict
sich herab-lassen condescend
herab-orgeln pound out
herab-setzen disparage
herab-stören scatter
herabzog pulled away
herangewachsen grown up
heran-rücken draw near

heraus-bilden develop
der Herausgeber — editor
herausgerissen (reißen) torn out
heraus-lehnen lean out
heraus-zupfen tug at
herbergen lodge
her-blinken shine hither
herein-bemühen trouble [to come] in
herein-brausen roar in
die Hereinfahrt return trip
her-fallen über befall
hergebracht traditional
hernach afterwards
die Herrlichkeit splendor, glory
her-schlängeln wind hither
her-stellen restore
sich herum-beißen i i bite at, fight
herumgeschlichen (schleichen) slunk about
herumgetrieben (treiben) driven about
sich herum-jagen chase after
herum-krabbeln crawl about
herum-kreuzen cruise around
herum-rücken move around
herum-schauen look around
herum-schleppen drag about
herum-schweben float about
herum-schweifen roam about
sich herum-spaßen have fun
herum-taumeln stagger about
sich herum-wälzen thrash about
hervor-brechen a o flash
hervor-bringen bring forth, create
hervor-keimen bud, bloom
hervorquollen (quellen) flowed out
herzen embrace
herzhaft brave
herzlich hearty, cordial, warm, intimate
hetzen provoke, hunt
heulen howl, scream
der Hieb –e blow, cut
hieher here
hielt ab detained
hielt auf stayed
hienieden here below
hierauf to this
hierzulande in these parts, hereabouts
hiesig local
es hieß (heißen) it was said
hin lost, gone
sich hinab-begeben retire
hinab-blicken look down

hinab-stürzen plunge down
hinauf-bilden erect
hinaus-laufen end up, amount to
sich hinaus-setzen über disregard
hindern prevent
hin-fahren ride along
hinflösse (fließen) flowed away
hin-führen lead along
hin-geben surrender; sich — sacrifice or devote oneself
hingegeben resigned
die Hingegebenheit apathy
hingerissen (reißen) transported
hin-lenken divert, change
hin-reichen get along on
hin-reißen i i impel, draw, carry away
hin-schlummern doze off
hin-schlüpfen glide away
hin-sehen look to
hinsterbend waning
hin-taumeln stagger about
hintergangen cheated
hinterlassen posthumous
hinüber over there
hinunter-schollern tumble down
sich hinunter-stürzen leap down
hindzu-denken complete [in thought]
hinzu-fügen add
hinzu-setzen add
hinzu-tun add
das Hirngespinst –e chimera
hitzig hot, violent
hochadlig highly aristocratic
die Höflichkeit politeness, respects
der Hofrat ⸚e court councillor
der Hofmeister — private tutor
die Höhle cave
hold gracious, sweet
die Hölle hell
die Hüfte hip, haunch
der Hügel — hill
huldigen pay homage
hundertfältig hundredfold
der Husten — cough
das Hüttchen — cottage

I

ihrentwegen on her behalf
imstande able
indem meanwhile
indes meanwhile, however
der Inhalt –e content

inkommodieren inconvenience
die Inkonsequenz inconsistency, stupidity
das Innerste innermost core
innig fervent, deep, intimate
insofern insofar as
inwendig within
inzwischen meanwhile
irden earthenware
die Irre error, wandering
sich irren err, make a mistake
der Irrsinnige –n madman
der Irrtum ⸚er error
die Irrung confusion

J

der Jagdhof ⸚e hunting lodge
das Jagdschloß ⸚er hunting lodge
der Jäger — hunter
jäh steep
das Jahrtausend –e millennium
jammernd wailing, agonizing
jeglich each
von jeher from time immemorial
der Jelängerjelieber — honeysuckle
das Joch –e yoke
die Jungfer maiden, girl, Miss
das Juwel –s –en jewel

K

das Kabinett –e study, small room, summerhouse
der Käfer — beetle
der Kaffee breakfast
der Käfig –e cage
kaltblütig cold-blooded
kam an arrived, was received
die Kammer bedroom; treasury
das Kanapee –s sofa
der Kanarienvogel ⸚ canary
die Kasse till, cash box
der Kastanienbaum ⸚e chestnut tree
die Keckheit impertinence
die Kehle throat
der Keim –e bud, germ
der Kelch –e cup
kennen-lernen become acquainted with
die Kenntnis –se knowledge
die Kette chain

der Kerker — prison
die Kirchhofmauer churchyard wall
das Kissen — pillow
kitzeln tickle, titillate
klagen complain, lament
die Kleinigkeit trifle, detail
das Kleinod –e jewel
kleinsinnig petty-minded
klettern climb
der Knecht –e servant, man
kneten knead, mold
knien kneel down
knirren grind
knirschen grind one's teeth, groan
knistern crackle, grate
der Knochen — bone
der Knoten — knot
der Kohl cabbage
das Kollegium –ien cabinet
die Kombinationsart logic
das Königreich –e kingdom
das Konto –s account, bill
der Kopfputz coiffure, bonnet
das Körbchen — little basket
das Korn ⸚er grain
körperlich physical
kostbar precious
kosten savor
köstlich precious
die Kraft ⸚e force, energy, resource
kraftlos impotent, indifferent
der Kragen — collar
kramen rummage
der Kramladen ⸚ small shop
krampfen cramp, convulse
der Kranich –e crane
kränken grieve, offend
kränklich sickly
der Kräusel — frill
das Kraut ⸚er herb
das Krautfeld –er vegetable garden
das Krauthaupt ⸚er head of cabbage
der Kreis –e circle
das Kreuz –e cross
der Kreuzer — small coin
kriegen get
die Krone crown
die Krönung coronation
krumm crooked
die Krümmung winding
die Kugel bullet
kühn bold, fierce

die Kühnheit impropriety
der Kummer grief
künftig future, in future
das Kunstwort ⸚er technical term
die Kur cure
die Kutsche carriage, coach

L

laben refresh, comfort
das Labsal –e comfort
lächerlich ridiculous
lackiert lacquered
die Lade chest, coffin
der Laden ⸚ shutter
laden u a load
der Ladstock ⸚e ramrod
lähmen paralyze
lakonisch laconical
das Lamentieren wailing
das Lämpchen — little lamp
ländlich rustic
die Langeweile boredom
der Lappen — rag, patch
der Lärm –e noise
die Lässigkeit idleness
die Last burden
das Laster — vice, crime
das Laub –e leaves
die Laube arbor
der Lauf ⸚e course, career
das Lauffeuer — wildfire
die Laune mood, whim
der Laut –e sound
laut werden become known
die Lebensmüde weariness with life
die Lebenswonne rapture
lebhaft lively, vivid, animated
lechzen pant, pine, languish, yearn
sich legen cease, subside; apply oneself, take to; plant
die Lehne arm (of a chair)
das Leiblied favorite song
die Leiche corpse
leichtfertig sprightly
die Leichtigkeit lightness
der Leichtsinn joviality
leden itt itt suffer, allow
die Leidenschaft passion
leidig empty
leidlich tolerable
leiten lead
die Lektion lesson
die Lektüre reading

letzthin recently
leuchten shine, flash, light
leugnen deny
liebenswürdig charming, amiable
der Liebhaber — lover
die Liebkosung caress
das Lieblingsgericht –e favorite
   dish
lindern alleviate, soothe, relieve
die Linse lentil
lispeln whisper
die List cunning
das Lob praise
die Locke lock (of hair)
locken coax
der Lohn ⸗e reward
lose roguish, naughty
lösen loosen
losging walked up
los-reißen i i tear away
die Losung keyword; receipts, tak-
   ings
die Lücke hole, gap
lud (laden) invited
lullen lull
die Lumpenbeschäftigung shabby
   occupation
die Lumperei triviality
die Lustbarkeit festivity
das Lusthaus pavilion

M

der Mai(en)käfer — cockchafer
malerisch artistic, picturesque
mancherlei many things
mangeln lack, be wanting
die Mannigfaltigkeit variety
die Manschette cuff
durch Mark und Bein gehen cut to
   the quick
der Markt ⸗e marketplace
der Marmorfels –en marble rock
das Maß –e measure, way
sich mäßigen control oneself
das Mäuerchen — little wall
das Mäulchen — pursed lips
die Maulschelle slap in the face
die Maus ball of the thumb
der Medikus (pl. Medizi) doctor
meinetwegen it's all right with me
der Meistbietende –n highest
   bidder
sich melieren mix, mingle
menschenfeindlich inhospitable

das Menschengeschlecht –er human race
der Merkstein –e symbol
merkwürdig remarkable
der Meuchelmörder — assassin
die Miene countenance
mildern soften
mischen mingle
das Mißfallen dissatisfaction
mißlungen (mißlingen) failed
der Mißmut discontent
mißt bei (messen) attributes
das Mißtrauen distrust
das Mißverständnis –se misunder-
   standing
mit-empfinden a u feel too or with
das Mitleid sympathy
mitnichten by no means, not at all
das Mittel — means, remedy
mit-teilen communicate
mittler medium
die Mode fashion
modeln shape, mold
das Moos –e moss
das Mückchen — midge
der Mückenschwarm ⸗e swarm of
   insects
mühselig laborious
die Mündung muzzle
munter cheerful, gay, lively
murmeln mutter, murmur
murren grumble
müßig idle
das Muster — pattern, model
der Mut courage
die Mutmaßung surmise
der Mutwille mischievousness

N

die Nachbarschaft vicinity
das Nachdenken thoughtfulness
der Nachen — skiff
der Nachfolger — successor
das Nachforschen inquiry
sich nach-lassen slacken, give way
nach-legen replenish
die Nachrede gossip, rumor
die Nachricht news, information
nach-sagen repeat
die Nachsicht forbearance
der Nächste –n fellow man
nach und nach gradually
nach . . . zu toward
der Nagel ⸗ nail

sich nähern approach
nahm sich zusammen pulled herself together
nahm teil took an interest
nähren nourish, encourage
die Nahrung nourishment
nämlich same
der Narr –en fool
närrisch foolish
naseweis pert
das Nasloch ¨er nostril
das Naß wetness, dew
der Nebel fog, mist
die Nebelsäule column of mist
neblicht misty
das Nebenzimmer — adjoining room
necken tease, nag, annoy
der Neid envy
der Neider — envier, enemy
sich neigen bow, incline, tend
die Neigung inclination, affection
das Nest –er village, hole
nett clear
netzten wet, moisten
neugierig curious
die Nichte niece
nichtswürdig unworthy
niedergeschlagen dejected
sich nieder-lassen sit down
sich nieder-legen subside, settle
niedlich pretty, dainty
die Not need, distress, anguish
die Notdurft necessities
nötigen compel, oblige
nüchtern sober
nunmehr by this time
der Nußbaum ¨e nut tree

O

obendrein in addition, as well
die Oberfläche surface
der Obstbaum ¨e fruit tree
der Obstbrecher — fruit picker
öde desolate
offen frank
öffentlich public
öfter repeated, frequent
ohnedies besides, anyhow
ohnegleichen incomparable
von ohngefähr by chance
die Ohnmacht fainting spell
ohnmächtig unconscious
die Ohrfeige box on the ear

das Ölkrüglein little oil jug
opfern sacrifice
der Ort –e and ¨er place

P

der Pack ¨e package
packen lay hold of, capture
das Paket –e package
patsch! whack!
die Pein agony, anguish
peinigen torment
der Pfad –e path
das Pfand ¨er forfeit
der Pfarrer — pastor
der Pfarrhof ¨e parsonage
der Pfeil –e arrow
pflegen tend, care for
pflücken pluck
der Pflug ¨e plow
Pfui! shame!
der Philister — Philistine, Babbitt
picken peck
plagen torment
der Plan ¨e dance floor
plan plain, simple
platt low
der Platz ¨e place, square
plaudern chat
plump clumsy, coarse
das Polster — cushion
der Pöbel — mob
die Posse foolery, farce
der Postill(i)on –e coachman
das Postpferd –e stagecoach horse
prächtig grand, splendid
die Prätension claim
predigen preach
die Predigt sermon
der Predigtstuhl ¨e pulpit
preisen ie ie consider, praise
pressen oppress, strain
die Prüfung trial, test
der Pulsschlag ¨e pulse beat
das Pult –e desk
das Pulver — gunpowder
pünktlich punctilious
die Puppe doll
der Putz finery
putzen clean, decorate, dress up

Q

die Qual torture
quälen torment

qualvoll tormenting
die Quelle spring, source
quellen o o flow, gush

R

das Radotage absurdity
radotieren ramble
die Rangsucht snobbery
der Raritätenkasten ≃ peep show
rasch swift, lively
rasend frantic raging, mad
die Raserei frenzy, madness
rasseln rattle
rastlos restless
rauben rob
rauh rough
räumen clear
rauschend roaring
die Rebe vine
rechtfertig righteous, anxious to be just
rechten dispute, sit in judgment
rechtschaffen upright, solid
recht sein be acceptable
recken stretch
redlich honorable
regieren govern
regnicht rainy
das Reh –e roe, deer
reichen reach
die Reinheit purity
reißend raging
der Reiz –e stimulus, charm
die Reihe series; **der — nach** in a row
der Rest –e remains
retten rescue, save
rieb (reiben) rubbed
reuen cause regret
rief aus (rufen) exclaimed
der Riese –n giant
rings umher round about
riß (reißen) tore, snatched
das Röcheln death rattle
das Röckchen — skirt
der Rockknopf ≃e jacket button
roh crude
das Rohr –e reed
das Rotznäschen runny nose
rücken move
das Rudern rowing
der Ruhm renown
rühmen praise

der Saft ≃e juice, sap
sammeln gather, collect
sanft gentle, soft
der Sänger — singer
der Sarg ≃e coffin
satteln saddle
die Sattigkeit surfeit
der Sauerteig leaven
saugen o o suck
säuseln pour
das Sausen roaring
schaden hurt
schadlos halten compensate, indemnify
schaffen do, get
schallend sounding
schalt (schelten) scolded
die Schande shame
der Scharfsinn alertness
die Scharren (pl.) scrapings
der Schatten — shadow
das Schattenbild –er silhouette
der Schattenriß –e silhouette
schattieren shade
der Schatz ≃e treasure, dear one
schätzen value
der Schauder — shudder
schaudernd shivering, shuddering
der Schauer — thrill
schauerlich thrilling, awful, awesome
die Schaufel shovel
schäumend foaming
der Schauplatz arena, stage
das Schauspiel –e spectacle
die Scheidwand ≃e barrier
der Schein –e semblance
scheitern founder, become a wreck
die Schelle bell
der Schelm –e rogue
schelten a o scold
die Schenke tavern
schenken dispense
der Scherz –e joke
scheu shy
die Scheuer barn
schicklich proper, appropriate
das Schicksal –e fate, destiny
schieben o o shove, blame
schieden (scheiden) separated, parted
schiedest (scheiden) would depart
schießen o o shoot
der Schiffer — sailor

304

schimmern gleam, shimmer
der Schirm –e screen, protection
die Schlacht battle
schlachten slaughter
schlaff limp
der Schlag ⸗e [carriage] door
schlangen (schlingen) threw, turned, wound
schlank slender, slim
schleichend creeping, lingering
die Schleife bow
schleppen drag
schließen o o infer
die Schlingung interlacing
die Schlittenfahrt sleigh ride
das Schloß ⸗er castle
mich schloß clung
die Schloße sleet
schluchzen sob
schlucken swallow
der Schlucker — playboy
schlug aus refused
der Schlummerer — slumberer
schlürfen drink in
die Schmach disgrace
schmachten long for, pine
schmählich shameful, disgraceful
schmecken taste
die Schmeichelei flattery
schmelzen o o melt
das Schnäbelchen little bill
schnappen gasp
schnellen spring; bob
das Schnittchen slice
schnoben pant
das Schnupftuch ⸗er handkerchief
der Schnürleib –er corset, stays
schnurren whir
schob (schieben) thrust
schonen spare
schöpfen draw
der Schoß ⸗e lap
die Schoten (pl.) green peas
das Schrecken — terror
das Schrecknis –se terror
der Schreiber — clerk
schreien ie ie cry, shriek
Schritt vor Schritt step by step
die Schublade drawer
die Schüchternheit shyness
schuf (schaffen) created
die Schulstube schoolhouse
der Schulze –n village mayor, steward
der Schurke –n rogue
der Schuß ⸗e shot

schütteln shake
der Schutz protection
schützen protect
die Schwäche weakness
schwadronieren swagger
der Schwall undulation, surge
schwanken sway, float, totter
die Schwärmerei enthusiasm, mysticism
schwatzen chatter, talk
schweben hover, float
schweifen roam
der Schweinhirte –n swineherd
die Schwelle threshold
schwellend swelling, effervescent
schwerlich scarcely
die Schwermut melancholy
das Schwert –er sword
schwindlig dizzy
das Schwirren buzzing
schwören o o swear
schwül sultry
schwur (schwören) swore
seebespült sea-washed
die Seelenfreude joy
das Seelenvergnügen mental pleasure
seelenvoll passionate
seeumflossen sea-surrounded
das Segeln sailing
der Segen — blessing
segnen bless
die Sehkraft vision
sich sehnen yearn
sehnlich yearning, fervent
das Seil –e rope
seither since then
seitwärts to the side
selbig same
die Seligkeit bliss
die Selbstgefälligkeit self-complacency
das Selbstgespräch –e soliloquy
der Selbstmord suicide
die Selbständigkeit independence
das Selbstvertrauen self-confidence
seufzen sigh
die Sicherheit security
sichtlich obviously
das Siechbett sickbed
sieden sott gesotten boil
siegrückkehrend returning victorious
siehe zu see to it
der Silbenfall intonation
der Sinn –e mind

die Sinnesart state of mind
die Sinneskraft reflective power
sittlich moral
die Skripturen papers
sogenannt so-called, aforesaid
die Sohle sole
sonderbar strange
die Sorge concern, care
sorgfältig careful
sorglos carefree
spannen strain, make tense
sparsam thrifty
der Spaßvogel ⸗ buffoon, joker
die Spazierfahrt excursion
der Spazierritt –e horseback ride
speisen dine
sperren lock
aufs Spiel setzen risk
das Spielwerk –e toy
spitzen point
spornen spur
spotten mock
sprühen spray
der Sprung ⸗e jump, leap
die Spur trace
spüren perceive, feel
der Stab ⸗e staff
der Stachelgürtel — belt of
   thorns
der Stahl steel
der Stall ⸗e stable
der Stamm ⸗e clan, race
stammeln stammer
stampfen trample
der Stand ⸗e position, class, rank
   — halten hold one's own
standhaft steadfast
die Stange pole
die Stärke strength
die Stärkung strength
starr stiff, rigid, frozen, blank
die Stätte place, abode
statt-geben grant
stattlich stately
der Staub fleck, dust
staunend astonished
stecken hide, be
steif stiff, artificial
sich stellen act, pretend
der Stempel — stamp, mark
steuern steer, divert
der Stich –e stab, sting; — halten
   stand the test
sticht ab (stechen) contrasts
stieben drizzle
der Stiefel — boot

stimmen tune
die Stimmung mood
stöbern blow about
der Stock ⸗e cane
stocken falter; constrict, be
   blocked
die Stockung estrangement
das Stockwerk –e floor, story
stolpern stumble
stoppeln scrounge
der Stoß ⸗e thrust, blow
stottern stutter
strafbar culpable
die Strafe punishment
der Strauß ⸗e bouquet
der Streich –e trick
der Streit –e conflict
der Strich –e stroke, line
strich mich (streichen) slipped
stricken knit
strudeln gush, bubble
die Stube parlor
stumm mute
stumpf blunt, flat, dull
die Stumpfnase pug nose
stündlich at every hour
stürbe (sterben) should die
stürmen storm
stürzen sink, collapse
die Stütze support
stutzen be taken aback
stützen support
sudeln scribble, smear
summen hum
die Sünde sin
das Süppchen — soup
der Surtout –s overcoat
die Süßigkeit sweetness
die Szene scene

T

tadelhaft blameworthy
tadeln rebuke, censure
zu Tafel for dinner
das Tagebuch diary
tagtäglich daily
der Taglöhner — day laborer
tapfer brave
tappen grope
der Täter — criminal
tauen thaw
taufen baptize
die Taufhandlung baptism

306

der **Taumel** delirium, intoxication
taumeln stagger
täuschen deceive
tausendfach thousandfold
das **Tausendgüldenkraut** ⁓er centaury
teilhaftig werden share, enjoy
teil-nehmen participate, sympathize
teils partly
der **Teufel** — devil
tiefsinnig brooding
das **Tischtuch** ⁓er tablecloth
toben rage, fume
der **Todesschweiß** sweat of death
der **Todfeind** -e mortal enemy
toll insane, furious
der **Ton** clay
der **Topf** ⁓e pot
der **Tor** -en fool
das **Tor** -e gate
die **Törin** foolish person
töricht foolish
die **Tour** turn, round
das **Trachten** aspiration, contriving
die **Tracht** garb, dress
trafen (treffen) met
die **Trägheit** indolence, sluggishness
die **Träne** tear
tratschen chatter, talk nonsense
trauen trust
die **Trauer** sadness
der **Trauring** -e wedding ring
trefflich excellent
treiben ie ie carry on, perform
die **Treue** loyalty
treuherzig loyal, sincere
der **Trieb** -e drive, instinct
die **Triebfeder** motive
tröpfeln drip
der **Tropfen** — drop
der **Trost** consolation
trösten comfort, console
trostlos without consolation
trüb gloomy
der **Trübsinn** melancholy
der **Trunkene** -n drunkard
der **Trupp** -s -en band, troop
die **Tugend** virtue
das **Tulpenbeet** -e tulip bed
tun affect; **es tut nichts** it doesn't matter
tuschen quell, suppress
der **Tyrann** -en tyrant

U

übel dran badly off; **— nehmen** resent
überbracht delivered
übereilt precipitate, overhasty
überein-kommen agree
die **Übereinstimmung** harmony
überfallen attack
überfließen overflow
der **Überfluß** profusion; **zum —** needlessly
übergehen pass over, disregard
das **Übergewicht** upper hand
übergnädig supergracious
sich **überheben o o** boast
die **Überlegung** meditation
übermannen overpower, shake
der **Übermut** arrogance
die **Überraschung** surprise
überreden persuade
überreichen present
überschattet shaded
überschauen survey
der **Überschuß** ⁓e excess, supplement
überschwemmen flood
übersehen survey, perceive
überspannt excessive, wild, exaggerated
überstehen endure, survive
überstiegen (steigen) exceeded
überstimmen drown out, outvote
über-strömen overflow, overwhelm
über-treten overflow
übertrieben (treiben) exaggerated
über und über all over
überwältigen overpower
überwinden a u overcome
überzeugen convince
übrigens otherwise
das **Ufer** — shore
die **Umarmung** embrace
um-bringen destroy
umfangen i a encompass
umfassen embrace
umflocht (flechten) wove round
umgaben (geben) surrounded
der **Umgang** ⁓e association
umgeben surround
umgekehrt vice versa
umher-gehen wander
umher-schleichen i i sneak about
umher-schweifen roam about
umhin: ich kann nicht — I can't help it

um-kehren turn round
um-kommen perish
der Umlauf cycle, course
der Umriß –e outline
um-sausen blow, roar about
um-schütteln stir around
um-schweben permeate
um so mehr all the more
umsonst in vain
der Umstand ⸗e circumstance, fuss
umwandeln transform
der Umweg –e roundabout way
um . . . . willen because of, for
die Unart wantonness, naughtiness,
    nastiness
unaufhaltsam irresistible, inevitable
unaussprechlich unspeakable
unausstehlich intolerable
unbändig uncontrollable
unbedeutend insignificant, trifling
unbefangen natural, simple, naïve
unbefriedigt unsatisfied
unbegreiflich inconceivable
der Unbegriff stupidity
unbehaglich uncomfortable
unbekümmert unconcerned
unbeschadet unharmed
unbescheiden immodest, aggressive
unbeständig fickle, inconstant
unbezwinglich unconquerable
unbiegsam unbending
undurchdringlich impenetrable
unergründlich unfathomable
unersetzlich irreplaceable
unerträglich unbearable
unerwartet unexpected
unfähig incapable
der Unfriede –ns –n discord
ungeachtet in spite of, notwith-
    standing
ungebahnt untrodden
ungebildet uncultivated
die Ungeduld impatience
ungefähr approximately
das Ungeheuer — monster
ungeheuer enormous
ungehörig improper
ungekünstelt artlessly
ungemessen boundless
ungemischt unalloyed
ungenossen (genießen) untasted
ungenügsam insatiable, greedy
ungenutzt unused
ungerecht unjust
ungeschickt clumsy
ungespannt unstrung

ungestüm impetuous
die Ungewißheit uncertainty
ungezogen spoiled
der Unglaube –ns skepticism
unheimlich weird
unhold irritable
das Unkraut ⸗er weed
unleidlich unendurable
die Unlust apathy
der Unmut ill-humor
unmutig irritating
unpaß indisposed
unrein messy
die Unruhe restlessness
unsäglich inexpressible, boundless
unscheinbar threadbare
unschmackhaft unsavory
unschuldig innocent
unsereiner the likes of us
unsersgleichen like us
unsinnig senseless, wild, insane
der Unstern misfortune
unstet unsteady, unstable
die Untätigkeit inactivity
unterbrach (brechen) interrupted
unterdrücken suppress
untergegangen ruined, perished
untergehend sinking, perishing
untergraben u a undermine
der Unterhalt way of life
unterhalten keep going, entertain;
    sich — talk
unterliegen be defeated, succumb
die Unternehmung undertaking
die Unterredung conversation
der Unterschied –e difference
sich unterstehen presume, dare
die Untersuchung examination, in-
    quiry
der Untertan –en vassal, subject
unter-tauchen engulf
unter uns between you and me
unterwegs on the way
untreu unfaithful
unüberwindlich unconquerable
unveränderlich unchanging
unverdorben (verderben) unspoiled
unverdrossen (verdrießen) patient
unvermeidlich unavoidable
unvermerkt unnoticed
unvermutet unexpected
unversehens accidentally, unex-
    pectedly
unwahrscheinlich improbable
unwegsam untrodden
unwiderruflich irrevocable

unwiderstehlich irresistible
unwiederbringlich irretrievable
der Unwille –ns –n ill-will, disaffection
unwillig sullen
unwillkürlich involuntary
die Unwissenheit ignorance
die Unwürdigkeit unworthiness
unzählig innumerable
unzertrennlich inseparable
unzugänglich inaccessible
die Ursache cause
das Urteil –e judgment

V

vaterländisch native
verabscheuen abhor, abominate
verachten despise
verändern change
die Verantwortung responsibility
verarbeiten work away
verbergen a o hide
verbessern improve
die Verbindung union, attachment
die Verblendung delusion, blindness
verborgen (bergen) concealed
der Verbrecher — criminal
verbreiten extend
verbildet spoiled, badly educated
verbot (verbieten) forbade
verbunden (binden) united
der Verdacht suspicion
der Verdammte –n condemned man
verdenken blame
verderben a o spoil, destroy
verderbt corrupted
verdienen earn, deserve
verdrängen drive out, replace
verdrießen o o annoy, vex
der Verdruß vexation
verdunkeln darken
verdürben (verderben) spoiled
verdürsten be parched
verehren respect, admire
vereinigen unite, concentrate
verfallen fall into, decay
verfaulen rot
verfertigen make, create
verfiel lapsed
verfolgen pursue, hound
verführen mislead, seduce
vergällen embitter

das Vergangene past
vergänglich transitory
vergeben given away
vergebens in vain
vergeblich useless, vain
die Vergebung pardon
vergehen vanish, pass away, faint
vergießen o o shed, spill
vergleichen i i compare
die Vergleichung analogy
vergnügen please, content
vergönnen grant, allow
die Vergötterung apotheosis
vergröbern coarsen
verhallen die away
das Verhältnis –se relationship, situation
verheimlichen conceal
verheiraten marry off
verherrlichen glorify
sich verhetzen become harassed
sich verirren go astray
verkehrt depraved
verklagen complain
verkleidet disguised
verknüpfen tie, connect
verkündigen proclaim
das Verlangen desire
verlängern prolong, extend
der Verlauf lapse, expiration
verlecht leaking
die Verlegenheit embarrassment
verleiden mar
verleiten lead astray
verletzen hurt, wound
verleugnen deny
sich verlieben fall in love
verlobt engaged
verlöre (verlieren) would lose
verlöschen o o become extinct
der Verlust –e loss
vermachen bequeath
vermehren increase
vermeiden ie ie avoid
die Vermessenheit presumptuousness
vermindern reduce
vermissen miss
vermochte (vermögen) was not able
vermodern molder, decay
das Vermögen ability, power, fortune
vermögen be able, have power
vermuten surmise, suspect
vernachlässigen neglect

309

vernehmen perceive, hear
das Vernehmen terms, relationship
vernehmlich audible
vernünftig sensible
verpalisadieren entrench
verphantasieren dream away
verplaudern chatter away
verraten ie a betray
der Verräter — traitor
verreisen go on a journey
verrichten perform, achieve
verriet confided
versagen deny, refuse
versah slipped, missed
versammeln gather
verschaffen provide, procure
verschieden (scheiden) passed away
verschieden differing
verschlang (schlingen) devoured
verschlingen a u swallow up
verschlucken choke back
verschmachten languish, pine away
verschnaufen recover one's breath
verschwand (verschwinden) vanished
verschweigen ie ie keep silent about, suppress
verschwenden squander
verschwimmen a o be submerged
sich versehen realize
versengt singed, burning
versetzen reply, rejoin, add; transport, transpose
versichern assure
versiegeln seal up
versiegt dried out
die Versorgung provision
der Verstand understanding, intelligence, reason
sich verstellen dissimulate
verstimmen upset, be out of tune
verstorben (sterben) deceased, late
verstört ruined
verstrichen (streichen) elapsed
die Versuchung temptation
versunken absorbed, steeped
verteidigen defend
vertieft absorbed
sich vertrauern grieve to death
vertraulich familiar, intimate, cozy
verträumt dreamed away
vertraut intimate
verübeln resent
die Verunreinigung contamination
verwachsen overgrown [with moss]
verwandeln transform

verwandt related
verweben interweave
die Verwegenheit audacity, boldness
verwehen blow away
verwehren forbid, prevent
der Verweis –e rebuke
sich verwickeln become complicated
verwirren confuse
die Verwirrung confusion
verworren confused
verwunden injure, wound
die Verwunderung wonder, astonishment
verzagen despair
verzärtelt sentimentalized
verzehren eat up, consume
verzeihen ie ie forgive, pardon
verzerrt eccentric
verziehen delay, put off
verzog distorted
die Verzückung ecstasy, rapture
die Verzweiflung despair
das Vesperbrot supper
vielmehr rather, much more
vollbracht (vollbringen) completed
vollenden accomplish
vollends completely
völlig exactly, completely
vollkommen perfect
voraus ahead, in advance
vorbei-kreuzen pass in crossing
im Vorbeigehen in passing
das Vorbitten intercession
vor-bringen produce, bring forward
vor-bringen produce
der Vorfahr –en ancestor, predecessor
der Vorfall ‑e incident
vor-führen present
vorgefallen happened
das Vorgefühl –e anticipation
vorgefunden appeared
voran-gehen go ahead, proceed
vorgekommen seemed, occurred
vorgenommen undertaken; sich – resolved
vorgeschrieben prescribed
vorgeworfen (werfen) reproached
das Vorhaben — intention, plan, proposal
der Vorhang ‑e drape
vorig former
vor-laufen outdistance

vor-legen put before (one), serve
vorliegend lying in front
vornehm elevated, elegant, distinguished
sich vor-nehmen plan, resolve
vornehmlich mainly, principally
das Vorrecht –e superiority
der Vorsaal — säle anteroom
der Vorsatz ⸚e resolution, intention
der Vorschlag ⸚e proposal
vor-schwatzen chatter to
die Vorsicht caution
sich vor-spiegeln imagine, picture
sich vor-stellen imagine
vorstellend representational
die Vorstellung notion
der Vorteil –e advantage
der Vortrag ⸚e proposal, speech
vor-tragen explain, expound
vortrefflich excellent
vor-trommeln pound out
vorüberfließend flowing by
das Vorübergehen passing
vorübergehend transitory
das Vorurteil –e prejudice
der Vorwand ⸚e pretext
vor-werfen reproach
der Vorwurf ⸚e reproach
die Vorzeit ancient times
der Vorzug ⸚e preference
vorzüglich principally

W

das Wachs wax
das Wachsstöckchen wax taper
das Wachstum growth
der Wächter — watchman
wacker brave, gallant, good
der Waffenträger — warrior
wagen dare, risk
der Wahn illusion
wähnen fancy, imagine, be under a delusion
der Wahnsinnige –n madman
während endure, last
wahrhaftig truly
wallen float
der Waller — pilgrim, wanderer
die Wallfahrt pilgrimage
wälzen roll, tumble
wandte ein (wenden) objected
wandte sich (wenden) turned
wanken waver, totter
warb (werben) wooed

ward = wurde
die Wäsche linen
weben stir
wechselnd by turns, at intervals
wechselseitig mutual
wechselweise interchangeably
der Weck –e roll
weg-fangen i a snatch
weg-gaukeln fritter away
weg-spülen wash away
weg-weihen remove by blessing
weh tat hurt
wehe! woe!
das Wehen breathing
die Wehklage lamentation
die Wehmut melancholy
das Weib –er woman
weichen i i retreat
die Weide willow
weiden feast
der Weinstock ⸚e grapevine
weisen ie ie turn away
weis-machen deceive, hoax
weissagen foretell
das Weitere further details
weitläufig extensive
das Welken fading
das Weltgeschäft general work
das Werkzeug –e implement
wert precious
das Wesen being, essence, nature, character; fuss
das Wetter lightning
der Wetterbach ⸚e cataract
das Wetterkühlen heat lightning
die Wetterkunde meteorology
das Wetterleuchten lightning
die Wetterschnelle speed of a storm
widerfahren happen, fall [to one's lot]
der Widerpart: — halten contradict
die Widerrede objection
widerriet (raten) dissuaded
der Widerschall –e echo
der Widerschein –e reflection
widersprechen contradict
widerstehen disagree
der Widerwille –ns disgust, repugnance
widmen devote, dedicate
widrig obstinate, repulsive, ugly
wieder-käuen chew over, ruminate
wiegen rock, waft
der Wiegengesang ⸚e lullaby

311

wies ab (weisen) rejected
die Wiese meadow
wiewohl although
willig receptive
wimmeln teem, swarm, crowd
der Windstoß ≃e blast
der Wink –e trace
wirbeln eddy
wirken auf effect, produce
wirksam active
die Wirkung effect
die Wirtin landlady; hostess
die Wirtschaft commerce
wispeln whisper
die Wissenschaft knowledge
wissentlich deliberately
die Witwe widow
der Witz –e wit, intellect
witzeln joke; **sich herum —** joke
  around, mock
woanders somewhere else
wöchentlich weekly
die Wohlfahrt welfare
wohlgeordnet well-ordered
der Wohlgeruch ≃e fragrance, perfume
wohlgewachsen well-formed
wohlmeinend well-meaning
der Wohlstand comfort
wohltätig beneficent
sich wölben arch, curve
die Wollust, delight, bliss
die Wonne bliss, delight
worein into which
der Wortkrämer — phrasemonger
wühlen stir up; **–d** turbulent
die Wunde wound
die Wundererscheinung marvelous
  sight
wunderlich strange
die Wunderquelle miraculous
  spring
der Wunderstreich –e illusion
die Würde dignity
würfeln throw dice
das Würmchen — little worm
wurmen gall, annoy
die Wurzel herb, root
die Wut fury, rage
wutsch! zoom!

Z

das Zagen timidity, wavering
das Zähneknirschen gnashing of
  teeth

zanken fight, quarrel
die Zartheit tenderness
die Zauberkraft magic power
die Zauberlaterne magic lantern
das Zaudern hesitation
der Zaun ≃e fence
zeichnen sketch
zeither for the present
eine Zeitlang a while
die Zelle cell
zerbrechlich fragile
zerbrochen (brechen) broken
zerfallen quarrel
zerlegen dissect, cut up
zerreißen i i tear up, break, rend
das Zerren tugging
zerrütten shake, shatter, rend
  disturb, ruin, derange
zerschlagen demolish
zerschmettern crush, smash, shatter
zerstoben (stieben) dispersed
zerstören destroy, ruin, devastate
zerstreuen disperse, distract
zerstückt fragmentary
das Zettelchen — little note
das Zeug –e stuff, thing, harness
der Zeuge –n witness
das Zeugnis –se testimonial
das Zettelchen — slip of paper
das Ziel –e goal, aim
ziemlich rather
zögern hesitate
zog sich descended
der Zopf ≃e pigtail
der Zorn wrath, anger
zu-bringen spend (time)
zuck! zoom!
zucken quiver, twitch, shrug
das Zuckerbrot –e cookie
die Zuckererbse sugar pea
das Zuckerwerk candy
das Zudringen pressure
der Zufall ≃e chance, accident
zu-fallen close
der Zug ≃e pull, urge, move, feature
die Zuflucht recourse
zu-geben admit, add
zugedacht destined, intended
zu-gehen come to pass, happen,
  proceed
zugetan attached, devoted
das Zugeteilte –n allowance
zu-greifen take hold

zugrunde gehen be destroyed; — **richten** destroy, ruin
zu-halten close off, plug
zuließ permitted
zumal especially
zu-messen a e measure out
zumute sein feel
zu-muten expect, demand
zupfen tug
zu-pressen constrict
zurecht-legen adjust
zurecht-machen repair, prepare, fix up
sich zurecht-setzen settle down
zurecht-weisen reprimand
zu-reden counsel, urge
zürnen be angry
zurück-beben recoil
zurück-klingen a u reverberate
zu-sagen promise
zusah watched
zusammengeschafft accumulated

sich zusammen-halten compare oneself
zusammen-pferchen coop up
zusammen-ziehen contract, gather
zu-schreiben attribute, ascribe
zu-sehen look on
der Zustand ⸚e condition, situation
zu-stutzen fashion, trim
zu-teilen allot
zuteil werden fall to [a person's] share
zu-trauen expect from
zu-tun add
die Zuverlässigkeit trustworthiness
zuvor-kommen anticipate
zuweilen sometimes
zuwider repugnant, odious
zu-winken wave to
zwar indeed, in fact, true, to be sure
der Zweck –e purpose, goal
zweideutig ambiguous
der Zwischenraum ⸚e interval

BANTAM DUAL-LANGUAGE BOOKS

An entirely new concept in publishing, created after much research by Bantam Books and hailed by critics and public alike. The Dual-Language format presents works in their original language with the English translation on facing pages. Here is a new, stimulating approach to the fascination of literature in its native language. Each book is complete with notes and study aids.

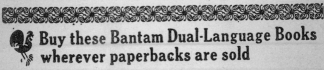